GUNNY

The point man stopped in his tracks and didn't move.

I went forward to see how bad things were. Pulling back some brush, I bent over to crawl. Suddenly, something popped and caught my eye. Then I saw a bright flash and an explosion. Everything turned red, and I felt myself flying through the air. I landed on my butt, then my back, but I didn't seem to care. Someone was shooting. I could hear someone screaming in front of me. I tried to move, to roll over or sit up. *Damn. I can't move.* My chest felt like something heavy was sitting on it. I kept seeing everything in red, and my skin was burning.

"My legs! My legs!" I heard someone scream. Thank God—it wasn't me.

I kept trying to raise my arms and open my eyes. Then I heard a voice next to me. "Oh shit, it's the gunny. Get a corpsman! Gunny, can you hear me? Say something, Gunny."

I'm talking. Can't you hear me? Shit, and I began to laugh. *Oh God that hurts. What the hell am I laughing at?*

"Gunny is hit bad. Get on the radio and ask for the chaplain."

"No way is he going to make it," I heard another say.

What the hell are you saying? Can't you hear me? I'm screaming as loud as I can. Still, no one heard me.

"Gunny, talk to us."

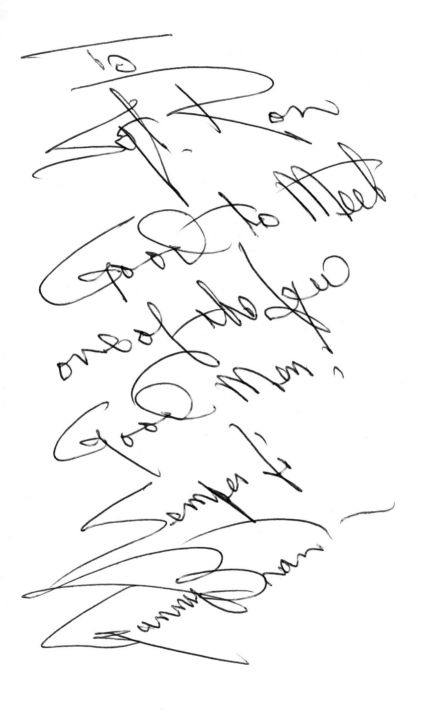

To Ron

Good to meet
one of the few

Good men

Semper Fi

GUNNY

by P.E. "Gunny" Brandon

Third Edition

GUNNY

Third Edition

Library of Congress Cataloging-in-Publication Data
Library of Congress Catalog Card Number: 95 - 94460

Brandon, P.E.
    Gunny / P.E. Brandon
    p. cm.
    ISBN # 1-883901-25-1
    I. Title

Third Edition, First Printing, softcover, August 2007. Edited by Mike Blackwell, Print Northwest, McMinnville, Oregon. Published by P.E. "Gunny" Brandon. Printed by Oregon Lithoprint, McMinnville, Oregon.

Printed in the U.S.A.

Dedication

To my brother, Pfc. Howard S. Brandon, who was killed in action at Iwo Jima on March 9th, 1945, and whose shoes I tried so hard to fill.

Howard looking sharp in his dress uniform

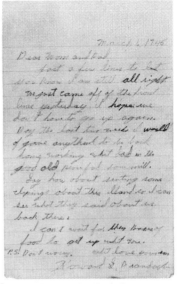

Howard's last letter home,
just two days before he was killed

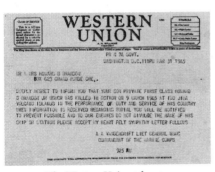

The Western Union telegram
informing my family of Howard's fate

...and the envelope in which it arrived

The condolence letter
from USMC Commandant Peck

Additional Dedications

**To Shirlie, my wife for over fifty years, who is known to my
Marine buddies as "Saint Shirlie" for putting up with me!**

In the Marines we have a saying: Behind every good Marine is a good wife.
Shirlie stood, not behind me, but beside me: during the drinking years, rodeos,
fighting and playing football. During the years I was a drill instructor and
seagoing Marine infantry, combat, and the years in the hospital Shirlie went
through hell and never once did she fall back. When she has to make that
final roll call at Heaven's Gate, she can stand proud with the Marines and say,
"Another Marine's wife reporting; I have spent my time in hell."

To my brothers...

John and Gary (the sailors), Bill (Air Force), and Howard, who gave his life for
his country on March 9, 1945 during World War II on Iwo Jima as a Marine. I
tried so hard to fill his shoes.

To Lance Corporal David R. Bingham...

We knew him as the "Gunny's Shadow" (U.S. Marines), who gave his life for
the Marine Corps because he followed orders. I have cried and felt his death
a thousand times. He never had to die in that dirty war. He begged to stay; he
gave the Marine Corps his all.

David R. Bingham died in Vietnam on May 2, 1968.

To my children...

Jan, Russell and Rita, whose childhoods were spent in the Marine Corps.
Thank you for understanding and for letting Shirlie be both mom and dad.

Acknowledgements

To the friends who knew what I was going through and
understood that my story needed to be told—thank you.

To Katherine Huit, for the cover photos.

To Mary Rash and the Easy Writers group, for their support.

To Wendell "Bud" Holst, for helping me get my papers in order.

To Carla Hopp of C.H. Hardcopy, Inc., who could read my mind
and make the final words come out in print.

To my granddaughter Crissandra, who did her best dealing
with her Grandpa and the mess of paperwork I would give her.
With all the changes, she must have retyped my story a hundred times,
and though I called her "pickle breath" for all the pickles she ate,
she stuck through it all.

To Becky Haggard, who helped read my story and sort it out when
I was unable to read it myself. I think it even got to her in the end.

To my friends Eric Fricke and Mike Blackwell of Print Northwest, who did
many layouts and put the book together; I would have quit if not for them.

To the hours and months which turned into years,
almost driving me nuts trying to put my thoughts into words.
I don't know how I ever got my first two prints done.

To all my Marine buddies and the ones who have gone to
the big parade ground for their last formation: Semper Fi!

To all the people who read my first books and wanted to know
what happened to me after I was wounded the last time that ended
my career in the Marines: your letters made me write my last chapter.

And to everyone else who made it happen—*Semper Fi!*

Contents

Author's Notes
(a Preface to the Third Edition)

September, 2006

My first book ended the day I was wounded the last time, June 28, 1968, one day before my 33rd birthday. Something about writing that book helped put my life back in order and I was moving on with my life looking forward to the day I would have enough money to retire and learn to play with my computer.

The computer woke up a whole new nightmare for me. I kept finding a lot of guys who had the same trouble I had getting over Vietnam and the Marine Corps and sooner or later I knew someone was going to come online that I had served with or maybe looking for me. When it happened it took me back into the nightmares and the flashbacks, the dreams all came back.

A Marine I was with in Vietnam killed himself twenty-five years ago and his family was still trying to deal with it. A friend was looking for someone who knew him that could maybe help the family understand, what or why he would kill himself. I knew everything about this Marine; he had been in my dreams for almost thirty years.

I was just getting over helping the family deal with the loss of their son and brother when a Sergeant Major in the Army contacted me. He was looking for someone who had known his brother who was killed in March 7, 1968 with F co. 2nd bn. 4th Marines that were in my company in Vietnam. He had been in the Marines before going in the Army and had another brother and also his father who had been in the Marines. The one brother was a book author and wanted me to go with him back to Vietnam to show him where his brother was killed.

I never thought I was going to stop, I think I was in the worst shape I had been. In my mind after coming back from Vietnam I was sick for six months and had to go to the Veterans Hospital and deal with the head doctor again. It seems like the only thing that works for me is to write about what is going on and clear my mind.

I'm at the point that I can put together a third print of my books and see if I can add a chapter of what I have written since then. I never thought I had any more to say and I'm still not sure I have.

Many readers of my book wrote to me and gave me hell about leaving them hanging about what happened to me after I was wounded the last time. Well, I lived and I wrote a book, didn't I?

But I do have an ending this time, and I want to call it "Gunny's Last Chapter, His Liife Without the Marines." The Marine Corps asked me to come back and allowed me to give my last two commands and then shut my mouth as the most Senior Gunny in the Marine Corps…that is just my opinion.

As I have said in my book, I was wounded for the last time on June 28, 1968, and in May 1969 they sent me home to recover from my wounds. They never called me back to retire on April 1, 1973, when they should have. After twenty years they sent me my retirement in the mail delivered by a long haired hippy mailman and that pissed me off.

A few weeks before September 8th, 2006 I got a call from Marine Corps Recruit Depot San Diego California Base Sergeant Major B.B. Woods.

He said, "I don't think you know me, but I know you and about that you have never retired and we don't do that, but we would like you to be our 'PRO' (parade reviewing officer) for the parade on Friday, September 8, 2006...kind of like your retirement parade."

Well, I got my parade and got to give the last commands that I will ever give to the Marine Corps, until I get to report to that big parade ground where all Marines go.

My last two commands were "PASS IN REVIEW" and "DISMISS THE STAFF."

Now you can just call me Percy.

2006:
My buddy, Sgt. Major Woods

San Diego, September 8, 2006:
Observing the Marine Color Guard

Award presentation by Sgt. Major Carter

* * *

As I write this, more than 38 years have passed since I took off my uniform and tried to fit into the life of a former Marine and make a life for me and my family. The worst hell I knew was being stupid, drinking and raising holy hell with my life, wanting to be the best I could, fighting cancer and all my operations just to keep my body going.

I'm not going to go into details, but will add to my story some of the many letters I have received over the years, including one that brought me to add more to my first book. This third edition will now also tell the story of what has driven me all the years since May 1969, when the Marines sent me home to recover from my wounds.

When I first wrote my book, I called it "Mostly a True Story." I don't think anyone can live the life I have lived and tell a true story. Sometimes, I'm not even sure I can believe it myself.

The only thing I *can* believe is what the Marines say:

"ONCE A MARINE, ALWAYS A MARINE."

GUNNY

Prologue

P.E. "Gunny" Brandon had been hit forty-three times in both eyes, both arms and both legs. Every rib, his left forearm, right leg, right wrist, right shoulder and right knee were broken. He suffered stomach and right testicle injuries. His left thumb had been blown off, as well as the tip of one finger. Three knuckles had been broken. The right side of his head had been torn in three places and every tooth was loose. His right ear and left lung were punctured.

His spleen was removed and the lower intestines sewn over. Hundreds of pieces of metal were left in every part of his body.

* * *

Gunny spent the next several years in and out of hospitals. He was eventually allowed to return to limited duty and nearly returned to full duty. He passed his mental and P.T. tests with flying colors, even after experiencing the hell he'd seen and been through. Before his last medical board review, he was once again hospitalized to remove a piece of metal from his stomach and went into shock on the operating table. The medical board recommended that he be retired due to his wounds or placed on temporary leave until he recovered.

* * *

With over twenty-five commendations-including four Purple Hearts, the Vietnam Cross of Gallantry. Navy commendations with Combat for Valor and Combat Action ribbons, Gunny Brandon ended his twenty years in the Marine Corps. He was never allowed to return to active duty.

For the next twenty-two years Gunny suffered severe flashbacks (delayed stress syndrome) trying to relive the years between 1953 and 1973. Being a Marine, doing what Marines do, working hard and playing hard almost cost him his life.

In 1993, under the supervision of a Veteran's hospital counselor in Portland, Oregon, Gunny wrote this book as therapy. There were times he had no knowledge of sitting at his typewriter or writing down what he was reliving.

He has not suffered a flashback since the completion of his book.

* * *

His marriage to Shirlie Bird Brandon survived the storms and nightmares they both lived through. They have been married, as of this printing, over fifty years and reside in McMinnville, Oregon.

Since 1973, Gunny has owned and operated several business ventures, including a rodeo town tavern, a veteran's club and a private fitness gym.

He is a noted lecturer and forum panelist on combat and Marine Corps life, as well as on delayed stress syndrome.

* * *

"If I get nothing more from this book, at least I now understand that I can take my pack off and stand easy. I am still a Marine at heart and truly believe the words: *Semper Fidelis.*"

Chapter 1
The First Flashback

"Get the hell away from me, Gunny, you crazy asshole. You draw incoming!" That's what my company clerk shouted at me while we were pinned down near the Cu-Vet River near Do Ha, Vietnam.

It was hot, I was sweating my butt off, and my new boxer shorts were halfway up my ass, cutting my balls in two. I rolled onto my side, got out my K-bar and tried to reach through the fly of my jungle trousers. I was trying to cut the crotch out of my shorts when my company corpsman started laughing.

"Hey, Gunny, you look like a monkey fucking a balloon!"

"Fuck you, Doc," I said. "If you were worth a shit, you'd come do this for me." He was still laughing when I got done, but it sure felt good!

I looked around for my clerk; he and my radio operator had crawled forward about fifty meters. *Damn those assholes,* I thought, *now I have to crawl up there just to get my radio.* I needed to call to see what was holding us up. The more I crawled, the more pissed I got.

They were about twenty meters away when I saw a dead water buffalo; it was laying about three meters away from them and had bloated from being in the hot sun. I was still mad-as-hell as I pulled out my .45 pistol and shot it directly in the guts. Poof! It looked like gray steam and, damn, the smell was bad!

"Goddamn you, Gunny. What the fuck did you do that for? That smells bad!"

"Well, maybe you shitheads better stay near me," I said, "so this doesn't happen again."

After initiating the call, our company XO said we were held up by sniper fire; 2nd Platoon had men hit and needed Medevac. We moved forward to set up a landing zone.

Second platoon's commander had been shot through the neck. Another Marine, by the looks of the bandages on him, was also hit about three times. We had just pulled them out when I got another radio call; they had another wounded man. This one had been shot in the foot with a .45 slug. (After what we'd just been through, if this was a self-inflicted wound, I would kill the son of a bitch myself.)

"Hold him where he is," I said. "I'll try to get him Medevac'd from over there." The Marine was seventy meters away, across a rice paddy, which meant I would have to carry him back at least fifty meters to a spot where the helicopter could set down. (While crossing the rice paddy I stopped to talk to a lance corporal smoking a cigarette behind a dike. After a minute or so I had to move on. I remember, he said that he was going to finish his cigarette and then get back to his platoon. Funny how you remember those minute details.)

I had just taken a few steps when I heard rocket rounds coming in. I dove for a bomb hole just a second before three other Marines with the same idea jumped in on top of me. The hole was full of water and I was on the bottom. I shouted, "Get off of me!" I stopped when I heard a Marine scream that he'd been hit. That was the last thing he ever said: he was dead. I looked back to the lance corporal. He was still there, but he too was dead. A round had landed on his legs.

That made two dead Marines and one wounded.

It took two Marines to get one dead and one wounded to the landing zone. That left me to retrieve the other dead Marine. While crossing the rice paddy, I heard the rocket rounds coming in again. I started to run with the body; I had to get him on that helicopter before it took a hit. I got him to the landing zone and was trying to push him through the helicopter door when the door gunner tried pulling me in with them. The pilot had taken off the instant he saw the rocket rounds start to hit.

"Let go of me, you asshole! I'm not going with you," I shouted as I pulled away, not realizing there wasn't anything behind me but a hundred feet of air. That free-fall sensation in dreams doesn't come close to the terror of the real fall.

SPLASH!! The water in the rice paddy must have reached thirty feet in the air. I landed on my back and, Oh God, did it knock the wind out of me! My mouth, nose, everything was full of water. I thought that I was certainly going to drown. (It still seems amazing that I can remember hearing my corpsman yelling, "Gunny was hit by a rocket round; it blew him a hundred feet in the air! I saw him hit the ground!") *Get over here and help me out of the mud, you assholes,* I was thinking. *I didn't get hit. I fell out of the goddamn helicopter! HOW IN THE HELL DID I GET HERE?*

Chapter 2
Where It Really Started

In hindsight, it seems it all started, not in that fateful rice paddy, but in November 1952 in a small, rural Oregon town a very long way from Vietnam. I was seventeen years old and in my junior year at Willamina High School. One Friday night, I and a couple of buddies had just finished a football game and were headed uptown to cruise the "gut." Our turnaround point was the VFW Club at the end of town. There was a dance that night at the VFW, so the parking lot was full.

Driving my 1949 Buick Roadmaster and making my turn through the parking lot, I spotted my brother Gary and some of his old school friends. Since they had beer, I stopped to talk.

I must have had about three beers before I spotted the chief of police coming our way. Trying to make a clean getaway wasn't in the cards: I fell flat on my ass while running to my car. The chief told me and the rest of the guys to get in his car. About that time, Gary told me not to mention him being in the Navy; he was not supposed to be home. (Great! Just great!) Well, the chief chewed our asses out good, then told us we could go but not before he made it clear that he was going to tell the football coach that I had been drinking beer.

It didn't seem like things could get much worse, but what does a wet-behind-the-ears teenager know? The "worse" happened afterward: my brother borrowed my car, fell asleep at the wheel, rolled the Roadmaster and totaled it. I could just see it—now I would have to ride the bus to school and would be kicked off the team for drinking. I thought, *Piss on it. I'm going to play sick and skip school.*

The next day I hitchhiked to Salem, about forty miles away from my home town of Grand Ronde, and ended up at the Navy recruiting office. *If my brother can make it in the Navy, I can, too.* No such luck, they had a waiting list six months long. Little did I know that a Marine recruiter, a sergeant, was standing nearby listening to my story. "If you want, I'll have your ass out of here in one day," he said.

"If I'm tough enough to play football," I retorted, "I can make it in the Marines. But I'm only seventeen years old and my mother won't sign for me. She always told me that everyone gets killed in the Marines. I had a brother and a cousin who were killed in World War II and another cousin killed in Korea."

"I'll give you a ride home and talk to your mother," he offered. "You are only seventeen, and by the time you're eighteen, you'll be on a permanent base. You won't have to go to Korea."

During the subsequent barrage of debates my mother finally tired of listening to me cry about my smashed-up car and signed my enlistment papers.

* * *

Things happened fast: just as fast as the sergeant promised! I was to leave the next day, so my mother invited a few guests over, mostly family, to have a big dinner before I left. My aunt was there. She talked about her son, Charles, being in trouble at school and thought my cousin should go with me. Believe it or not, the next day she drove both of us to the Marine recruiting office in Salem.

At the office we met two other young men also joining the Marines: Gordon Selby and Elmer Bice. They were from Dallas and Rickreall, respectively: both small, rural Oregon towns just like Grand Ronde.

Selby was a damn good bullshitter so, of course, he was put in charge to make sure we got to Portland and finished our paperwork. He was sure as hell going to get us in shit. He had a burp louder than any I'd ever heard. On the bus ride to Portland, he got his kicks by walking up behind someone and burping at around ten or twenty decibels. He would scare the shit out his victim and then laugh. The bus driver wasn't enjoying this any more than Selby's victims and was close to kicking us all off the bus on his account. I'm sure there were more than a few "second thoughts" going through our minds, with someone like Selby in charge, during the ninety-minute drive from Salem to Portland.

That night in Portland was the first time I had ever been in a big town. It was kind of scary for me, coming from a small, rural town. Grand Ronde only had one store, one gas station and one diner.

Boy, there were a lot of Marines in Portland in 1953. I guess maybe about twenty of us were enlisting on that day. We endured a more-than-thorough "going over," but we all passed. An ex-Army man was put in charge of us to keep us out of trouble. We were given meal tickets to eat at a nearby greasy spoon, then taken to a hotel. Of course we were supposed to stay at the hotel until midnight, before catching our flight to San Diego.

Selby claimed to know his way around Portland, so we sneaked out of the hotel and went to the Skid Row area. He also said we were all going to get laid. (Just the thing for a seventeen-year-old enlistee!) Well, he and his twenty-decibel burping landed us in trouble with a few local boys who wanted nothing better than to kick our asses. Before they could get that far, they made the wise decision that we were too tough for them, thanks to Elmer Bice. He was a great fighter and beat the shit out of two of those local boys.

We returned to the hotel unharmed and in one piece only a few minutes before we were bussed to the airport. I was half carsick on the ride there, I never could ride in the back of a bus. Boy, was I going to make a hell of a Marine!

June 29, 1946: Gunny's birthday. Five will grow up to be Marines.

We met two more Marines at the airport who were home on leave from Korea. Selby bragged about how we were going to show the Marine Corps how "bad" we were. These two Marines must have seen how green we were from a mile away, because they sure set us up for a world-class ass kicking! They were kind enough to show us how to do things the *Marine* way; just to help us look smarter than the other guys from other states once we got to boot camp. God, if we only knew what a bunch of dickheads we were. Our supervisor, the ex-Army man, didn't tell us any different.

We boarded a four-engine plane sometime after midnight. I was still feeling carsick, and by the time the plane taxied down the runway, I was full-blown airsick. I threw up and puked all over my cousin Charles who was sitting next to me. I was sick throughout the entire night flight to San Diego. It was the longest four hours of my life. I didn't think that plane would ever land but was thankfully glad when it did. I was never so glad to get fresh air, but not before I was made to clean up my own mess.

As I stood in front of the airport, a transport Marine, driving the biggest truck (called "cattle cars" in the Marines) I had ever seen, pulled up to collect us. He was trying, military fashion, to ramrod us onto the cattle cars, when our supervisor informed him that we were going to eat first. That really pissed off the driver. Little did I know that we were going to eventually pay for that. If I had been smart, I would have gotten on the truck, but I had puked up all my food and I was hungry. So, like everyone else, I stayed to eat.

"Get on the truck, you pigfuckers," shouted the transport Marine, once we'd had our meal and returned to the truck. I knew he wasn't going to go easy on a bunch of kids who'd just made him wait. The truck must have been ten feet tall. A fat kid ahead of me couldn't pull himself up into the truck and fell back on me. After about ten tries, the Marine opened the tall gate for us to board. "Pussies," he muttered. Forty of us piled into a space I was sure was only big enough for half of us, but fit we did. I had three guys on top of me and felt all of them as we hit every bump in the road on our way to boot camp. At the base, payback time came when our supervisor got the shit beat out of him for not instructing us to board the truck at the airport. Boy, I was glad I wasn't him!

"Stand at attention, you shitbirds! Let your arms hang at your sides and curl your fingers. Turn your feet to form a forty-five-degree angle and hold your chin up!" (Shit! That wasn't what the two Marines home on leave had told us at the airport! This was our chance to show them how smart we were in Oregon.) *Oh, damn!* I thought, as I got hit in the guts. Down went my cousin, then Selby, and then two or three more. "What's wrong with you pigfuckers? Did you not hear me tell you how to stand at attention? You pigfuckers trying to piss me off?" the drill sergeant shouted.

We had all been standing at attention, just as the Marines in Portland had so

1951: Age 16, working in a sawmill

kindly instructed us, still unaware we'd been royally set up. I decided I didn't
need to be punched again and stood the way the DI told me, but not that damn
Selby. Another punch in the guts and down he went again. "You pigfucker, can't
you hear? I told you how I want you to stand at attention. Where did you dumb
fuckheads come from?" After about ten minutes of getting the shit kicked out of
us, we finally knew we had been set up.

I remember learning how to duckwalk that day, with a footlocker overhead.
I could only take a few steps before falling down. I also remember having, only
been there a few hours, before I had been kicked around ten times, was hungry
and my mouth was dry. I'd been running, standing at attention or duckwalking
since I got to the base.

* * *

"GET OUTSIDE, YOU SHITBIRDS, and stand on the yellow footprints.
It's time for chow. You may take all you want, but you will eat all you take," the
corporal said.

He tried to march us, but we stepped all over each other to get in front of
what he said was a Marine mess hall. We were told to hold our metal food tray
in front of our faces with both hands, so we could just see over the top. "Close it
up tight, until the asshole in front of you smiles."

*Shit, this place smells bad! Oh my God, they have potatoes cooked with onions.
Why are they throwing all that food on my tray? Oh shit, I'm supposed to pull my
tray back if I don't want it. It's too late now, I hope I can eat all this,* I thought,
looking at the heap of food on my tray.

"Set your trays on the tables," we were told. "When I say *ready seats,* I want
you to jump inside between the table and chair until I tell you to sit." We tried
it once. "You're too slow! Get out and do it again!" We must have done it twenty
times before we got it right. Maybe I wouldn't have to worry about all my food
after all: I was working up quite an appetite.

Oh, this tastes bad! The butter is frozen; how do you spread it?

"Get on your feet and pick up your tray. There had better not be any food
left on your trays," the corporal snarled. I still had two measly cubes of butter left.
The guy across from me took the bread off his tray and stuck it to the bottom
of the table. *Good idea,* I thought, and stuck my butter underneath the table,
too. Without warning the corporal picked up the end of the table and dropped
it back to the floor. "Do you think I was born yesterday?" he said. All kinds of
food fell to the floor. "Get down on the deck, pick that food up and eat it!" As
I grabbed a piece of bread, he yelled, "Don't swallow it! And keep your mouth
open." I took the bread out of my mouth and, as soon as we went out the door,
dropped it on the ground.

Once we were outside, the corporal picked out those who had dumped
food. Shit, I was proud I didn't get caught and was I glad! They must have beat
the shit out of those guys for a half hour for "wasting good Marine chow."

At last, our first day was almost over and we returned to our barracks.

"Get your dirty asses in the shower," we were instructed, none too gently.
"Shower and shave." There were forty of us trying to use only six showers and,
because I only had a little fuzz on my chin, this seemed worse than gym class in
high school. Finally, after a disorganized effort, a little bald-headed man lined
us up and filed us through. He had been in the Navy during World War II and

that was the way they did it, according to him. He certainly looked old to be in the Marines.

I was finally going to get some sleep. God, I don't think I had stopped for two days and damn!—there was only a skinny little mattress on the bed, and no sheets or blankets. Contrary to popular belief, it sure can get cold in California in January.

* * *

The next morning, bright and all too early, we were greeted by our drill instructor, Staff Sergeant Baker, throwing a trash can down the aisle. "Get out of those racks, you maggots. Get your clothes on, you pigfuckers, and get outside on the yellow footprints." This was without a doubt the biggest man I had ever seen. He sounded just like a cowboy herding sheep. I then knew who was in charge of the epithet *pigfucker*, everything Staff Sergeant Baker said started with pigfucker. We were soon to find out that the less we saw of him, the better off we would be.

"It looks like there are about a hundred of us here, but it turns out there are only seventy," Staff Sergeant Baker began. "You are platoon number thirty-three, First Battalion, A Company. The other two drill instructors will be Sergeant Gilmore and Corporal Colby. You pigfuckers will be with us for the next twelve weeks. The only way you will get out of here is if we want you out of here. You can only get out of here two ways: one as a Marine, and the other in a pine box. You make it as a Marine or you're fucking dead!

"Line up as I call your name. I will call your last name and you sound off with your first name and middle initial, and make sure you end it with SIR. IS THAT CLEAR?"

"Yes, sir!" we all said, like a bunch of little kids.

"I can't hear you little pussies. Sound off all the way from your asshole!"

"YES, SIR!"

Abrahamson was called first, then I heard 'Alifolitolie.' I thought: *Shit! What kind of name was that?* God, he looked like an ape, and I hoped I didn't have to sleep next to him. To this day, I don't know how I remember those first names of newly enlisted Marines back in 1953.

Finally, "Brandon!"

"Percy E., sir!" I said.

"Well, what the fuck do we have here? A violin player? Come here you red-cheeked little pussy. Where the fuck you from?"

"Oregon, sir."

"I hear they only have Indians and loggers up there. What the fuck do you log? Pussy willows?" One of our platoon laughed. "What the fuck you laughing at?" Baker said to the guilty man, then to me, "Get out of here, I'll rip your fucking head off?" Thank God, he told me to get back to the barracks; I barely heard the "thump" as the DI punched the laugher in the guts.

* * *

As luck would have it, my bunk was under Alifolitolie's. *Oh shit!* I thought. "You help me make my bed," he would say.

Boy, he talks funny.

"I'm from Solomon Island." I was scared shitless of this guy; he was tough-looking and as big as an ape. "We are friends. You help me and I will help you. I was a school teacher and a boxer back on the island."

My first Marine friend, and I couldn't even pronounce his name!

* * *

"Get your asses out in the middle of the barracks," Sergeant Gilmore commanded the platoon. "Bring all your lighters, matches and cigarettes. There are two boxes in the middle of the floor. Throw your cigarettes in one box and your matches and lighters in the other. You will get three cigarettes a day—if you're lucky. The best thing for you to do is quit now."

I must have been the first one there: I had only started smoking about two weeks earlier and it sounded like a good way to get rid of them without looking like a pussy. Some of the older guys held back, as they had been instructed to put their cigarettes in a holder on the wall.

* * *

During that first week, we were taught how our bunks should be made and how to fold our clothes in the military style. Damn, I thought that was great! I got two pair of boots, three sets of work uniforms, six pair of socks, shorts and T-shirts. I also got a bucket full of goodies: tooth paste, shaving cream, razor blades, soap, towels and laundry bags. "Shit, this is just like Christmas, and we get to keep the bucket," I said. Damn if there wasn't more: boot polish, two belts, buckles, some kind of Brasso polish and Marine Corps stationary picturing the flag-raising on Iwo Jima. "My brother was on Iwo Jima," I said, without thinking.

One of our DIs heard and said, "You want to talk, you asshole? Get up here—tell us all what's so important that you want to run your fucking mouth."

I repeated with more conviction, "My brother was a Marine."

"If you don't shut your fucking mouth and learn to say sir, you will never be a Marine!" He then pulled my hat down over my ears and made me stand in place and jump up and down while saying, "I'm a shitbird, I'm a shitbird." God, I knew I was going to cry. *I hope he doesn't see the tears*, I thought.

"Well, look, the little girl is crying. Do you want to go home to your mommy? What the fuck you crying for? Do you think you're at Boy Scout camp and we're here to play games? You goddamn little cunt, if you're not man enough, we can send you across the fence to the queen farm. Then you can be a sailor."

Damn asshole. I'd kick his ass if I ever got the chance; but that was just wishful thinking.

We resumed with our gear allotments and I thought, *Shit, aren't they ever going to stop giving us stuff?* We were given other sundries, a tent, our own rifles, bayonets and belts. *Shit, let anyone fuck with me now!*

* * *

"Pick it all up and move out."

We were miles from our barracks and I wondered where the cattle cars were. As a unit of seventy, we strung out almost the entire length of a football field.

"Close it up, you assholes!"

God, with everything I have to pack, I feel like I'm carrying a hundred pounds!

"Who told you to put your gear down? Move it out...run...run, you assholes…get to your barracks…get back out here…you're too slow!"

As the orders were shouted the men were falling down right and left, their gear all over the ground.

"You shit-maggots will never make it," we were told.

God, my arms are coming off; sweat's running down my face. This was worse than football wind sprints.

"Put all your shit on your bunk, get in, and make a head call."

At "head call" we walked sideways down a long trough to take a piss, and damn if I could get started! Nearing the end of the trough, I tried to stop walking, in order to finish what I had a hard enough time starting. A big Indian pushed me, causing me to piss all over my own leg. "Get the fuck out of my way," he said.

All I could think of was, *God, what am I going to do if I have to shit? Maybe we don't get to shit!*

We had about an hour to put our gear away, Marine style. We learned all bunks were head-to-toe; our rifles hung on the end of our bunks; our packs were made up to hang on the same end; and our towel and laundry bags hung at the opposite end. We practiced tearing them apart several times until we got it right.

"Platoon thirty-three! On the road for chow," Corporal Colby said.

I was so tired I couldn't remember what day it was, or when I ate last. We lined up in four squads, according to height. I was in the third squad, about seventh from the front. My cousin Charles was in the fourth squad, one man in front of me. Shit, this was the closest I'd been to him since we got there. It was good to see him, and I thought about sitting together at mess hall. We did sit at the same table but were scared to talk. If we got caught, we would, sure as shit, get our asses kicked.

After eating, we were to get out of the mess hall and form up on the east side of the building. I didn't even know where I was, let alone which way east was. Charles and I ran out at the same time; there were platoons all over the place. *Where the hell is my platoon?* I spotted Colby talking to another DI and told Charles I thought that we probably were over in that direction. We ran over and started to get into our spots when the other DI shouted at us. "Get the fuck out of here, you pigfuckers! What the hell you doing trying to get in my platoon?" Shit! Another screw up! We got knocked on our asses by a platoon full of men we didn't even know. Damn, I wouldn't do that again.

Back in our own platoon, Colby started drills. "Right face!"

Shit, I did a left face! I turned back to the right, double-fast, hoping to God he didn't see my mistake. Maybe I'd get lucky. Some of the other men had made the same mistake; I might be able to blend into the crowd. I could hear him walking up behind me. *Please let him pass me.*

"That's your right foot, you asshole," he said as he stomped on my foot. "It's the one that hurts."

No shit! Two others got stomped, so at least I wasn't the only one with a sore right foot—not that that was any consolation. We must have been at boot camp about a week, and by that time, we were marching fairly well. Some of us, including myself, were daydreaming when our DI halted the march; half of us didn't stop.

"Get down on the deck for push-ups," we were ordered. *Shit! On a full stomach!* Then Colby threw in duckwalking on top of the push-ups. Some of the men puked.

* * *

When we were finally allowed to write home my first letter said:

Dear Mom, please come and get me. I want to go back to school; I promise I will never skip school again. I will cut wood and ride the school bus. Anything, just get me out of here. PS., Charles wants to come home, too.

A lot of good that letter did me. My first letter home and, shit, I didn't finish in time to put it in the mailbox. I promised myself I would next time.

* * *

"Third and fourth squads, get in the head for showers."

Shit, I hated this. Two squads trying to get in only six showers. The big Indian guy turned out to be from Oklahoma and must have been close to seven feet tall. He wouldn't let anyone stand under the showerhead with him. Personally, I thought he was jacking off in the shower, but no one was brave enough to look.

One night, one of our drill instructors called out six names, mine included. "You will be on firewatch tonight. Your job will be to make sure no one gets out of their rack at night, except to go to the head, and then only one man at a time. You will wake up the next man in two hours and make sure he is ready. Private Brandon, you have the first watch from 2100 hours until 2300 hours." (That was the nine to eleven p.m. shift.) I hoped that while I was in charge, nobody would fuck up.

"Come here, Brandon," one of the men said. "You watch for Colby while we crawl out the window and smoke a cigarette."

"Shit," I said, "I don't think you better; you might get caught."

"Ah, hell, we do it every night," he said. "And I'll kick your ass if you don't watch out for us." What choice did I have? And like he said, they'd been doing it every night. What could go wrong?

"Turn on the lights, firewatch," Colby's voice boomed out.

Oh, shit! I thought. The men were still outside smoking; we were caught.

"You asshole!" he said as he slapped me alongside the head, "What are those privates doing out of their bunks?" The four men were trying to crawl through the window, all at the same time. Everyone in the barracks was sitting up in their bunks watching the show. I was the first to get punched. You're going to jail for not following your firewatch orders," Colby snorted, then punched me again, before starting on the other four. Shit, he was pissed! We lived through an hour of beatings, before he left us alone.

I woke up my relief at 2300 hours. I had a swollen eye and my guts were awfully sore. "I thought Corporal Colby was going to kill you," my relief said.

I was scared all night, knowing I was going to catch hell in the morning and, come morning, I did.

"Brandon, you'll be standing firewatch every night until you get out of boot camp," were his final words—after he beat the shit out of the five of us again. Sure enough, every time we had to leave a firewatch, I got the duty.

* * *

During the coming weeks, while my platoon went to chow, I stood firewatch. The good part was: it always gave me a chance to rest. The bad part was: I had to join another platoon at mess, after I was relieved each time from watch duty. This DI screwed with me all through training. His platoon pulled my hat over my ears or said my DI was a shithead, then threatened to tell him I'd done the name calling. I had to finish eating and be ready to leave the mess hall by the time my own platoon was done. Most of the time that meant I didn't eat much or had to run like hell to catch up. Sometimes I'd be late and get my ass kicked.

Another bad aspect of my firewatch duty was that it took place during the time our DI usually taught new marching movements to the rest of our platoon. I would miss this instruction because I did not march to mess hall with them. Sometimes the guys would help me, but most of them would teach me incorrectly and I'd get my ass kicked anyway. *Shit, I'm gonna be one tough son of a bitch or one black-and-blue Marine—if I ever get out of here alive*, was my thought on the matter.

We were coming back from chow one day, when the DI said, "Left step… right step…double to the rear…march!" I had never heard this move before and got stepped on, pushed and knocked all over the place. "What the fuck's wrong with you? Can't you hear?" he asked.

"Sir, I thought the drill instructor was joking." (I'd been the butt of so many jokes at boot camp that I thought this was just one more.)

"You're the only fucking joke here," he said as he choked me and threw me back into the platoon.

Firewatch caused me more than my share of headaches.

* * *

During boot camp we had complete medical and dental checkups and received our immunization shots. I had never been to a dentist in my life and was starting to sweat as we filed up the stairs to the second-floor level for our checkups.

What is that smell? I thought. *I'm going to be sick.* I didn't remember a thing and woke up outside laying on the grass. When I looked up, Corporal Colby was standing over me.

"What the hell is wrong with you, you goddamn little pussy," he said.

I tried to get up. *Oh my God, my balls hurt. I feel like I've been kicked by a horse.*

"Get back inside!" So, in I marched. The others were already standing in line, buck naked.

"Get your clothes off," I was told, "and get back in line with your number."

I was still hurting like hell and wondering what the hell had happened. Then the doctor asked, "What's wrong with your penis and testicles?" They were black-and-blue and swollen. He called Corporal Colby over, and two or three other people came to look, as well.

"You been loping your mule?" Colby asked.

"Sir, I don't know what that means."

"Are you pounding your pud? Jacking off?"

"No, sir," I said. "I really don't know what happened."

The doctor's diagnosis didn't alleviate my fears. "This man has to be circumcised." He pulled my foreskin back so tight that it hurt like hell.

I could only think: *What happens if I get circumcised? Am I set back any in training?*

After the doctor finished looking up our asses and grabbing our balls and making us cough, we got our shots. *Lots* of shots.

While marching back to the barracks, I must have looked like hell. My balls were killing me.

Colby finally said, "Get out of the platoon and walk in back. You look like you have a corncob up your ass."

Back in the barracks, during a head call (the only time we dared to speak to each other), I asked Charles what had happened back during the checkups. Why had I ended up outside, lying on the ground.

"You shithead," he laughed. "You passed out at the smell of that place and did a three-sixty down the stairs. Colby and some others packed your ass outside. I think it was a good thing you woke up when you did, or more than your balls would hurt about now!"

* * *

By the time we got back to barracks and were called for chow, I still wasn't happy about the prospect of being circumcised.

"Platoon, outside for chow!" (Shit! We had a new drill instructor. I wondered what had happened to Colby. Then I wondered if this new DI had been told I might have to get my pecker fixed.) "I'm your new drill instructor, PFC Thomas. Corporal Colby is on orders and will be going to Korea."

What are the chances of everyone keeping their mouths shut about the doc cutting on my pecker? I wondered. As it turned out, good. No one ever mentioned the circumcision to Thomas. One of the men in my platoon even gave me some tips to reduce my swelling—if you call running ice-cold water over my pecker and wearing swim trunks under my pants when I ran, good tips! The next few days were hell, but the swelling went down and Thomas never knew I was to go back to the doctor. And I damn sure didn't tell him!

* * *

That night Staff Sergeant Baker announced a "smoker" the following Sunday and said that if any of us could box or was a good fighter we could sign up. Well, shit, I had boxed a little in school, and because I'd had the shit beaten out of me over the last two weeks, I signed up at one hundred and fifty pounds. All in all, about eight men signed up. Among us were Douglas D. Dunkin, a little red-haired Scottish man, who signed up at one hundred and thirty pounds; and Henderson, the big Indian who pushed me around in the john. He signed up just to fight.

We were all surprised that everyone in our platoon won their matches! I only had two fights and won both; Henderson must have fought at least six times. Dunkin was the one we all had doubts about, but he proved that he could sure box for a little guy. The kid from the Solomon Islands nearly killed everyone he matched up against. We sure made a name for 33rd Platoon; the rest of the platoons stayed clear whenever we went to chow.

We dared anyone to cross us. No one ever made the mistake of trying to walk between our platoon and our DI, for they were sure to get their asses kicked.

It worked to my advantage, too. Everyone quit calling me a "little pussy."

Even the drill instructors started leaving me alone: most of the time anyway.

* * *

Sundays were always good days. We had most of the morning off to wash clothes and write letters. (We could also use the head without asking!)

One morning, after I thought I was surely off the hook, I heard my name being called out. "Private Brandon, report to the drill instructor." PFC Thomas was on duty and I was sure he had suddenly remembered about the smoking-on-firewatch incident. I just knew he was going to kick my ass. "Brandon, you have a visitor. Get your cousin and report to the visiting center in clean uniforms." My next thought (after my heart skipped a beat or two) was. *Shit, my mother's come for me!*

As was usual when visitors came, the platoon asked us to buy cigarettes and candy bars from the vending machines in the visiting center. They must have given us ten or fifteen dollars.

The visitor turned out to be my brother Gary, who was still in the Navy. One of his buddies had come with him. They looked as through they had been on an all-night drunk, but I was sure glad to see him. I was glad to see *anyone* from home at this point.

I must have eaten every candy bar I bought. Gary told me not to sweat it, since I'd probably get the shit kicked out of me if I got caught sneaking the stuff in. He said that if I gave him the money, however, he could walk by and drop the stuff off. Always the sucker, we told him where our barracks were located. I still had three Oh Henry candy bars, so I hid them in my socks before we returned. Charles hid some cigarettes and a candy bar in his socks. When we entered the barracks, Thomas asked if we had brought any candy or cigarettes. We said no—as innocently as we could muster.

"Well," he said, "you smell like you did!"

He ordered us to do jumping jacks in the hallway outside his office. One of my candy bars fell to the floor. "You goddamn pigfuckers lied to me!" Thomas screamed.

I'm not sure his feelings were really hurt at finding our lie. In fact, I'm almost certain he was enjoying it. All three of my candy bars were shoved into my mouth, wrappers and all. Charles, too, had candy and cigarettes stuffed in his mouth. Thomas covered our heads with buckets and ordered us to run up and down the hallway for the better part of an hour. Every time we passed the DI, he whacked the bucket with a broom handle. Candy was running out of my mouth and I was choking, but I kept trying to swallow while I ran. In the end I got sick and puked up everything.

I guess the best part was that the men in my platoon thought we had been caught with their goods! That asshole brother of mine—surprise!—never did show up. Damn, the platoon would have killed us!

* * *

By March, three weeks into boot camp, we saw big changes as we loaded onto cattle cars and rode ten miles up the road to Camp Mathews and the rifle range. As there were no extra barracks at this base, we camped six men to a tent. That was great! The DI never checked on us, so we had a good time talking to one another.

One day, when we were ordered into platoon formation, half the men didn't hear the DI. It seemed we were having a little too good a time talking.

Good old PFC Thomas came up with the idea of having us pack our seabags over a mile to a hill called "Big Aggie" for our punishment. We ran up and down that hill with seabags overhead, and it only took till the second time before half of us were falling down.

Next was duckwalking *down* Big Aggie. God, if that wasn't even worse! We were soaked with sweat, but we got smart fast. From then on we took turns standing watch at the front of our tents. If we spotted a DI, we had time to cover our asses. This was great for those who smoked: after dark they could sneak into the PX and buy all the smokes they wanted.

* * *

We finally saw our first day at the rifle range. It was also our first contact with Marines other than our own DI. We marched to the rifle range and were turned over to the range instructor. Our first instructor was, coincidentally, from Oregon. It sure made me feel good to have a Marine from Oregon teaching us, but we found out fast that it wasn't to our advantage.

When we were seated he said, "All privates from Oregon, stand up."

I think there were twelve of us, and I'm sure we thought we would be getting special treatment: that we'd found a kindred soul in this hell hole. He then said, "All of you had better shoot expert or I'll kick each one of your asses." He was on our butts all the time. He had bragged that Oregonians already knew how to shoot, so at his rifle range they just got better. He was going to make damn sure we didn't prove him wrong and screw up.

I never knew a body could get into so many different positions. In the kneeling position, we sat on the side of one foot. Damn, I could barely sit on my foot, let alone try to shoot a rifle from that position. Those five shots, however, would be worth twenty-five precious points.

The worst part seemed like the rapid-fire prone position. We had to drop as fast as possible, get into position and be ready to shoot. In only sixty seconds we had to have fired ten rounds. It had been almost four weeks since I fell down the stairs at the infirmary, and it seemed like I should have healed in that time. I was still hurting like hell; my balls felt as though they were falling off each time I hit the ground.

One day a private in my platoon wanted to put some luber plate (grease) on his rifle and asked the DI for the grease for his "gun." The DI had him stand on a trash can, pull out his pecker and grease it up. He then ordered the private to hold his rifle over his head with one hand and onto his pecker with the other while yelling in cadence as loudly as he could: "THIS IS MY RIFLE. THIS IS MY GUN. THIS IF FOR FIGHTING. THIS IS FOR FUN." Some of the men laughed and joined in as they got caught up in the fun. I nearly bit my tongue in half, but I did not laugh. I'd pretty well learned what earned me a beating and what didn't.

That evening someone asked the private how his gun was. He didn't see the event as humorously as the rest of us and decided to take the man on. The DI, also pissed, made the two beat the shit out of each other until they dropped.

We had a week of rifle practice. I thought: *Practice, shit! Are we ever going to shoot this gun? Oh, shit, don't call it a gun!*

* * *

The next Monday morning we were kicked out of our tents at four-thirty for chow, in order to be on the firing range by six o'clock. Shit! It is pitch dark at that time. We tried to march without stepping on the man in front of us, but that was unavoidable in the dark. I heard a lot of grumbling from the private in front of me.

Boy, I still remember the butterflies in my stomach. Charles and I were on one target together, side-by-side. There must have been a hundred targets. Our instructor was a sergeant just back from Korea, who didn't give a shit about anything. He had been wounded and awarded a Purple Heart and Bronze Star—whatever those were.

"Whoever of you two shoots best gets the other's dessert at chow." (Shit! That was the best part of chow for me!) *Well, that asshole cousin of mine isn't going to beat me!*

Damned if Charles didn't shoot the shit out his target that morning. Nothing like incentive, I guess. My balls felt like they were shoved up my ass each time I hit the ground, and I thought I missed the whole target: all I could see was a blur. I actually did hit the target, but my shots were all over the place.

"What the fuck are you using, a shot gun?" my instructor asked. Damn, he was pissed!

That asshole Charles hit every shot in the bull's-eye. That shithead would surely be eating my dessert. Every time he looked at me, the son of a bitch smiled and licked his lips. I even heard him thinking about how good it would taste. *I'll fix that bastard,* I thought, *I'll spit on my dessert, then laugh back! Screw him!*

* * *

Every morning it was the same old shit. Out of the bunks at four-thirty, off to chow and stumble to the rifle range in the dark.

Charles was shooting a higher score each day, and I was barely making it by the skin of my teeth. We had one day left before we would shoot for the record. As we marched back from the rifle range before that last day, Charles was doing the same old shit: smiling and licking his lips. *I hope our DI catches the bastard, then maybe he'll get his ass kicked.* I got as close to an answer to a prayer as I could get: Charles' rifle fell off his shoulder and the sights hit the pavement.

"You pigfucker," Thomas screamed at Charles as he slapped him alongside of the head. "What the fuck are you doing, dropping your rifle like that?"

I thought Charles was going to cry, I don't think he even heard what Thomas was saying or knew that he'd been slapped. And I was such an asshole. All I could think of was how Charles had fucked up his sights—and that I could outshoot him now!

* * *

Friday morning everyone was awake early, making sure things would be ready for that last day.

Charles had stayed up all night sweating. Sure enough, his first shot missed the target.

I was shooting all right, but not hitting many bull's-eyes. Finally, the five-hundred-yard line! Only ten shots left. I knew I wouldn't fire expert, but if I could hold on, I could make sharpshooter. In the end, I scored two hundred eight, only a marksman rating. But that marksman rating was good enough to beat Charles by one point. He was so pissed! He had not only hoped to win my dessert, he hoped to be the highest scorer in the platoon. I, of course, wouldn't leave it alone. I was on his ass for dessert.

"Fuck you," he said. "I'm not giving up my dessert because of a shit accident with my rifle."

When our instructor asked who won, I told him I had, but that Charles was going to welch on the bet. I was assured that our DI would make sure Charles didn't. All the way back, I rubbed it in. I knew that, if I kept it up, Charles would probably kick my ass; he was already so pissed-off that he wouldn't talk to me. During our last three weeks at boot camp, I gave him such a nice smile each time he gave me his dessert.

* * *

I could tell we were almost done with boot camp the first week we returned to San Diego. We were allowed to unbutton our top uniform button and starch our hats. Shit! We almost looked like Marines!

We also got a week of mess duty upon our return. We had to rise at 3 a.m. and ready the mess hall for chow. It wasn't all that bad: we sneaked all the food we could eat. I remember how I thought that one week of mess duty went by faster than all the others combined!

We stayed with an incoming platoon that would be taking our place, just long enough for us to show them what our jobs had been. My own relief, with his arrogant, know-it-all attitude, reminded me of myself. He even told me to fuck myself, that he didn't need to do things per my instructions and challenged me to a fight.

I was feeling mighty tough. I'd been through ten weeks of boot camp and was seasoned enough to know there was no such thing as cheating when it came to beating the shit out of someone. The new enlistee went out the door first, with me right behind him. I had a big, old mop in my hand and used it to smack the back of his head. I knocked him off a six-foot-high platform and that ended the fight.

Damn, I was proud of myself! A few of my platoon saw the fight and were fast to tell the rest how I had kicked this kid's ass. I was nicknamed "One-Shot Brandon."

* * *

Incredible! Only two weeks of boot camp left! Spit and polish, march, march, march, march, press those uniforms.

That damn Charles actually bought an ironing board and iron. He charged everyone two bucks to press their uniforms, but he was still so pissed-off at me that he'd tell me to go fuck myself and charge me double.

I remember my last Sunday in boot camp. I was put on a working crew to move things from one building to another. The rest of the platoon stayed to work on their own gear. Shit, I was pissed: that was going to make my stuff look bad. While I was gone, my platoon schemed up one last boot-camp sucker's joke. When I got back to barracks, they told me they had all been tattooed with a heart and the number thirty-three on their right leg to symbolize the bond between the members of our platoon. I was the only one left to get the tattoo.

A Mexican kid from Arizona was the artist. He took a needle, heated it with a match, dipped it in ink and started on my leg. Goddamn if this didn't hurt! Pussy or no, I told him to quit. I let myself be persuaded to finish the heart portion of the tattoo; then the pain got to be too much. I demanded to see the rest of the platoons' tattoos before I went any further. Only two others had gotten a tattoo! What a shithead I was!

* * *

Before we were to ship out, it was a tradition to hold a drill competition among the platoons. We placed second to 34th Platoon but didn't mind all that much, because their senior DI was a DI we began boot camp with.

God, I could almost taste it—we were just about finished! I remember it was April 3, 1953. One more day left.

At 0700 hours we filed out for final inspection.

"Brandon! What the hell did you do to your finger? Wipe your ass with it?"

When I looked down, I saw shoe polish on my fingertip from shining my shoes. *Damn! I'm going to get my ass kicked one more time before I get out of here!* I thought. I tried sucking off the polish while the captain fetched the senior DI. That didn't do much, so I tried clipping it off with my nail clippers before their return. By that time my finger had started bleeding. I knew the next inspection was with the senior DI, and he was going to kill me. But no. He looked at my finger and, surprisingly, said, "Get back to the barracks and take care of that finger."

He had told me not to return, so I stayed in the barracks until I saw my platoon coming back. *PFC Thomas is with them! Oh, shit!* Then I knew I was going to die.

"Get your packs, gear and rifles," he said. "Fall in outside to turn in all equipment."

For once in four months I got away clean. No one said anything.

* * *

Friday morning came, April 4, 1953, and we walked back to the barracks after chow in full uniform. Seabags were left in the barracks and the cattle cars were parked in front of our building. We were herded into cattle cars headed for Camp Pendleton—wherever the hell that was.

"When I call your name, sound off. First name, middle initial and rank. BRANDON!"

Shit, it was my turn. "Percy E., PFC, sir!" *Good Lord! I'm done! I'm a fucking Marine at last!*

April 4, 1953: A Marine at last!

Above: USMC Platoon 33, San Diego 1953

Below: My classmates' signatures on the back of the photo

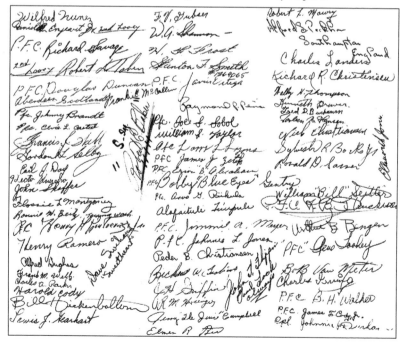

Chapter 3
Camp Pendleton

This was only the second time I had been off the base since I'd arrived at boot camp on January 19, 1953. The ride that Saturday seemed long but really took only about an hour.

Camp Pendleton had hills everywhere. Marines with packs were moving everywhere, mostly up the hills.

"Everyone off the trucks. Fall in according to last name. Form up four ranks!" A sergeant, with rows of ribbons and ladders on his shooting badges, walked down the middle of the group. "Last names *A* through *H* take eight steps to the left," he shouted. We split in half. "Are any of you married, and is your wife here?" A few raised their hands. They were given liberty for the weekend. The rest of you get back on the trucks with your seabags." For the first time in my life, I seriously considered marriage a viable option in the Marine Corps.

Our group of three hundred was divided by last name. *A*'s through *H*'s went to First Combat Training Center, and *I*'s through *Z*'s went to Second Combat Training Center.

I saw my cousin Charles board the second group's truck and waved at him. Like always, he gave me the finger, and we both laughed. I guess he finally got over being pissed at me. As we drove between those big hills, all I could see were rows and rows of Quonset huts.

When we stopped in front of ours, we were welcomed to Dog Company and instructed to fall into three ranks. That was a change for us: the last four months we had been forming four ranks with a full platoon.

Our troop leader, beginning at the front of each rank and moving toward the back began with, "You first three Marines will be squad leaders, the next three team leaders, the next three riflemen, the next three automatic riflemen, and the last three will be assistant automatic riflemen." That made me an automatic rifleman (Shit!). He repeated this three more times so that the fifteen of us would understand, without a doubt, our assignments. I wondered what Charles had been assigned.

One of our group, with past experience, was assigned as our guide.

This will be your team for the next four weeks. Get to know each other. You will work, sleep and live together. If one of you fucks up, you all pay." Thinking about our recent history at boot camp, I didn't have a lot of confidence in our ability to stay out of trouble.

I was still awaiting our orders for drills or marching when the troop leader surprised us.

"Put your seabags away and get back here on the double. You'll soon get combat gear and rifles. If you get your asses in gear, you get base liberty until midnight Sunday. "

Liberty! A day and a half of liberty!

* * *

My squad leader turned out to be a kid from Idaho named Buchannon. "Let's go find a Slop Chute," he suggested.

"What the hell is a Slop Chute?" I asked.

"That's where we can get all the food and beer we want."

"Well, shit, man," I said. "I'm a Marine! Let's go!"

The place was full of Marines, from old-timers to the guys I had just gone through boot camp with. I remember being impressed with those men who had rows of ribbons from other wars. They were sure pouring down the beer! As a new Marine, I felt it my duty to keep up. I'd only had a few beers in my life, but Buchannon was an old hand and downed three beers to my one. I was soon getting plowed. After much more than I could handle, I knew I had to quit or die intoxicated.

"I'm going back to the hut," I told Buchannon.

"I'm staying until they throw my ass out of here!" he said.

I must have walked for hours, trying to find my way back to my hut—they all looked the same to me. I puked all the way back and had shit all over my shoes. Amazingly, I found my hut but was so sick that I didn't bother taking my clothes off when I finally hit the rack. I couldn't have been asleep but a few minutes when I heard Buchannon come in.

"Get your ass up, Brandon! We're going to town. I got a taxi waiting at the gate."

"We can't go to town," I said. "We only have base liberty."

"Fuck it! We're Marines, let's go!"

"Don't you know what the brig is?" I thought throwing a scare into him might change his mind. "If we get nailed going off-base, they'll lock us up."

"Shit! I know we can do it." He was sure.

"Fuck you, go by yourself," I said. "We only have one month here before we get to leave."

Buchannon departed with, "You chickenshit, Brandon!"

* * *

Come 0600 hours we fell out for roll call. No squad leader.

"PFC Buchannon? Anybody know where he is?" our troop leader asked. I didn't speak.

We were marching to chow when I saw Buchannon coming down the road. He was drunk on his ass, and his uniform looked like shit. Goddamn it! They were going to hang his ass for this and probably the whole platoon's, too.

"Where the fuck have you been, Buchannon?" the corporal asked.

"I got lost last night and ended up in another camp," he innocently began, "and some Marines got me drunk and lost, and I've been walking all night trying to find my hut."

"Get the fuck back to your hut and out of that uniform. Be in my office when I get back."

Damn, he looked like a sad case. We laughed our asses off at him. A good start on our first day.

After chow that Sunday, we had the morning to attend church and work on our gear. We had been told that we would be in full training. If we missed one day, we would be set back to the beginning and have to start over.

Poor old Buchannon, he had to spend the day digging a hole. I asked him if he'd like to go have a beer with me that night and was told to fuck off.

* * *

"Make sure you have two full canteens of water; we won't get back until late tonight. You'll have C rations for noon chow and field mess for evening chow."

We were on our way to the fields.

Damn, all the classroom benches were cut into the sides of the hills. We hiked to one, then another, and another—up one hill and down the next. *Why the fuck don't we just stay at one?* But then, I didn't get paid to think.

"Squad leaders, send two men to pick up your squad's C rations." I realized I was really hungry and two green cans were all I got. *Shit, I'll never make it!* I thought.

We had one can opener for our squad of fifteen men. They called the opener an "Itty-waah," whatever that was. I just knew it opened my chow. When I opened a can, the contents looked like some kind of greasy patty. After I scraped away the grease, it turned out to actually be four patties of some unidentifiable meat. The other can held a round candy bar, cocoa, hard crackers and a flat can of jelly.

We threw our cans into the bushes and our troop leader went ape-shit. "You think you're the only fucking Marines that ever trained here? Get your goddamn asses out there and clean up that trash!"

Shit, I guess we *weren't* the only Marines to train there. We found cans a hundred years old. We had to pick them all up.

* * *

Our next class was about a three-mile hike up one side of a mountain. My ass was dragging by the time we got there. We sat on the side of a hill that did not have cutaway benches and damn near slid off.

The "gunny" (a gunnery sergeant, ranking just above a staff sergeant) who was giving the class was a mean-looking asshole and hard to understand. I saw a huge black beetle crawling toward me, so I picked up a small stick and poked at it. I was having a hell of a time teasing it when Gunny jumped off his platform and landed smack, square on top of me.

"You fucking asshole!" he yelled. "You think I'm up there for my fucking health? Get your fucking rifle over your head and run down that hill! When you get to the bottom, turn around and get back up here before I'm finished talking to these fine Marines, or I'll kick your ass back down there again!"

Shit! It must be two miles to the bottom! I thought. I found out you don't run downhill holding a rifle overhead. My rifle was a Browning automatic that weighed over twenty pounds. I thought I was dying and could hardly move by the time class was over. My company was moving uphill, and I wasn't going to catch up. I hauled ass, trying to catch up with the rest of the group, and passed Gunny.

"Did you learn anything?" he asked.

"Yes, sir," I said and kept moving along.

By the time we caught up with my troop, we saw tents about three miles downhill.

"Get your mess kits and fall in—chow time."

God, we were going to walk all the way down to eat. Back up the hill for two more classes, then back down to the huts. I was halfway to being a mountain goat by the end of the day.

Back at the hut we were told about a rifle and equipment inspection due at 1900 hours.

"Everyone who passes gets a movie call tonight."

I hadn't seen a movie in six months. What a great theater: the seats were benches with no backs, outdoors under the stars, no fucking popcorn or pop and bugs up the ass. *Shit, what a treat!* No wonder Marines are so tough. *Damn, I have three more years of this.*

* * *

It *did* get better. With only ten days left, word was, that if we did well in the field, we would get liberty from noon Saturday until midnight on Sunday. I was already looking forward to liberty call the next day.

A colored kid named Green was scared of everything, but mostly snakes.

During a break, someone found a dead snake. We tied it to Green's pack with comm wire, and when Green got up, the snake moved. The faster he ran, the faster the snake followed.

We were all dying. The last we saw of Green he was doing about fifty miles an hour down the side of a mountain. What a great prank! When no one got liberty except Green, however, the joke wasn't nearly as funny.

* * *

I was cleaning my gear one day when Charles walked up the road in uniform. Damn, I hadn't seen him in over a month.

"Hey, fucker, what's going on? How the hell did you get liberty so early?" I asked.

"I was the only one to hit the target on the rifle grenade range!" He smiled cockily.

As I only had base liberty, we headed to the Slop Chute for beer. At the Slop Chute we ran into a still-pissed-off Green, but he joined us in a good laugh, and we took pictures in a photo booth. I had picked up a knack for holding on to things and keeping them in fairly good shape. I'll never know how I stuffed those old photos in my seabag—folded, crumpled and bent—and, in the long run, they survived better than I did.

Charles and I were about to finish training on the same weekend. We planned to meet at the bus station in Oceanside, California at twelve noon to catch a bus to Los Angeles. From there, we would board a train to Salem, Oregon and home.

I was one tough son of a bitch by that time. I could hike with my seabag, a handbag and a clothing bag without ever putting them down. Damn fine!

In Oceanside we all joined up: Bice, Selby, Charles, myself and a few more from boot camp. We didn't have much time to chat, as the bus to L.A. was already loading. Originally we only had a one-hour layover before the train left for Salem, but when we got to Frisco, we had a three-hour layover. Hot damn!

* * *

We hit the streets. Big tough-ass Marines with a few bucks and a bunch of hard-ons. We set out to find a piece of ass.

The whores looked like female wrestlers and wanted twenty bucks a throw, plus we would pay for the rooms. That was way more than I had, so the four of us went back to wait for the train.

On our way back, we ran into some soldiers and gave them holy shit. They didn't want to screw around with us; everyone was scared to death of us.

On the Shasta Daylight train to Salem, I must have slept most of the ride. The next thing I knew, we were in Salem. It was two o'clock in the morning and raining like a son of a bitch. There wasn't a bus or a taxi in sight. *Shit, now I'll have to hitchhike home!* I thought. It was at least five miles just to the other side of Salem, let alone getting the other twenty miles to Grand Ronde. *What the hell, I'm a bad ass Marine.* I had just started walking over the bridge when a pickup truck pulled up beside me.

"Where you heading, Marine?" the driver asked.

"Grand Ronde."

"Get in, I'm going to Rose Lodge." Shit, what luck! He had to drive right through my hometown to get to Rose Lodge. He dropped me off about a half mile from home.

* * *

It was around six o'clock Sunday morning, just about the time Mom would be cooking breakfast, when I walked in the house. God, how I remember this. My older brother Stubby had been a Marine and was killed during World War II on Iwo Jima eight years earlier. Whenever he came home on leave, he would sneak in on Mom. On his last leave he stayed eight days; it was the last time we ever saw him. Now it was my turn. I was going to sneak up on Mom. When I walked up to the door, she was making a fire in the kitchen stove.

"Hi, Mom," I said.

"Oh, my gosh!" she exclaimed. "It's Gene. He's home."

My younger sister Mary and brother Bill were staying with the folks.

"Daddy, get up! Gene is home."

Mary had a little girl and a good old boy for a husband. He came from Arkansas and was a big, tall shit.

Boy, what a breakfast: bacon, eggs, fried potatoes, deer meat, the works! I was eating and telling them all about the Marine Corps. Without thinking I said, "Pass the fucking salt."

It got dead quiet around the table. Mom began to cry and left the table. Mary was smirking at me. "What did I say?" I asked.

Dad almost bit his lip off, trying not to laugh out loud. I went after Mom, feeling like shit.

"Mom, I'm really sorry. That's the way Marines talk all the time. I guess it just slipped out. Can I go to church with you? I am sorry."

It must have been the right thing to say, as she hugged me and stopped crying. After that I was scared to talk. It seemed like I would always swear.

* * *

I had planned, on Monday morning, to go to my old high school to sort of show off. Everyone in school had thought I was too big a sissy to make it in the Marine Corps.

I climbed the front steps and saw Fritz Misler. "Hi, Percy. I didn't know you worked for Coca-Cola," he said, dead serious.

"I'm not a Coke man. I'm a Marine," I stated, sticking out my chest. Everyone around sure looked pale. I had a great tan from being in the sun all day during my training. I couldn't help gloating.

The school looked smaller than I remembered. Then I spotted my first love, Sharon Blackwell.

"How has school been?" I asked her.

"Fine," she said. "How are the Marines?"

"It's tough, but I made it. I guess I will be going to Korea," I lied, hoping for some sympathy and an invitation to visit her. All I got back was her stare.

"Are you going with anyone, now?" I asked, stumbling around awkwardly.

"Yes."

"Steady?"

"Yes," she said. "Sorry." She turned and just walked away.

Someone told me once that, when you leave, you can always go back; but you can never really go *home*. Even though this was the only the first time I'd been away, I knew it was true. I wanted to leave. I wanted badly to get back to the base and my new life. I only stayed home eight days, then said my good-byes.

Chapter 4
My New Life

I viewed things differently back at Camp Pendleton. I no longer thought of myself as a boot-ass Marine. I was a tough-as-nails Marine.

I reported to Receiving for assignment on a Saturday—a day early—and was told I still had liberty until midnight the next night. Afterward, I would be going into the 3rd Marine Division.

Since coming back from leave, I was stone-cold broke. I found a base bus and rode around. The driver asked where I wanted to go.

"Just for a ride," I said despondently.

The driver had been a Marine during World War II and proceeded to tell me stories of his Marine days. I rode the bus, listening, as far as it went. Its furthest point took us way up into a canyon to North Tent Camp Three-and-a-half. *I sure hope I don't get sent up here. There's nothing but hills on all sides!* I thought.

* * *

Come Monday morning, we heard the list of names called for assignment, mine among them.

"You're going to First Battalion, Third Marines, Third Marine Division. Climb aboard!" Two hours later we arrived at North Tent Camp Three-and-a-half. *Shit! The asshole of the base, and I got stuck on it.*

"Get off those trucks and line up by last name, starting with A. PFC Brandon, PFC Kyle, you'll be going to B Company. Get your seabags and report to Staff Sergeant Dembroski."

Dembroski was the size of a truck. He was the fattest man I had ever seen. *Shit, I thought all Marines were in good shape.* Dembroski had ribbons all over his chest and wore a .45 pistol—although it took two pistol belts to go around him. I spotted yet another huge sergeant on my way in. *Are all the sergeants fat around here?*

"Where the hell did you get a name like Percy?" Dembroski asked.

"My brother named me after an uncle. He, my brother, was killed in the Marines, so I guess it's an okay name." That was the last time anyone made fun of my name.

"Brandon, you and Kyle are in First Platoon, Staff Sergeant Brankie and Lieutenant Cheatham in charge. Corporal Canneryberry is squad leader and will take you to your hut."

Corporal Canneryberry asked where we were from.

"Oregon," I said.

"Texas," replied Kyle, southern drawl and all.

Well, you're in luck, Kyle. Brankie is from Texas, and Lieutenant Cheatham is from New York—I think. He is so fucking big that he can be from anywhere he wants, and he is meaner than shit. He even swings between the huts." I wondered what the hell that meant, not realizing he was calling Cheatham an ape.

Staff Sergeant Brankie turned out to be a little guy with a bald head. His chest hair stuck out of his shirt, and he had a cigarette hanging out of his mouth.

"We work hard here, and we play hard here," he said. "If you fuck up doing either one, I will personally kick your asses up between your shoulder blades so hard that you'll have to take your shirts off to shit!"

He assigned us to 2nd Fire Team, me as an A-BAR man and Kyle a rifleman.

Shit, I thought, *I wanted to be a rifleman, damn that old, heavy A-BAR!* Brankie assigned me an A-BAR, after finding out I'd done A-BAR in combat training. I hated lugging the thing around, but it seemed my destiny was already written.

* * *

"We wear working uniforms for all meals, with the exception of uniform-of-the-day at evening chow—unless we are in the field. Same thing for the Slop Chute located in Tent Camp Three. Tent Camp Three is three miles down the road."

"Shit, I don't care if it's ten miles away, I'll go," bragged Kyle.

"You will, if I say you will," Staff Sergeant Brankie said. "You go down there and those assholes in Second Battalion are likely to kick your ass. We don't get along much with Second Battalion, so keep your mouth shut when you go down there."

We had guard duty that weekend. Some general was coming to inspect camp, so everything had to shine. Shit, all week we cleaned, painted rocks, raked dirt and trimmed ice plants.

Kyle and I were trimming ice plants, with our hats on the back of our heads, when I heard, "Who told you to wear your hats that way?"

I looked up—and up—and up: it had to be the man they described as Cheatham, whom I still hadn't seen.

We jumped and said in unison, "No one, sir!"

"What platoon are you in?" Cheatham asked.

"First Platoon!" I said.

"Don't ever let me catch you wearing your hat on the back of your head again."

"Yes, sir—I mean, no, sir!"

"Damn, he sure is one big asshole," Kyle said after Cheatham walked away.

"I hope he doesn't tell Brankie," I said, "because for sure *he* will be in our shit."

* * *

It was becoming a regular habit to show up at the Slop Chute, after chow, for a few beers. I was getting better at handling my booze and was looking forward to drinking with Kyle that night.

"Brandon, Kyle, make up a marching pack tonight and report to me after evening chow," Corporal Canneryberry said. Apparently Lieutenant Cheatham had told him about our hats.

"See that bench marker on that hill?" he asked.

"I can't see it, sir," I said.

"Well, trust me. It's there. You and Kyle take a hike up there tonight after chow. Then come back and tell me what it says on that marker."

We started out after chow. It was nearly dark by the time we found it. Kyle had thought to bring matches, so we were able to read the marker: PFC

CANNERYBERRY WAS HERE. Goddamn!

"What time is it?" I asked Kyle, when we finally got back.

"About two a.m."

"Shall we wake up Canneryberry and tell him we made it back?"

"He's not even in his bunk. Fuck him, we'll tell him in the morning," replied Kyle.

The next morning we were asked what we read on the marker.

"Canneryberry is a prick, and he was here," said Kyle. I almost shit.

Canneryberry said, "You're half-right, Kyle. What did you read, Brandon?" *Well, we were in this together,* I thought. "The same thing Kyle did, sir."

"Well, that's not right," he said. "So, go back tonight and make sure of what you saw."

"Shit, shit, shit, shit, shit! What the fuck did you say that for? Damn it, Kyle! Now we have to go up there again tonight!" And we did.

That night we again returned about two o'clock in the morning. This time, however, I woke up Canneryberry and told him exactly what I had read.

"Get the fuck to bed, Brandon," he said.

"You prick," I muttered.

* * *

The next morning, Brankie assigned Kyle and myself to guard duty for the weekend. "Report to the guard shack at 0700 hours with your rifle and helmet liner."

Because I carried an A-BAR. I was told to borrow the fire-team leader's rifle for guard duty. I can recall how I felt, thinking I was never going to get liberty. I hadn't even made it to the Slop Chute.

Kyle was posted around the supply hut. I was posted to the mess hall and PX. Guards had to carry rifles at "shoulder arms," unless challenging someone during their post. When reporting, the post rifles were carried at "port-arms." These were both grueling positions to maintain for four hours at a time. After four hours of walking around the two buildings, I thought: *I'll be glad when I turn eighteen. I'm going to ask to go to Korea.*

I'd just rounded a corner of the PX and—man! I swore I'd never seen so much brass in my life!

"Where in the hell is the Slop Chute? Is this all the Marines have to drink around here, damn pop machines?" an officer asked me.

My God, this man looked like a bulldog.

Shit, I'm about ready to piss my pants. What the hell do I do? A rifle salute? I'm not even sure who this guy is, but he's packing a bunch of brass!

"Morning, sir!" I said and kept on walking.

"Morning, Marine," the general said. Just that one encounter and my ass was all sweaty. By 1100 hours the officer of the day called for a report.

"PFC Brandon reporting. Post One all secure. All post and orders remain the same, sir!"

"Did you see the general come by your post?"

"Yes, sir," I said.

"That," the officer said, "is General Puller, the most famous general in the Marine Corps. He said we better have a fucking Slop Chute the next time he comes out this way."

That made me smile.

This general has five Navy Crosses and had been wounded several times, I was told. The enemy even has a price on his head. I wondered what that meant, but was too scared to ask. Besides, all I could think about was getting off the post and going for beer.

"Brandon, stay here in the guard shack on standby. You have the same watch again tonight from 2000 hours to 2400 hours and again on Sunday." Goddamn! Things just weren't in the cards for me. I had to sit in the guard shack all weekend, on duty.

While I was on guard duty, I saw a car with Oregon plates. I wondered where in Oregon they were from, then I recognized them. Damn, it was Charles' parents. I wondered what the hell they were doing here.

"It sure is good to see you," I said. "What are you doing clear down here?"

"We had to bring Charles down. He and another Marine from Rickreall came home without leave."

"Oh, shit," I said, "are they in jail?"

My aunt said, "No, they are just up the road from you at the next camp."

"Well, they must be with Second Battalion. When are you going back to Oregon?"

"Now," she said. "We heard you were here and wanted to say hello."

"Tell my folks I'm doing fine," I said. "Tell them not to worry. I like it here and don't think we will be leaving for a while." (I'd heard we would be in the field for another two weeks. Well, at least that meant I wouldn't have to stand guard duty.)

* * *

I found out what a field transport pack was. Shit, it had everything I owned in it, and more.

We'd been moving up a canyon all day and training as we went along. Everyone talked about all the pussy they'd gotten over the weekend: everyone except me; I'd been on guard duty for wearing my hat backwards.

We'd heard that some of C Company had got the shit blown out of them in a mine field, and one guy was hurt bad. I remember hoping it wasn't anyone I knew.

On our fourth day out in field, a fire got out of control and the entire canyon was ablaze. Shit, there were rabbits all over the place. That ended our field training, but we learned quickly how to fight fire.

"Hey, Brandon," someone yelled, "did you hear that it was Dunkin who got blown up?"

"Shit, he's a guy I went through boot camp with. He's from Scotland and was a great boxer. I sure hope he makes it." I truly meant it.

When we got back, I visited a friend from my old platoon named Bingham. Bingham was now in C Company. I asked him what had happened to Dunkin.

"He stepped on a dud that went off. It blew off part of his leg and put a hole in one of his lungs." I could tell it bothered Bingham as much as it did me.

I asked if anyone else got hurt, and he told me of a kid from Oklahoma, McCulliam, also from our platoon in boot camp, had been bitten on the hand by a snake.

Geez, these were stories I wasn't sure I was ready to hear.

* * *

Because the fire ended our field training, we ended up with about six hours of unexpected liberty.

"Let's head over to Tent Camp Three and have a beer," I offered.

"Hell, we don't have to," replied Kyle. "They opened a hut down here by the outdoor theater. We now have our own Slop Chute."

Great! "Let's get drunk and go fuck with my cousin Charles. He and Bice are on mess-hall duty at Tent Camp Three for the next thirty days, because they went AWOL."

On the way over, I told the story of Bice and Charles' over-the-hill trip. Damn, at 2200 hours they were still in the hall cleaning up.

"Hey Charles," I said, ready to fuck with his brain, "you want to go drink some beer?"

Before I knew what happened both Kyle and I were on our asses.

"Fuck you! We're restricted to the barracks and have to sign in every hour."

"What the fuck did you go home for?" I asked. "We went home only a month ago."

"Hell, I don't know. I just did it."

I can't say I didn't understand why he did it. I did.

"Did you hear about Dunkin?" he asked me.

"Yeah, but he's going to make it; he just won't be able to stay in the Marines."

Kyle must have known his beer-drinking time was being severely cut into with our chit chat.

"Let's go. Let's go drink some more beer."

It was too late, however; the Slop Chute was closing.

Just to prove, in front of my cousin, how tough I still was, I said, "Hell, let's run back to our camp; it's only three miles."

"Yeah, us First Battalion Marines are tough!"

My parting shot to Charles was, "See you assholes later. See if you can get liberty when you get off mess duty, and we'll go to Tijuana, Mexico for a piece of ass! It's only five pesos, I hear."

* * *

"Hey Brandon, you wanna chip in ten bucks to go to Woodard's place in Laguna Beach? He's going to buy the beer and food, and we can stay all weekend."

I had a cousin living in Compton, up near L.A. somewhere. "How far is Compton from Laguna Beach?" I asked.

Woodard told me it was about twenty miles, so I pitched in my ten bucks. I could hitchhike to Compton later during the weekend and look him up.

Woodard had a nice-looking wife, for being the ass-eye that he was. All he ever did at the base was sleep. Corporal Boyd always went home with Woodard. It was rumored he was screwing Woodard's old lady. I could believe that. Woodard, as usual, went to bed while we stayed up drinking. Sure as shit, Boyd went outside with Woodard's old lady.

I decided to head for Compton to look up my cousin. It only took me an hour to get there, and I asked at a barbershop how to find his street. What luck! I was only five or six blocks away. I hadn't seen Joe since he was in Oregon hunting with my dad four years earlier.

Joe and I had a few beers and some chow, and I spent the night. He gave me a ride to the highway so I could hitch a ride back to Laguna Beach.

I stopped by Woodard's house to see if the guys were still around. Woodard told me he and Boyd had gotten into a fight, after he'd caught him screwing his wife. He'd beaten the shit out of Boyd, and Boyd was a lot bigger than Woodard. None of this surprised me much, but I was glad I hadn't been there when he caught them.

Back at camp, I stopped to see Charles and Bice. They were still on mess duty. Playing with Charles' mind was a favorite pastime of mine, so I told him a very different version of my weekend. "I went to visit Joe in Compton and met this woman in a barbershop. She took me home with her and screwed me all weekend. She just dropped me off." I said it all with a straight face.

The funny part was that they'd been busted down to privates. I didn't know they'd lost their stripes until the next day when I saw them in uniform. God, Charles just kept giving me more to dish out at him! This was too much fun.

Bice heard part of the 3rd Marine Division would be going overseas. *Well, I thought, it won't be me. I'm not eighteen yet.*

* * *

Corporal Boyd looked like he'd gotten the shit beat out of him. Speaking through swollen lips, he told me to be ready to pack my seabag in the morning as we were going to go to San Diego to work the docks, helping load ships. I was told to take everything, including my rifle. We would be going to Hawaii by the weekend. He told me to send my green uniforms home. That took money that I didn't have, so I asked permission to hitch a ride to Compton to leave my greens with Joe. I told him I could make the round-trip in three or four hours.

I barely made it back through the gates in time. The MP gave me shit and told me that, if I'd been ten minutes later, he would have locked my ass up.

Not a car on the road and I still had six miles to go before I got back to my camp. *Shit, I guess I'll have to run,* I thought. I only had an hour of liberty left and was in uniform and dress shoes. I made the run in record time, but looked like shit when I walked into my hut. The duty NCO questioned me, and I told him about my six-mile jaunt from the gate. He laughed but must have understood the weekend I'd just gone through. He told me I'd have until 0800 the next morning; we didn't stage until then. At least I was going to get some sleep.

All night I wondered what the hell we were doing going to Hawaii. It sounded like a good deal to me: sandy beaches and lots of sunshine.

I decided to write to my mother. I believed that that's where Stubby is buried: a place called Punch Bowl, home of the 5th Division dead. I would check with Mom.

I was turning eighteen years old in three days. That damn recruiter had sure fed my mom a line of bullshit.

Chapter 5
Shipping Out

My old buddy Kyle was headed out to help load ship, too. We were headed for one of the bases south of San Diego.

"Where is the ship?" he asked. "In San Diego?" I nodded. "Shit! Maybe we can make it down to Mexico and get laid," he said excitedly.

We boarded the trucks the next morning. On the ride to San Diego, I remembered the set of khaki uniforms I'd left at the laundry. Kyle was good enough to tell me I was shit-out-of-luck.

We went onto the navy base and stopped at the docks.

"I hope we don't have to load all those ships," I said.

About six of us were still under eighteen and were assigned guard duty when we arrived.

"Shit! I don't get to go to Mexico with you."

"You fucking sissy," Kyle replied. "Sorry, buddy, I'll be down in Mexico tonight getting a piece for us both."

The officer in charge said, "You Marines who are standing guard stash your seabags at the end of the docks. Brandon, don't let anyone off the docks unless I okay it. PFC Parrish, you stay here with Brandon." Parrish was from another platoon in boot camp and had, for a colored man, the longest eyelashes I'd ever seen.

Back then, I thought we had it made on guard duty. At least we didn't have to load ships. The best part was the snack bar. We didn't have to eat C rations all the time. After standing guard for two days, I began to wonder if we would stand guard yet *another* night.

"Brandon," the officer called, "there's someone here to see you."

I saw some sailor and wondered what in the world he wanted to see me for. Then, hell, I realized it was old Howard Fuller from high school. I was given an hour to visit Howard before returning to duty.

Howard said that he had heard I was now a Marine. He'd seen our troop at the docks and asked the officer in charge if he happened to know a PFC Brandon from Oregon. *How often does that happen?* I thought. *I'm standing less than fifty feet from them?*

Howard was in one of the navy specialty schools but was headed for Korea sometime that month. I mentioned that, as of that day, I was eighteen years old.

"Hell," he said, "I'll go buy a cake."

Cake wasn't a commodity at the snack bar, so we settled for jelly rolls.

Camp Pendleton, 1953:
Tent Camp 3-1/2 waiting to go overseas

Still, someone from home was celebrating my birthday with me. We talked about the good old days at high school and all the girls we tried to score with. We both lied a lot during that hour.

When my company returned I spotted their truck pulling up to the docks I knew my time was short.

"See you overseas," I said.

* * *

I didn't see Corporal Canneryberry with my company or with the rest of the platoon. Once again, we had a new platoon sergeant and squad leader, as Canneryberry and Brankie would not be coming with us.

"Grab your gear, Brandon, we're going aboard ship," said Bray, another guy from my platoon. He'd managed to pick up my khakis from the laundry, and I owed him two bucks. That was cheap compared to the shit I'd have caught if the sergeant had found out I'd lost a uniform.

We boarded a shithole ship named *USS Minfee APA*. I had no idea what that meant, or if it symbolized anything at all.

"This will be your home for the next twenty days," Sergeant Lessier, our new platoon leader said. He was a gunnery sergeant and stuttered terribly when he talked. Corporal Hingee was my new squad leader.

Our bunks were just pieces of canvas tied to a metal frame, thirteen racks high. There was barely enough room to lay down, place our rifles and packs on the end of our bunks and store our seabags underneath the ladderway.

Our first lesson onboard was about living on a ship.

"Left is port, right is starboard. Move forward on the port side and aft on the starboard side. If you try going any other way, you'll get knocked on your ass. There are two thousand Marines on this ship, plus three hundred sailors. If you *don't* move accordingly, it won't work.

"You'll hear a whistle: that's the boatsmate. He will tell you everything the ship is doing, so shut your fucking mouths when you hear that whistle and listen up.

"All chow lines form on the starboard side. When you finish eating, come out on the port side. We eat by numbers and that does *not* change.

"We all have stations we report to in case we must abandon ship." Boy did that get everyone's attention. Shit, everyone sat up and started to listen.

"Abandon ship? You mean we might sink?"

"Well, this tub has been around a while and anything can happen," the instructor replied. "If we make a landing with this ship, we will be assigned debark stations. We'll debark down the nets into the waiting mike boats."

God Almighty! A sinking ship never crossed my mind when I signed up!

* * *

"All hands man the rails. We are underway!"

As the ship pulled away from the docks, we all stood along the sides watching the tug boats push us away.

Well, this can't be too bad. What can we do but sit on our asses or lie in our bunks? There are too many troops aboard to do anything. Those were my thoughts on the present situation. Well, hell, I was only eighteen years old; I didn't know there was no such thing as a free lunch.

"Move off the fan tall and wash down decks."

"Move aft and wash down ship sides."

"Move forward…."

"Move…."

"Move…."

Shit, all we did was move and tried to keep from being washed down. The fucking Navy…if they weren't washing it, they were painting it or chipping it. And of course you know who got to chip, to do the grunt work: the United States Marine Corps!

* * *

"Chow call! All hands form on the starboard side for chow!" We were called out numerically by company and attached units.

Damn, my belly feels funny. I feel like I'm carsick…shit; I hope I don't get seasick. We'll be here twenty days; I will die! Oh God, greasy pork chops. The next thing I knew I was running for the head, and I wasn't sure I would make it. I was heading for the rails when I puked up all over myself. *Good guess, I didn't make it to the head!* I thought. At least I wasn't alone. There were all kinds of men puking all around me. *Oh shit, let me lie down, I'm dying!*

It wasn't enough to be suffering on deck. Those goddamn sailors wouldn't leave us alone.

"Get the fuck out of the road, jarhead, or we'll wash your ass over the side!"

Someone replied, "Fuck you, swabby, we ain't moving."

Getting doused with saltwater, however, did take my mind off being sick, but only for a while. I snuck down to my bunk, but, shit, there was too much cigarette smoke. A dice game was going on in the corner.

* * *

It seemed there was no getting away from being sick. The next couple of days didn't get much better; nor did I get used to feeling sick.

"Brandon, you have guard duty. Report to the officer of the day."

After grabbing my belt and helmet liner, I reported up top.

"You have the forward hole where the trucks are stored," he said. I was instructed to keep everyone out and make sure no one smoked in the area. The routine called for four hours on and four hours off, so I took a sack lunch to tide me over, seasick or not.

Oh, shit, the smell of diesel. Now I know I'm going to die. Fuck this, I'm lying on the hood of this truck. I'll watch this hole to see if anyone comes.

"WHAT THE FUCK?" the officer of the day shouted at me as he headed out another hole I hadn't seen. "You don't lie down on your post!"

"Sir, I've been sick for two days. I'm too weak to stand up."

I was relieved of duty and instructed to report to the corporal of the guard.

"What the hell is wrong with you?" the corporal asked, none too kindly.

"Sir, I'm seasick, and the OD told me to leave my post."

"Oh, go hit your rack, you little pussy."

Oh God, I don't care. Call me anything you want, I'm dying.

What a night! I was sick, couldn't eat and could barely move. PFC Prines, a

Mexican Indian from my platoon, tried helping by making me eat crackers and drinking water.

"Okay, I think I feel a little better," I told him. I sure hoped I was going to get over it soon.

* * *

"Guess what First Platoon? We have rifle inspection this morning. Big Cheatham is going to inspect!"

Shit, I could hardly sit up. How the hell was I going to stand for inspection? And, damn, my BAR looked like shit. I remember hoping there wasn't any rust on the damn thing but was still too weak to do anything about it.

"Brandon, your rifle looks like shit. It has dirt and rust all over it!" Cheatham shoved the rifle into my gut. "Get that thing over your head and start double-timing in place till I tell you to stop."

Please, God, help me. I know I'm going to die. I had dry heaves, but Cheatham didn't spare me.

"Get down on that deck and do push-ups." Double-timing didn't seem like punishment enough, I guess. Afterward, I was given one hour to clean my weapon and have it inspected again. At that point I was more scared than sick.

Prines came along to help me. God bless his soul! This was twice he was saving my life.

I was feeling better, and the ship wasn't rolling as badly. When I reported back for inspection, Lieutenant Cheatham looked over my BAR, asking a lot of questions. I knew most of the answers. Luckily for me, he didn't say much: only that I had better not fuck up like that again. "Or I'll break your fucking neck." I believed him.

Rifle inspection everyday. Jumping jacks everyday. Push-ups everyday. Anything to keep busy.

Chapter 6
Hawaii

Twelve days aboard the ship and we spotted land. *Damn! 1 hope that's Hawaii. I'm so tired of this ship.*

God, what a beautiful island: miles and miles of beaches—and Pearl Harbor! I'd heard a lot about that place.

When we moved out onto the docks, we were greeted by a Marine Corps band and all kinds of hula dancers on the beach. *Damn, I must have died and gone to heaven! Let me off this garbage scow!*

Man, I remember the fresh pineapple and milk! I hadn't seen milk for weeks. I could hardly believe I ate so much.

We reported to Kaneohe Bay, a base with brand-new buildings. God, what a change from that garbage scow and Quonset huts! Hawaii was like another world to me, so different from California and that damn ship.

The base was great. The barracks were three levels high with all brand-new lockers, mattresses and bunks, and there were showers at each end of the barracks. The mess hall was huge! Damn, we thought we were living!

"Get your gear stored for inspection. If everything goes well, you'll have liberty all weekend."

Three days! Man, oh, man, we shone. Even big Cheatham said we looked good.

The only bad news was that we were restricted to base liberty. I didn't care. I just wanted to find the Slop Chute.

The Slop Chute was an airplane hangar renovated into a club called The Big E-Club. Shit, everyone was there! Guys I hadn't seen since boot camp! Hell, the whole regiment must have been at Kaneohe Bay. I saw Charles and Bice and a few more guys from boot camp. Beer was ten cents and mixed drinks were twenty cents back then. I had three week's pay, almost sixty dollars! I never drank so much beer in my life.

"What are you guys drinking? Tom Collins? Screw Drivers? Bloody Marys?" I'd never heard of these drinks before and decided to try a Tom Collins. The drink seemed passable enough to me, so I drank two more.

Man, what a night. We stayed until they threw us out. We were so sloshed that we sang songs as we headed back to the barracks.

Somewhere off the coast of Hawaii, 1953

My first day on Hawaii, 1953

* * *

Oh God, I'm losing my head. I can't open my eyes for the pain! The entire platoon had hangovers the size of Honolulu. Thank God, we had the day off. We slept until noon before grabbing chow, then checked out the base and went swimming, hangovers and all.

Sunday was a great day. There were still a lot of Marines with hangovers: many of us just walked around in a daze.

I couldn't believe that just a short seven months earlier I was trying to get out of high school and think up a way to avoid telling the football coach I'd been drinking beer after that game. Now, here I am, a thousand miles away, a Marine, on my way to the other side of the world—maybe even to the war in Korea.

I loved the beaches. I wanted to go to the beach every day and lie in the sun. I remember wondering if we would be doing any training while we were there, that would severely cut into going to the beach! Little did I know then, that we would run mile after mile up and down those beaches.

I began to hate the beach. Every morning and every evening—down to the beach to run in the soft sand. After a few grueling miles in soft sand, I found out that running closer to the water, on the hard pack, made for easier running. Shit! You'd think that asshole Cheatham would have figured that one out. What the hell did he do in college, sleep?

* * *

Believe me, I was glad to see the weekends come: I really looked forward to getting a break from the regular routine. We got an hour off for lunch on those days. Most of us would sneak into the barracks and hit the racks for a little sleep during our lunch hour. Corporal Singer, one of the NCOs, was a big son of a bitch: about six foot three and two hundred and twenty pounds. It seemed like he always slept. He'd jump into the bunk, boots and all. If we'd have done that, he would have had our asses.

"Let's tie his bootstrings together and sound off that the first sergeant is coming! Then watch him bust his ass," Corporal Hingee said. Hingee's bright idea seemed good for a laugh or two.

Yeah, it was good for a laugh, but not for long. Singer busted his ass all right; then he busted ours. Boy was he pissed.

"Get your fucking footlockers over your heads!" he shouted.

"Fuck you, Singer, I tied your boots," confessed Hingee. "How about setting an example and keeping your ass out of the bunk?"

"Yeah, and while I'm at it, I'll kick your ass, too, and set an example about fucking with me."

Hingee only hit him once in the nose; Singer went down, hitting his head on a bunk. There was blood everywhere. The two men taking Singer to sick bay weren't quite out the door when the sergeant entered the barracks demanding to know what happened.

"Who the fuck did that?" No one said a word. "I want you assholes here tonight at 1700 hours. After chow, we'll see how smart you really are. You will take all the footlockers to the top deck of the barracks."

Big deal, I thought. *We'll have that done in an hour.* Hell, I should have known we wouldn't be getting off that easily. We carried up one footlocker at a time, up three floors and then the full length of the barracks. We carried them down the back stairs and around the barracks, then up the stairs again. During that hot four hours, we went around and around in circles. Damn, you'd think we would have learned. At almost 2100 hours we got to secure. Man, our asses were dragging. No one tried sneaking off to the E-Club for beer that night. We were awfully quiet and I thought, maybe, even we'd quit screwing around after we learned our lesson. Ha! Fat chance.

* * *

Morning PT came and the same old shit. Just as we got outside, it began to rain, but no one gave a damn. The rain in Hawaii is mostly warm.

"First Platoon, fall into the rear of the company." We were going to run it seemed. Guess big Ernie Cheatham heard about us screwing around the night before, after all. Well, big deal. We could run. There was nothing but blacktop: easy running. Down the road we went, turning right and—oh shit!—we headed for the beach. *Shit, I hope we don't run on the beach. Hell, he won't take us down there. We'd be late for chow, and Cheatham loves his chow!* was the most desperately cheerful thought I could come up with.

"You shitbirds want to play games?" he said. Sure enough, down to the soft sand we went. For a big man, that long-legged asshole could sure run.

At first it didn't seem bad, and Cheatham knew we were in good shape. But, damn if he didn't run the shit out of us. All I could think about was that we'd never get back in time for chow. Well, at least the rain kept the sand wet, so it wasn't hard running. When we turned back to base, I hoped Cheatham thought we'd had enough.

"Hit the decklow crawl…get up, let's go! Hit the decklow crawl."

Goddamn sand in my face. Fuck all this, just for a little screwing around!

Chow was almost over by the time we got back. Sand and all, we put on our jackets and made it to the mess hall. We were the butt of the jokes of the rest of the company.

"Fuck you, assholes," one of our guys retorted. "We're the Cheatham Raiders! You can't *give* us enough shit!"

Oh God, who said that? Shit. I hoped that it wouldn't get back to Lieutenant Cheatham. That big asshole would eat it up and screw with us even more.

* * *

Finally, good news. We were going to the range for live firing. We all hoped for a little slack, as they tended to keep us on the ball when it came to live fire.

That was the best part of being A-BAR man: it was a great weapon to shoot, and I loved shooting it. I could shoot the hell out of a target, hitting a hundred and eighty-one shots out of two hundred, mostly in the black. I always got favorably noticed for my shooting.

Back at the base things were happening. Everyone was packing up.

"What's going on?" I asked. "Are we going to Korea? Oh, shit, the real thing. When are we leaving?" I was excited as hell.

The gunny told me to get my foot locker, but I was not going. I was to help load trucks, then I'd be stationed at Pearl Harbor. I knew better than to ask why.

We loaded trucks all night, and the next morning, I saw my platoon boarding. Soon the base was almost deserted; there were just a few men left in the office. I felt like crying and wondered why I had to stay. I knew I was going to miss those guys a lot.

After chow, sitting in the barracks, a kid named Parrash said he'd be glad when he turned eighteen. He was going to request Korea. Someone else said the same thing.

I said, "Are all you guys seventeen?"

"Yeah," they all said.

"Shit! I'm eighteen. I turned eighteen before we left San Diego."

I jumped up and headed for the office to see the first sergeant.

"Do we have to be eighteen before we can go to Korea?" I asked.

"That's right," he said.

"I turned eighteen several weeks ago," I said.

When he checked my record book, he said, "Sure as shit! Well, get your gear together and be ready to leave with the company headquarters tomorrow morning."

"Will I get to join up with my platoon?"

"Don't see why not."

God. I was excited.

* * *

I was heading back to the barracks to ready my gear when I ran into a private, a full-blooded Indian. I only remember his name being Jayneno. Can't remember if that was his first or last name. He'd been in the Marines a long time and had served in World War II and Korea. He was in full uniform.

"Your name Brandon? You an Indian?" he asked.

"Yes," I answered.

"You live in Santa Fe, New Mexico?"

"I used to. Now we live in Oregon."

He said that he used to know a girl named Jerry Brandon, who went to the Indian school he had attended. It turned out to be my sister.

Jayneno wanted to go to the E-Club and talk.

"I don't have any uniforms: mine are packed."

We went anyway. He said he'd get me in and, sure enough, no one said anything when we walked through the door. In fact, everyone seemed afraid of Jayneno.

I said, "You musta kicked somebody's ass…they always give me shit when I come over here!"

"See all these medals on my uniform?" he asked. "Nobody tells me anything!"

We stayed until the club closed, then went back to his barracks where he pulled out a bottle of whiskey.

"I have to get up early," I said, "and board a ship for Korea."

"War is tough," he told me. "Be tough and train hard. Never trust the enemy; they'll kill you. Kill 'em fast and kill as many as you can."

I stayed to listen to his war stories, until I saw the light go on in my barracks.

* * *

There weren't many of us on the trucks heading for Pearl Harbor. It was going to be good seeing my old platoon, after I thought I'd never see them again.

USS J.J. Pope, a general ship, was ten times the size of the garbage scow we'd come over on from San Diego.

"Hey Brandon, you fuckhead! It's about time you got here!" That was my old buddy Kyle.

"You red-headed prick," I said. "I heard you cried so hard to see me that the first sergeant said that I'd better get down here and take care of you! When do we leave for Korea?"

"Shit! I heard we were going to Japan," Kyle said, a little surprised.

"Japan? Are we going to fight them again?"

"Fuck no, we're going to screw them—or at least all the women. I hear they have slanted pussies. That's what the sailors say."

"What the hell do they know? All they do is screw each other, the queer fuckers!"

Kyle said, "Shit, don't let them hear you say that. We'll be chipping paint all the way over."

That shut me up. This ship was a lot bigger. There were more bunks, more space tables in the holes and more sit-down tables on the mess decks. (Our last ship only had standing room to eat. What a bucket of shit that was!) There must have been at least three mess halls and a lot more room on the main decks of the USS J.J. Pope. There were three movies each night.

Grateful as we were for the extra room aboard ship, it also gave us more room to conduct exercises and stand more inspections. Well, there's always a downside to everything. But the ship rode a lot better than the last one; we'd been underway about two days, and I hadn't been seasick at all. The chow wasn't as greasy as the other ship, or hell, maybe I just got my sea legs, and it didn't bother me anymore.

When we crossed the International Date Line, I remembered something my brother told me about a dragon but couldn't quite remember what it was. I know that whatever it was he told me didn't happen when we crossed the date line. What a shithead.

The sailors gave us all kinds of shit. We crawled through a paddle line of slop (or any other shit they could come up with). It was just like being a freshman in high school initiation.

We had great weather aboard the ship. Some nights we stayed up on deck all night and were the first ones in chow line. It seemed like all we did was eat. They say we will be within sight of Japan in the morning. I'm sleeping on deck tonight. I think it's been ten days since we have seen land. I was sure glad I hadn't joined the Navy: all they did was clean, chip paint and repaint what they'd just chipped off. I rationalized that we could forgive them, since they were taking us overseas to fight.

Chapter 7
Japan

Boy, I have never seen so many ships! I think they said this was Yokohama. Look at those Japanese boots alongside. What the hell are they doing? Tossing money or anything they can, then diving for it.

As the Japanese came alongside to take our garbage, I realized how small they were.

"Cigritt, jo die," they kept saying. I took it to mean they wanted cigarettes.

There was an army band on the docks to welcome us, and I wondered where they were from.

We started off loading the ship. I don't remember how many of us there were, but we filled up the docks. I hoped we wouldn't have to stay to offload the cargo, as well. It seemed like that was all I had been doing: unloading ships.

We stayed at an army rest and recreation center. I'd heard that was where men stayed when they returned from Korea for a rest. I'd also heard they had bars and whorehouses all around the R and R. *Damn! What a place,* I thought. There were rows and rows of little white buildings, and each building had the name of a state on the front of it. Kyle and I walked along, naming off all the states.

"Latrine? Where in the hell is Latrine?" Kyle asked, not familiar with that state.

"I don't know, maybe in the South. I never heard of it either," I said. We asked an army man where in the hell Latrine was.

"Right there," he pointed.

"I know, but where in the U.S. is it? Down south?"

"Hell no! They have them on all the bases," he replied, starting to toy with us.

"You mean Latrine is every state?" we asked, still oblivious to our ignorance.

"I sure as hell hope so," he said. "Where do you Marines take a shit?"

God, how fucking dumb we were. That's what the Army calls a shithouse? We call it a head! Well, at least we learned a little history.

* * *

Just look at all the bars and women all over the place!

"Hey GI, you want fuckie, fuckie?"

Shit, those whores looked good after being at sea for all those days. We damn sure never got any pussy in Hawaii. The only thing I did get in Hawaii was a tattoo of a fly, and that took all the money I had: three bucks. That tattoo got me into a few fights. Every time someone saw it, they felt compelled to slap me and say, "Kill that fly."

Because we were to unload ship the next morning. Lieutenant Cheatham assigned us guard duty that night to make certain no one left base before the unloading. Our first night in Japan and no liberty. Bullshit. Sure as shit, I had guard duty the first watch. That was the worst part of having my last name begin with *B*: they always called me first.

A short while later, I am walking the fence line, on guard, and all these women are raising their dresses to show their snatches. *Damn! I have never seen so much in my life.* It's pretty damn tough to walk your post in a military fashion with a hard-on.

I caught a lot of shit on guard duty, because I couldn't let the rest of the platoon near the fence to watch the whores' show. Eventually the men got bored and began a game of "king of the mountain." When that doesn't entertain them enough, they "pants" anyone they can get a hold of. Kyle pointed out my hard-on from looking at all the pussy. I was duly threatened with a pantsing when I got off duty.

"Yeah," I said, "and I'll kick the shit out of the first one who tries."

Sure as shit, they came after me. My own buddy Kyle was the first to try to grab me. I knocked him on his ass, hitting him square in the mouth.

"You cocksucker," he growled. I hit him again and the fight was on. It didn't do me any good to defend myself. The asshole was so mad he pulled my pants and shorts down around my ankles, then dragged my bare ass through the dirt and rocks. *Shit, rocks up my ass!*

"Hey, Brandon, you wanna fight now?" Kyle asked.

Each time I tried pulling up my pants, the asshole pushed me back down again. He was pretty smug.

"Let me get my pants up and I'll fight you, you chickenshit!" I said, then plowed into him bare-assed and all. (I wonder how we ever win any wars with some of the stupid shit we do.)

"THAT'S ENOUGH!" Corporal Hingee ordered.

"Go hit the shower, Brandon. Kyle, you stay the fuck away from him or I will personally kick your ass."

Kyle must have decided later to make it up to me. "Brandon, you want a candy bar?" he offered.

"Fuck you, Kyle, my ass hurts like hell. Don't you ever quit screwing around?"

"Oh, hell," he said. "Can't you take a joke?"

Not when he scraped half my ass off.

* * *

After four days of unloading ships, we headed north on some pretty damn rough roads. It looked like we were going to the end of time.

We ended up at an old Japanese Army base—about a hundred years old. The base was near Mount Fuji, the largest mountain in Japan. In comparison to Mount Hood in Oregon, it was huge. Not like the barracks. They had ridiculously small bunks and little lockers. I hoped we wouldn't be here for long.

"This is our training area," Lieutenant Cheatham said. We are here in support of the First Marine Division in Korea. We'll be training and on call for the troops in Korea."

During our training, we had only base liberty. Anyone caught "going over the fence" got thirty days in the brig. Base liberty was just like torture: there were all kinds of bars *outside* the fence; and where there were bars, there was pussy. That's what Kyle said.

Bright and early the first morning of training, we headed out the back gate to the hills and an old Japanese training area. The U.S. Army had been there for a year or two and had constructed a few new training areas by the time we got there. It took us only three hours to reach the training area.

We trained all that day, ate one meal of cold C rations, then humped back to base.

We didn't have to wear our uniform dress in the Slop Chute. There must have been a hundred men there. We heard stories from some who had been there a few weeks ahead of us about how they would crawl through the fence at night and get all the pussy they wanted for a pack of cigarettes. Their warning wasn't very reassuring: "Watch out for the guards. If they catch you, they will shoot at you."

* * *

Training was the shits and went on all day long, every day. I wondered if we were ever going to get liberty. Maybe by the weekend we would earn time off.

Our gunny told us, finally, that we were to get liberty that night at 1700 hours. Only half the company was allowed to go at one time. I guess having my name begin with *B* wasn't so bad after all—for once I got liberty the first night!

"Get on the trucks. We're going to a town called Gotemba. It's about ten miles away. The trucks have to be back through the gates before midnight. If you miss the trucks, you'd better grab a taxi or start humping. They lock the gates around here at midnight. No one goes in or out after that."

We were told about converting our money to yen and that we were required to carry at least five dollars in yen or we would not get to go on liberty.

"Man, oh, man," I said, "Look at all the women. Shit! Are they painted up! There are bars all over the place."

We hit the bars first to see what the beer tasted like. The bottles were about three times the size of our beer back home and only two hundred yen: about the equivalent of sixty cents.

"How much is that?" Kyle asked.

"Fuck, I don't know, but I have eighteen hundred yen. That should be enough to get drunk and screwed."

"Let's go see if we can get screwed! Hooray! At last!"

"How much for a fuck?" Kyle asked the first woman we saw.

"Five hundred yen," the old woman said. About a dollar and forty cents.

"Hell, I don't want to screw you, you're older than shit!"

"Me no screw. Me *Mama-san*. You pay me first, then you get the *Jo-san*."

"We want to see the Jo-san first."

They all looked like little girls. "How old, Mama-san? We're looking for big girls."

"These Jo-sans okay. They have hair pussy."

Turning to Kyle, I said, "Let's do it. We fuck around here too long and we'll miss the trucks."

We didn't see a bed in sight and were about to commence activities on the floor.

"You wait, I make bed," Mama-san

Me and my platoon buddies, 1953

said. Japanese beds were no more than a mat on the floor.

"You catch rubber, okay?"

"Yeah, no sweat. I don't want any V.D. You *don't* have any hair on your pussy! How old are you?" I asked, kind of shocked.

"Me okay, not cherry," the Jo-san said.

Damn, as horny as I was, I quit asking questions. That was one "wham-bam-thank-you-ma'am."

I thought Kyle would never get done. "What took you so long?"

"Hell, I went three times! I'm going to find another one."

Two Jo-sans later, we were both broke and headed back to the trucks. Our truck driver had had quite a time on liberty, too, and was half-drunk. He got lost on the way back to the base, and we really started to sweat, thinking about the thirty days of extra duty without liberty.

At last, I thought I saw the base. "What time is it?" I asked Kyle, scared to death it was past midnight.

"Hell. I don't know."

The gate MP gave us hell and said, "Ten more minutes and you assholes would have hung."

All we could think about was turning in our liberty cards before midnight.

"Let us go," we said like the scared eighteen-year-olds we were, "we have to turn in our liberty cards."

"Fuck you," he said. "Get out and walk. The driver stays here."

We took off running, hoping we could make it. Not knowing who our duty NCO was, we weren't sure if we'd catch hell or a little slack.

"Hey, we made it!"

Our NCO turned out to be Corporal Gordon. "Your ass you did! You're five minutes late!"

No amount of explanation was going to keep us off the hook.

"Don't tell me your problems. If you weren't trying to screw all the gooks in town, you would have been back in plenty of time."

"But the driver got lost," Kyle said, still hoping to talk our way out of being late.

"Bullshit. Tell your troubles to Lieutenant Cheatham in the morning."

Boy, what an asshole Corporal Gordon was. Five minutes late and he wrote us up.

"Looks like we'll get about three hours of sleep," I said.

"We can skip chow."

"Not me. We're going to the field with only one C ration, and I never get enough to eat. Besides, with all that screwing, I'm hungry."

Kyle retorted, "Yeah, if you screwed as much as I did, I'd have to carry your ass to chow."

* * *

The next morning it was raining, but we still went into the field. We were the only platoon going. Damn that Cheatham.

"That asshole always makes us go to the field," I whined to myself. "I wonder when he'll get on us about being late last night." My curiosity got the better of me. I asked Gordon if we were going to get extra duty or not.

"I haven't told the lieutenant, yet. Maybe, if you dig my foxhole for me, I might forget to tell him."

That seemed like a good trade-off to me. I had no idea what I was starting.

"Hey, Brandon," another corporal asked, "what the hell you digging a hole in the Third Squad area for?"

"I lost a bet to Corporal Gordon. Kyle and I both lost."

"Yeah? Well, I *bet*, when you finish that hole, maybe you can dig me one, too."

"You asshole, Brandon," Kyle said. "See what you started."

"If I remember right, you're in this shit, too."

"Just keep digging until we have a trench dug; then everyone will have a damn hole," Kyle snapped.

Sergeant Moe, our new platoon guide, came by and wanted to know why we were digging a trench.

"I think that's what the lieutenant told us to do," lied Kyle.

"Well, I don't see why the rest of the platoon doesn't help," Sergeant Moe said and made the others join in the digging.

"Kyle, you asshole," I whispered, "if the lieutenant asks Moe about this, and he ends up in trouble, he will kick the shit out of us. And he's big enough to do it!"

My timing couldn't have been better. Up walked Cheatham.

"How deep is the trench?" he asked.

"About four feet, sir, where I'm standing."

"Well, that's deep enough. That's the way Marines are fighting in Korea. They have trench lines all over the hills. You're lucky here. The ground is frozen in Korea."

We stayed the night in the field and slept in the trenches we dug. Boy, what luck.

* * *

"Hey, Brandon, the lieutenant wants to see you and Kyle."

Away we went. *Shit! Gordon turned us in,* I thought, not happy at the prospects.

"Sergeant Moe tells me you two started the trench, is that right?"

"Yes, sir!" I said.

"Well, that shows you're doing a good job and working to better the platoon. When we get in off the field, we'll see about getting you two extra liberty. We're also going on night raids tonight, and you'll get to come along with us. Be ready to leave after dark."

When we got back to our squad, Corporal Hingee asked how badly Cheatham had gotten on us about the trenches.

"He told us we were doing a good job, and we get to go on a night raid tonight." We gloated just a little.

"Yeah, and my name is Jesus Christ."

"No shit, Corporal, that's what he said."

New Year's 1953: A little Toddy for the body!

"Well, I'm telling him different. I know you two are fuck-ups."

Exasperated, I said, "I'm getting away from you, Kyle. All you do is give me a bad name."

"Fuck you, Brandon," he shot back and laughed like hell.

* * *

"Damn it's dark out. I wonder where we are going."

"I don't know, but I heard we are trying to get behind the company we're up against. We want to get behind their lines, so we can fuck them up."

"Quick," I said, "there is a truck and some troops up the road. Looks like they're setting up a line to their battalion. They're rolling out some comm wire."

The next thing I knew, we'd taken them prisoners, tied them up and thrown them into a truck.

Damn, it seemed like we drove for an hour before coming to a base. But it wasn't our camp! It turned out to be the 2nd Battalion, who wasn't even in on our operation. Cheatham and the platoon sergeant took out a deuce-and-a-half truck from the motor pool.

"Get in," Cheatham said. "We're raiding the Fourth Marine headquarters."

We drove right into the camp, right through the smoke grenades. We caught them with their pants down, and we didn't even have to get off the truck. We took off like a bat out of hell. The umpires were sure to kill us for this one.

We made a stop on the way back and Cheatham said, "Everyone off the truck and push it into the ditch." It rolled over as it went down.

Damn, I thought, *we are all going to go to jail.*

We made it back just before daylight and in time to load up and head downhill. We met up with the 4th Marines at the bottom of the hill. The umpires had ruled them "wiped out" and they were pissed.

I saw Henderson from my boot camp days and walked over to talk with him. I didn't get far before an officer told me to get the hell out of there, or he'd kick my ass. What a poor loser.

We were in our glory! Our platoon had spearheaded the raid and even the battalion commander told us how good we had been. Cheatham was smiling— the first time I'd ever seen him do that!

Kyle and I were about as happy as Cheatham was. We didn't have to stand inspection *and* we got two day's liberty! All for a stupid screwup!

* * *

"I'm going to Yokosuka," I said. "My brother Gary is there on a tin can called the *U.S.S. Henderson*. He's been over here about a year."

"I'm staying in Gotemba," said Kyle. "I'm going to drink and screw myself to death all weekend." Probably so.

It was about a two-hour trip on a damn small train, but I sure wanted to see my brother. The Japanese stepped all over my shoes.

When I got to Yokosuka, I wasn't sure how to find Gary. There were sailors all over the place. I went to the local E-Club where records of all ships in port were listed and talked to a clerk.

"We can help you get ahold of your brother," the clerk assured me. They had ship-to-shore phones. We reached the officer of the day. He told me Gary was restricted to the ship. I asked if I could visit him aboard ship but was told not until the next day, Sunday. That didn't help much, because I had to head back on Sunday. This was the fourth time I'd visited Gary, or tried to. The first was the time at boot camp, and the second and third times he was in a navy brig somewhere. When I visited Gary in the brigs, I taken cigarettes for him. But, as the brigs were run by Marines, they said, "no smokes." I only saw him for ten minutes. As I left, I was told to leave the smokes, and they'd see that Gary got them. It looked like we would never get together. *Why the hell was Gary always in the brig?* I wondered.

I headed back to the E-Club for some chow and a haircut. I had just sat down when I saw an old schoolmate. "Hey, Eggart!" I yelled.

"Percy, right?"

"Yeah," I said. "How long you been here?"

Eggart had been in Japan about six months. I told him where I was stationed; that I was only in Yokosuka to visit Gary, but that he was in the brig. Damn, this was like old-home week. Eggart told me of six or seven of our schoolmates from Willamina High. It looked like everyone had joined the Navy except for me.

"Any of you been to Korea?" I asked.

"We're waiting to ship out, but we don't know when."

We swapped more stories, comparing the Navy and the Marines.

"You damn sailors have it made!"

I talked with my old girlfriend's brother, Carl Blackwell, who was in Yokosuka, too. He hadn't been home in over two years and hadn't heard from Sharon.

"I wrote Sharon a few times," I said, "but she never writes back."

"Maybe she thinks you're over here screwing the gooks."

"Shit no, you sailors do that. Too much V.D. for me."

"Your ass, Brandon!" Eggart said. "You fucking Marines would screw a bush, If you thought there was a snake in it."

"You have to get it when you can," I replied. "The way it is in the Marines, we might be getting our ass shot off— so get it when you can!"

I didn't have a place to stay for the night, and the guys offered to let me stay on the ship. I had other ideas.

Man, what a night! My pecker was so sore I could barely touch it the next morning. I was going to try to catch Kyle at Gotemba and drink a few beers before our liberty ran out.

I found Kyle in a bar, half-shaved and hung over.

"You better find a place to get cleaned up and shaved," I said, "or the MPs will write your ass up."

"What the fuck for?" he asked.

"Because you're so fucking ugly.

1954: The Snows of Mt. Fuji. Ah so!

Damn! You look like dog shit wrapped in a uniform!"

While Kyle was cleaning up, I embellished the details about the Jo-san I'd been with all night and how she had shaved me. All I had to do was lay in bed. I told him the Jo-san said that Marines were better lovers than the swabs, who only screwed once a night. "I screwed once," I said, "but it was all night."

Chapter 8
The Military Police

Lieutenant Cheatham was leaving the platoon. He was going to Korea. We didn't go into the field that day, and Staff Sergeant Welch was put in charge until we had a new lieutenant assigned. Damn! Just when we were getting good, we were losing Cheatham.

"It's been great with you Marines," Cheatham said. "Maybe we will serve together at some other time." He went on to tell us that some of us, like him, would be going to other duties. Most of us would be going to South Camp Fuji to help fill a new company. This was to be our last weekend together. Cheatham wanted us to have a good time. He said, "I hope to see you again."

Of course none of us knew if we would. Nor could we know that Cheatham would become a two-star general and be awarded the Navy Cross, the second-highest combat award in Vietnam.

During that last liberty, we must have drank half the beer in the Slop Chute.

It was my idea to go into town. "We still have six hours of liberty left," I pointed out.

There was a new MP at the gate, a PFC Bernezo. We knew him from 34th Platoon back in boot camp.

He was a loudmouth ex-doggy who always asked questions.

"What the hell are you doing on the gate?" I asked.

"I received orders this week. You, Brandon. Let me see, you have orders to report to the military police!"

"Bullshit!" I said. "They asked, but I said no."

"Well, you ain't going out the gate until you check in with the desk sergeant."

I asked the guys to wait for me while I ran over to check it out. The desk sergeant told me I had to stand the midnight-to-four o'clock watch on the gate.

The guys all laughed at me. Someone said, "Sorry, buddy, we're going without you." There went my last six hours of liberty with my old platoon.

* * *

I didn't have any MP gear and was told to just trade with the man on the gate. I sat in the guardshack and read special orders for the MPs.

Shit, I really hate guard duty, and now I'm stuck with the MPs. That's all they do!

The desk sergeant had told me he expected me to be "tough at the gate." He told me that the usual habit of Marines coming back from liberty was to return, half-drunk, with jugs smuggled under coats or shirts, and that was usually how fights started in

1954: Me cuffing my buddy Pvt Martin, WWII M.P.

the barracks. Shit, how well I knew that. I think we had fights in our barracks every night.

"Don't let anyone stay on the truck when it comes to the gate," he continued. Shit! I knew how much that pissed me off when I came in half-loaded. The guys were going to be pissed at me.

"You'll have a Japanese security guard with you, in case you have trouble with the locals."

This had to be the worst night of my life. My whole company was coming back, and I had to be the one to make them get off the trucks and confiscate their booze. Damn, I could even hear them singing.

"Hey look, it's Brandon on the gate. Hey, Brandon, we screwed one for you."

"Everyone off the truck," I said.

"Fuck you, Brandon! Hey fucker, you want a drink?" asked my old Indian buddy Prines. He had a jug.

"Give me that and get the hell off the truck, or I'll write you all up," I said, hoping to put an end to a bad situation.

"I'll kick your damn ass," said Prines. Shit, I knew how mean he could get when he drank.

"Driver, get the truck out of here and take them down to the First Battalion area," I ordered, hoping the desk sergeant wasn't watching. He'd have my ass if he was.

The truck I'd sent through was all of my platoon—at least I hoped it was—and anyone else who came through wouldn't know me. At midnight I shut down the gate. Anyone left out was shit-out-of-luck.

As I was leaving, Sergeant Blair, the charge of the section, asked me where I had been during guard mount.

"I didn't know I was going to the MPs. I was headed out on liberty when Bernezo told me I had duty. I still have my bunk and all my gear back at my old company."

"Well, stand this same watch in the morning at 0800 hours. Go get your gear and get back up to the MP barracks."

Shit, I knew that, if I returned to my old barracks now, my platoon would still be awake and ready to clean my clock. I'd have to fight my way out.

"Is it okay if I go to the guardhouse and read up on some more orders first?" I asked, hoping he would let me get my gear later, after everyone had gone to sleep.

"I don't give a shit, just be ready for your post at 0800."

About four a.m. it was safe enough for me to sneak into the barracks and get out before anyone saw me. I was thinking over what I was going to do on the gate. Damn, what a change from being in the infantry. I wasn't sure if I was going to do MP duty full time.

The next morning Sergeant Blair came up to my post. I was praying I hadn't screwed up too badly last night.

"The desk sergeant said you were a little slack about making the guys get off the truck last night."

"They were my old company," I said. "They were on their last liberty together and were really drunk. I thought I might have to fight them all if they got out of the truck. There wasn't any trouble when they got back to the barracks."

"Well, it doesn't matter who they are. Don't take any shit from anybody, even an officer. If he's wrong, write him up." I continued to get a lecture about how we were the law, and if we let these guys get away with just a little shit, they would just cause more. We only had two MPs per town and had to keep the shit from happening, or we'd get fucked over.

I had hoped to get off duty in time to say goodbye to my platoon. I wasn't sure where they were all going. Oh, well, at least the trucks would have to go right by me as they left.

"Hey, Brandon, you lucky shit, guess where we are going?"

"To hell, I hope."

"No! South Camp Fuji! Come over and see us when you can."

That wasn't too bad. It was only about twenty miles away.

"We are just trading places with Third Battalion." I wondered why.

"Good luck, Brandon," said Lieutenant Cheatham. "You're a good Marine; that's why I sent you to MP Company."

Shit! I was the only guy to leave my old platoon. The rest were staying together. I had a hard time keeping from crying.

My parting shot to my buddies was, "HEY CHEATHAM'S RAIDERS, YOU'RE THE BEST IN THE MARINE CORPS!" I had tears in my eyes.

* * *

One good thing about the MPs were their barracks. They were a lot better than my old ones and had good lockers. Hell, we even had a houseboy to press our clothes and shine our shoes, if we all chipped in a few bucks each week to pay him. He ran out the gate and brought back chow whenever we wanted.

The best part of being an MP was not having field every day. The MPs seemed like a good bunch of guys; most of them appeared a lot older than the guys in my old platoon.

I stood gate duty one day on and one day off, until I had hand-to-hand training. Town patrol was pretty rough, and we were taught how to fight with

"B" Company 1st.Bn.3rd. Marine Regt.
3rd. Marine Divison FMF Japan 10/10/53
Lt.Ernest C.Cheatham Jr.

Japan, 1953: The Cheatham Raiders, my first Platoon - One Hell of a Team

a nightstick and how to fight more than two guys at a time. Man, these MPs fought all the time, mostly for fun!

"Brandon," I was asked one day, "Do you know any judo?"

"Just a little. We did some hand-to-hand in bayonet training."

"Well, you better learn fast or you'll get your ass kicked, even on the gate. Don't ever let anyone get close to you when you're on duty."

Then he knocked me on my ass, "Like that. See what I mean? Here, you try it on me."

When I tried it on him, he knocked me down again. I started to get up. He grabbed me around the neck, squeezed and pushed down on my head. Shit! I couldn't breathe. I ducked my head and somersaulted forward; he went over my head and landed on his back. He pulled me over but I landed smack-dab on top of him and knocked the wind out of him.

He just lay there looking at me. Everyone waited to see what I would do next. After a while the MP stood and looked me over for a while.

Then he said, "Where'd you learn that?"

"In high school. When you're a fat, little guy with a name like Percy, you have to be tough."

Shit, I thought they were going to die laughing.

The man I'd just knocked the shit out of turned out to be a PFC Gabba. He'd been an MP in Texas before he came to Japan. I told Gabba that infantrymen fought all the time, so I had a habit of being ready for shit.

"No shit," he said, still catching his breath.

* * *

There was a lot more to being in the military police. We learned about report writing, controlling traffic and underwent a lot of hand-to-hand training. We also trained with the Japanese judo instructors. I thought that was great because, when we finished judo instruction, we were allowed to stay on in town for the day. Everyone else had field training, while we had the women to ourselves. We were even taught by navy medical inspectors, so we knew who had V.D. and who was clean.

The women knew we could raid the cathouses whenever we wished, so they treated us good. We practically had our own bars: we'd post one of us MPs at the door to keep watch—making sure nobody screwed with us. It discouraged anyone else from coming in. It was great!

I found out fast that MPs were hated by everyone. It never paid to try to be a nice guy: that was when you got into trouble.

Gotemba, with all the bars and women, had three patrols at one time. You'd think knowing that would keep the Marines out of trouble, but shit, they had twenty fights a night.

I was starting town patrol. But only small towns. I found that patrolling towns near tank or artillery companies or headquarters wasn't nearly as tough as patrolling towns near the infantry units. The armored, artillery and the HQ boys never fought nearly as much as the infantry.

After about six months, Sergeant Blair assigned me to Gotemba. I was hoping, in a way, it would never happen. I thought I might run into some of my old platoon buddies and have to be the badass again. I saw a few of them, but mostly we just said our hellos. I don't think they trusted me, but I knew I would do all I could to keep them out of trouble.

I'd been in Gotemba about four weeks when I spotted a Marine out of uniform staggering down the street. He was on his ass, wearing a piss-cutter that looked army issue. When I got close enough, I saw it was Charles, my cousin. I thought, *Shit, how am I going to handle this?*

My duty partner, Keen, was a big, old guy from Texas who never took shit from anybody. He jumped on Charles' ass, took his piss-cutter and tore it in half. He chewed his ass out and told him to get his ass in a taxi and back to base before we locked him up. I didn't say anything.

"Hey, Percy, how come you let him fuck with me like this?" Charles asked pathetically. "Hell, I don't want to go back to the base."

"I'm sorry, Charles," I said. "You're out of uniform."

"Well, fuck you. You ain't any cousin of mine," he said as he took off in a taxi.

Not more than an hour later we walked into a bar and there sat Charles, still drunk on his ass and still out of uniform.

Keen grabbed him by the neck and dragged him outside the bar. He called a patrol truck to take him to the lockup, an old, cold Japanese jail. They took all Charles' clothes off and threw him inside onto the floor.

I just had to get him out of there. I talked to the patrol sergeant and told him about Charles being my cousin. The sergeant agreed that, if I could get Charles' clothes on and put him in a taxi, he'd let me send him back to base.

I tried my damnedest to get Charles to shape up, but he tried to knock the shit out of me.

"Fuck you, Charles. You can rot in here!"

I saw him two or three more times during the next year, but he would always turn and go in the other direction.

* * *

One day, while I was standing guard at the gate, a Marine in a jeep drove up. Man, he smelled like shit and was drunk on his ass. He had shit all over him and the jeep.

I asked him where he had been, and he told me how he had run off the road, trying to miss hitting a honeybucket wagon. I told him to pull the jeep into the motorpool across from the gate and park. As he pulled away, something dragging under the jeep caught my eye. It looked like a piece of metal or pipe. I walked over to inspect and—oh shit!—saw a bike underneath and a Japanese wound around the rear axle of the jeep. They must have been dragged over twenty miles. It looked like a mass of metal and meat. I could just make out part of the head. I began throwing up and called for the desk sergeant.

When he arrived I showed him the jeep.

The driver was still so drunk that he didn't know what was going on. I thought the sergeant was going to kill him as he took him over to the guard shack.

I threw up every time I thought about that scene. I must have lost ten pounds over the next couple of weeks. Whenever I tried to eat, I would see that mess under the jeep.

* * *

After two years in Japan, part of the 3rd Marine Division was assigned to another island, Okinawa, and two platoons of MPs were assigned to accompany them to control prisoners and beach traffic. I was going as traffic control.

We were going to be the first Marines to land in Okinawa since World War II. Only a few army units had been left on the island, and they would be acting as the enemy for landing practices.

The *USS Epping Forest*, our transport ship, was a landing-ship dock. There weren't many troops aboard, mostly equipment. I hadn't been aboard a ship since leaving Hawaii.

As I stood in the chow line, I saw Albert Clark, an old high school buddy. Clark had joined the Navy about six months before I joined the Marines. As it turned out, he wasn't the only one from back home on the ship.

"The boats down in the deck wells have a unit attached; that's where we're quartered," Clark told me and offered to get me a bunk with my old friends. That was great! I didn't have to sleep on deck and didn't have to stand in line with the Marines for mess. I got to eat in Clark's mess decks.

One day Sergeant Blair caught me and asked, "Hey, Brandon, how come I never see you in the chow line?"

"Oh, I always go early," I lied. I wasn't about to tell him I was sleeping and eating with the Navy, while he was sleeping out on a cold deck and standing in chow lines.

* * *

Okinawa, we had been told, had temperatures over a hundred degrees in the sun. They weren't kidding. It was so hot that I took my shirt off while I directed traffic on the beach. After an eight-hour watch, my shoulders were so sunburned I couldn't raise my arms. Sergeant Jones didn't have much sympathy for me or my shoulders, or anyone else for that matter. Everyone had sunburned just about every part of their bodies that had not been covered.

"Get your ass back out there and direct traffic," I was told. "If you don't, it's a court-martial! Heh! A court-martial for getting a sunburn that keeps you from doing your job?" I think he almost hoped I wouldn't go back out.

But back into the blistering sun I went.

Damn! I can't stand this pain when I raise my arms. I gotta do something.

I cut two sticks and tied two white rags tom from my T-shirt to the sticks, then used my "flags" to direct traffic. Traffic was moving along nice and orderly when Sergeant Jones and the Provost Marshal drove by. I couldn't resist flashing a smart salute with one of my stick-flags. From the comer of my eye, I caught a glimpse of Jones shaking his head. Later I discovered that Vaseline helped me move without as much pain, but I still ended up with blisters as big as pancakes all over my back and chest. It hurt so much to lie down that I even tried standing against a tree to sleep. I swore I would never get burned like that again.

* * *

Maybe something came of Jones catching me directing traffic with sticks after all. The next day I was taken off traffic duty and put on duty guarding prisoners. This suited me just fine. The army men, our stand-in prisoners, were scared shitless of Marines. Our makeshift POW camp was really only a big hole with barbed wire around it. Anyone we took as prisoner was thrown into the hole.

I remember thinking those army guys must live good lives. They had never heard of sleeping in the field, and they had some pretty fine equipment...so fine that we stole most of it.

Patrols were sent into town to make certain the Marines weren't raiding. It had only been a few years since the war ended, and the townspeople were still quite afraid of some of the stuff that was going on. We found bunkers and a few other things left over from World War II.

We weren't the only ones who were glad when the operation was over. From what I heard, the Army didn't want us back anytime soon.

* * *

We returned from Okinawa only a few months before my overseas tour was over. The rest of my company was assigned to other operations, but us "short-timers" were left behind. And there wasn't anyone else left behind! We could go to town where there were hundreds of women and no Marines except us. I seriously considered the possibility that I might screw myself to death.

* * *

When the division returned from ops, things really got wild. Lots of fights meant stepping up village patrols. Extra patrols were sent into the mountain area to artillery sites; there seemed to be trouble with the colored gangs knife fighting. Another time we were called in to stop a barfight where a colored Marine had broken a beer bottle and stabbed a local woman in the neck with the shards. The sergeant in charge just so happened to dislike anyone but whites and made no bones about it. While two of us went in the front door, the man jumped through a window in the back, right where the sergeant was covering. The next thing we heard was a gun being fired. The sergeant had shot the man through the chest. *Oh shit*, I thought, *we will never get off this mountain alive!* It was snowing like mad, and we stayed half the night trying to settle things down a bit.

When we finally returned, the company commander wasn't about to send the same men back up after that scene. Boy was I glad. Things stayed that way, and we had to secure liberty for about a month. The sergeant got a quick set of orders and was gone shortly after the incident.

* * *

Camp Fuji had some pretty horrific stories told about its brig. Because I was on temporary assignment, and we were short-handed at the time, I was assigned guard duty there. I didn't know if the stories were true—stories like prisoners being beaten with socks full of soap bars—and so I was a little

1954: Joe and Gunny (then a PFC): Military Police Town Patrol

apprehensive about my assignment at Camp Fuji.

On the first morning, we stood inspection in full-guard gear: white belts, gloves, and MP arm-bands. We looked sharp, but that still didn't change the fact that MPs weren't liked much.

The brig warden was a salty old master sergeant, C.S. Johnson. (Someone told me the initials stood for "Chicken Shit.") After inspection, Master Sergeant Johnson marched us through the middle of the base and around the barracks.

From inside the barracks, someone yelled, "Fuck the MPs!"

Master Sergeant Johnson took two guards into the barracks and returned with the only three Marines who'd been inside.

"Take them to the brig."

It didn't much matter which one swore at the MPs, and Johnson didn't bother finding out. Those three paid a hefty price in the brig. Johnson kept them busy all day busting rocks with a hammer, exercising, or he just kicked the shit out of them. During my eight-hour watch, the working or beating never once stopped.

* * *

Halfway through my watch, a new prisoner arrived. I recognized him from a radio company. The last time I saw him he was a sergeant. Well, he was a private now, and the guards were working him over but good. After about an hour, I was called to take him to his cell. I showed him the operation, how to store his gear and where the rules were posted. He had been beaten so badly he could barely stand by himself. I was showing him how to "cross the red line" when he asked me for a drink of water. I didn't think much about it and told the man, "Okay."

I'd been sitting on a stool, but the next thing I knew, I'd been knocked on my back, landing on the cement floor. I looked up to see Master Sergeant Johnson glaring down at me.

"Don't ever let a prisoner talk to you without saying sir."

Johnson nearly choked the man before I grabbed the prisoner and threw him into his cell.

Damn, these guys are crazy! If I can help it I'll never be a prisoner!

My platoon sergeant, Sergeant Jones, gave me the word the next morning.

"Turn in your gear, Brandon. You're going stateside in fourteen days."

In four hours I was checked out. No more guard duty.

Chapter 9
Almost Stateside

I had three days before I was to report to another base near the ship docks, and I thought I might go say good-bye to all the girls before I headed out.

Those of us going stateside ended up shipping out of Okaboo. There were over four thousand Marines, some back from Korea, finishing overseas tours at the same time as I was.

God—better stay out of the club. I see a lot of the men I picked up when I was on patrol. Needless to say, my ass would have been grass if I'd tried socializing with some of the guys I'd made enemies with.

Fortunately, I ran into Selby, Bice and Charles, as well as several others from boot camp. I was the only MP; the rest had stayed in the infantry and most were PFCs. Selby worked in an office and was now a corporal and Charles, well, Charles was still a private. What the hell, we all had a great time.

"Where in the States are we landing?" someone asked.

"Frisco, I hope. That's only six hundred miles from my home," Selby said.

He had friends in Oakland who were arranging a car for him to drive to Oregon. He offered us a ride if we'd chip in a few bucks.

The old Oregon gang was together again! It seemed like years since we came overseas, but it had only been two.

* * *

What luck! Another general ship with lots of room and no one in charge. I was thinking that we would get plenty of sleep and food during the fifteen days it would take to get stateside, when I heard my name called over the P.A. system. *I wonder what they want me for? I haven't even had time to get into trouble.*

I reported to the boatmate on watch. "Brandon," he said, "you were an MP, right? We have three Marines aboard being held for murder. They will be going to a federal prison in the States. We need trained personnel to stand watch. Bring your gear; you'll stay in a special compartment." Well, so much for my cushy trip home. At least we had two private rooms in officers' country.

I was senior PFC of the five of us standing watch. I set up watch for four hours on, twenty hours off. I also set the tone with the prisoners. "I won't screw with you, if you don't screw with me. Remember that, and we'll get along fine. The first time you give us *any* shit, I will strip you down naked, turn off the heat and feed you nothing but bread and water until we get back to the States."

Damn! Maybe this won't be so bad after all! At lost, guard duty is paying off! I thought. And that was good duty. We didn't have to stand in chow lines, and we had nice bunks. I only had to report four times a day: during prisoner meals and showers. The rest of the time was my own. Everyone aboard thought I was some kind of badass, being in charge of the Marine prisoners who committed murder. I was getting pretty full of myself.

* * *

I awoke one night to all hell coming down. The ship was rolling from side to side and shit was banging around the room. "What the hell is going on?" I demanded.

"We ran into some kind of storm. Shit, you should see the size of the swells on the deck."

"Hell, I'm not going on deck," I said, then thought to ask about the prisoners.

"They're sick as shit."

"Fuck them. Don't take them out for chow. Give them crackers and water, but keep them locked up."

The storm lasted three or four days. I'd almost forgotten what it was like to be seasick.

* * *

We were sailing under the Golden Gate Bridge, and all I could think about was that I'd never seen anything look so beautiful. I'd only seen pictures of the bridge, and with the sunlight hitting it, it really seemed to be made of gold!

"Brandon, the officer of the day wants to see you."

The OD told me the ship would be docking in San Francisco before noon that day. We were, however, going to tie up at Treasure Island just beforehand, so I could take the prisoners off. I was to do it as quickly as possible, then take them to the brig on Treasure Island.

I told the other MPs how we would be removing the prisoners and voiced my concerns. "I think if they are going to try to escape, it will be when we leave the ship. I know they will be thinking about it. All three got life sentences, so they have nothing to lose."

As the OD held the gangway open for us, I led the three prisoners off in front of the other MPs. There were ten guards and two brig vans awaiting us on the docks.

"Who is in charge of the prisoners?"

"I am, sir," I replied. "I have been since we left Japan over two weeks ago." He relieved the other MPs of duty, but ordered me to accompany the prisoners to Treasure Island.

"As soon as we check them into the brig, we'll return you to staging for orders and leave."

"How long will it take?" I asked.

"About an hour with the prisoners. But you'll be in staging about a week, maybe less. It'll take awhile to stage the four thousand Marines on that ship."

Treasure Island's brig looked like a hellhole. It sat on top of the island, on the side of a hill overlooking the bay.

"Good luck at your new base," he said when he dropped me off at the staging area.

Chapter 10
Stateside

Staging was done mass-production style. Everyone stood in formation under the letter of their last name. Boy did we move! First things were taken care of first. More shots, more physicals, more V.D. checks and more uniforms. The sergeant in charge didn't say much, unless we didn't move fast enough.

We were told where to stand if we needed new I.D. cards or dog tags.

Shit! They don't have our record books! How in the hell will they know how old we are? I'm getting new cards!

"What's your name?"

"Brandon, Percy E."

"Service number?"

"1372356."

"Date of birth?"

"June 29, 1933," I lied.

"Blood type?"

"OP."

Shit, he didn't even look up at me! Hot damn, now I'm twenty-one! I can hit the bars! raced through my mind, and we had liberty in two hours.

I had plenty of money and wanted to find Selby. If he'd gotten that car, I wanted to ride to Oregon with him. I checked out the base club first. It looked like everyone had the same idea; the club was packed tighter than sardines in a tin can.

It didn't take long before Charles came in; it hadn't taken him long to find the club either.

"Guess who's pouring beer?" he asked. Then, answering his own question, "Darrell Helerson! He's stationed here on Treasure Island." Darrell was another schoolmate who had joined the Navy.

"Are you going on liberty?" I asked.

"Hell yes! We're going to Chinatown."

"Chinatown? Fuck, we just got back from two years of looking at gooks!" I yelled over the noise in the club. "I'm going to see if Selby is getting that car. If he doesn't, I'll ask Darrell for the best way to get to Oregon from here."

We had a long wait to catch a taxicab, but hell, there was plenty of beer in town. Anyway, I had to try out my new I.D. Charles did too. I guess we were all twenty-one now.

* * *

"Don't fuck up in town or you'll never get off base," we were told. It seemed funny being around American girls again. They did look good, and it was great being able to speak English and not half Japanese.

There as many whores in San Francisco as servicemen. I guessed that they had heard that a bunch of drunken Marines were coming in—with their pockets full of money. Every bar was full of women.

I couldn't believe how quiet the Marines were, almost like gentlemen. Shit, in Japan they would have been kicking the shit out of each other by now.

I wasn't as horny as I thought I was, or maybe twenty bucks a shot for a piece of ass was more than I wanted to pay. Getting drunk sounded more my speed and, hell, I was heading home in a few days anyway.

We got back to base around three the next morning. We had had a great time. We sure spent a few bucks our first night home.

* * *

I finally caught up with Selby at chow the next morning. He had a car, and four of us would be driving together. One guy had his wife with him and would be riding as far as Eugene, Oregon.

We hit the road around noon, along with several hundred other Marines. We stopped at the first town we came to and picked up a case of beer and a jug of whiskey. I got so drunk that I couldn't help drive. From what I remember, which wasn't much, Charles and Selby did all the driving. We were in Eugene, dropping off the couple, before I knew it.

Boy, we drank a lot of beer during that road trip. It's a good thing Selby offered to take us all the way to Grand Ronde. He guessed we would get there around five in the morning.

"Maybe we can stop and get something to eat," I said. "I feel like shit."

Well, that dog didn't fly. I was told to wait until I got home, I could eat there.

* * *

Charles wasn't sure if his parents were in Grand Ronde or Nebraska, so we decided to go to my house first. My mother would know.

There were no lights on in the house, and no one was up at that time of day. I wasn't even sure I had told my folks I was coming home. *This'll be a shock! My face is all broken out with pimples, I've gained about sixty pounds, and I'm five inches taller than the last time I was home!* I pounded on the door loud enough to wake the dead, thinking, *Shit, I hope my parents still live here!*

Well, Mom almost didn't recognize me and had no idea I was coming home. She told us Charles' folks had moved to Nebraska a year earlier, but his sister was still in Salem.

"Why didn't you tell us you were coming home?" she asked.

"I wasn't sure how long we were going to be in San Francisco, or if we'd get to leave at all," I lied. *Too busy having a good time,* I was thinking. I promised to let her know where I was from then on. I thought that might be California.

"Well, maybe you can see your sisters Toni and Jerry. They both live there now."

My brother Gary was now out of the Navy and living in an apartment in Valley Junction, not too far away from my parents. After promising to return later to eat some home cooked food, we borrowed a car and headed off to kick Gary's butt out of bed.

* * *

A few minutes later, in Valley Junction, we realized we didn't have the slightest idea which apartment Gary lived in.

"There's only six of them, pick one. Honk the horn and holler for Gary. Maybe he will come out."

"HOW WOULD YOU LIKE THAT HORN STUCK UP YOUR ASS?"

someone yelled out from inside the house.

"You know anyone man enough to try?" I shouted back.

Good thing it turned out to be my cousin Jack. "What the hell do you guys want?" he asked.

Jack let us bum a couple of beers, being as it wasn't even light outside yet and the stores weren't open. Then he directed us to apartment number three, Gary's home.

"Who the hell you got in bed with you, Gary? Anyone I know?" we yelled as we barged in unexpected and uninvited.

"My wife."

"Your wife? When the hell did you get married?" I asked.

Gary had been out of the Navy for nine months and had gotten married three months after that.

"Shit, out of the pan and into the fire! Damn Navy didn't teach you anything."

"Hello, Gary's wife. Do I know you?"

After introductions and beer, we caught up on each other's lives and mishaps. Gary was driving log truck, and my other brother John was loading logs in Long Bells. I told Gary how I'd tried to see him while he was in the brig. Gary didn't miss the Navy much. He was glad to be home.

I got the same third-degree inquisition from Gary as I had from Mom. "What's wrong with your face? How tall are you? How much weight have you gained? Have you seen a doctor? How long are you home for?"

All I knew was: I sure hoped I had quit growing. I was broke from keeping up with buying so many uniforms.

* * *

Willamina High School was playing rival Sheridan that night. Charles and I and a few others met up in Sheridan to root for Bob Robinson, one of our old gang. Everyone went to the high school games back then, but not many had changed, except me.

Earl Homes, another younger cousin, showed up in his old Model A, a car he'd had before we left for the Marines. We joshed each other about playing "chicken" and nearly collided, before one of us turned off the road.

We decided to take the Model A to a dance in Grand Ronde after Earl took his girlfriend home. He was dating a girl named Shirlie Bird, who was not too happy that she was being taken home while her boyfriend's buddy dragged him off to a dance. Shit, was she pissed-off at me and said something I couldn't hear, but I'm sure wasn't too nice.

"Hell, Earl, she looks pretty good. Let's find some like her and I'll be happy."

* * *

Grand Ronde looked so small to me now. I guess that happens once you get out in the world.

The old dance hall brought back a lot of memories. Before Indians were allowed in the bars, we had dances there almost every night. My father played the piano, my uncle played the violin and another local Indian played the accordion. They always ended up drunk and picked fights with each other. Everyone used to make homebrew, but were in such a damn hurry to drink the stuff that they wouldn't wait for it to age. It was funny, seeing everybody end up with the shits from drinking green beer. Except me: I hated the taste and could not drink back then worth a hoot.

I remembered helping my brother make some home brew once. He'd heard that, if you put rice in the bottle, the beer would age sooner, and you could drink it in half the time. He stored the beer under the sink in the kitchen. After about five days the bottles blew up as a result of the rice expanding. Shit, what a mess!

* * *

By the time we caught up with everyone at the dance, they'd had quite a head start drinking in the parking lot. Same old rule applied: No drinking in the hall. I checked out the women and wondered who was good for putting out. I hadn't had a piece of ass since I left Japan.

I told Earl, "The Indian girl looks okay, but the other one is kind of fat. But what the hell, they're all the same in the dark."

"Shit, Brandon, I think you'd screw a bush if you thought there was a snake in it."

"Bullshit!" I said. "They need to have clean socks before I screw 'em."

"What the hell does clean socks have to do with screwing?" Earl asked.

"I'm not sure," I said. "Someone just told me if they have clean feet, they have a clean ass. It's easier to check their feet than it is their ass."

I danced with the Indian girl a few times, and she finally invited me and a case of beer to go back to her cabin. It was four o'clock in the morning, and Earl had left for work. There was me, the two women and a big kid named Roger. He was strong as hell, and everyone called him "Moose." Moose told me a story about how he was once bet five bucks that he couldn't push a pickup loaded with logging cable up a hill about two hundred feet. Of course no one thought even Moose could do it, but he backed up to the tailend of the pickup, grabbed the bumper and won himself five dollars easy. By the looks of this kid, I believed him.

I had the Indian girl in the bedroom, finally, when Moose decided to see what the hell we were doing. I was brave enough to push him out of the bedroom but had a hell of a time trying to keep my mind on what I was doing as Moose pounded away on the door.

"Go get some beer out of my car," I lied, hoping to get him out of the house long enough for me to finish what I'd started.

"You son of a bitch!" he yelled a minute later. "You don't even have a car!"

This poor girl was scared to death that Moose would tear up the house and made me quit. I wanted to kick his ass, but I wasn't that stupid.

I walked home with my head about ready to burst and half a hard-on to boot.

* * *

During the next twenty days, I blew my money pretty frivolously, including paying a doctor a full day's beer money to tell me to keep my face clean. Shit, I should have been a doctor.

I tried catching up with old friends, including Sharon Blackwell. I even put on my uniform before going to visit her. She wasn't impressed and, damn, I still had the hots for her. She didn't want to hear my sweet shit and didn't want to go out with me. I rationalized that she must be too tired: she and her mother were working in the bean fields.

I hooked up a few times with the Indian girl from Grand Ronde, but for the most part, I was just ready to go back to bed. Shit, I don't remember one good night's sleep out of the twenty.

My ride to the Salem bus station was a kid I went to high school with. He had joined the Marines two years before I had. Robert was a pretty shaky guy and liked to get things the easy way. I vaguely remember promising to go into business with him when I finished that last year in the Marines. What the hell. That was a year away, right?

* * *

It was good to get on the bus. There's one thing about riding a bus (besides being a good place to catch a few z's): if there are any women aboard, leave it to the Navy put the moves on them. It must be something in their training. The jerk in front of me was sure working a woman over pretty good. I wasn't jealous or anything. At the stop in Roseburg, I recognized the sweet young thing the sailor nearly undressed as a girl I'd gone to school with. Small world back then.

I looked forward to getting on a new base. Hell, I'd been in the service over two years and was still a PFC and wanted another stripe (and a few more bucks). Yep, I missed life in the Marines.

It was good to see Oceanside. I hadn't seen the place for two years. I had my fake I.D. and was going to grab a beer when I heard, "Hey, fuck you, MP!" Wouldn't you know, it was my old red-headed buddy Kyle! He tried to convince me he was on his first beer, but he looked like hell.

"Well, I have been drinking all night on the bus, but this is my first beer here!"

I was still hung up on being a PFC, and I asked Kyle why he was also still a PFC.

"Same fucking reason you are. Because we are both too fucking dumb," he replied, laughing. I threatened to go back into the MPs just to give him shit.

I checked into staging early, but there were no Marines returning from Korea or Japan. The Marines checking in that day had come from a base in North Carolina. They were a strange bunch and talked funny. They were headed for the Far East, and I thought they'd fit right in with that accent.

I was told I'd be in staging for two weeks before being stationed at Twenty-nine Palms, a place about two hundred miles from L.A. Everyone had to fire the rifle for the record. I was pretty nervous about it; it had been two years since I'd fired for the record. I also had an asshole Silver Star sergeant in charge to make things worse. *I only have to deal with him for two weeks,* I told myself.

My nerves needed some settling with a few beers at the E-Club (all the Slop Chutes were now E-Clubs). Charles and I started kidding around, competing, just like the old days.

"A bunch of us are going to start a new battalion called Recon. Only the badasses get picked for that."

"Well, what did they pick you for?" I couldn't resist. "I'm going to Twenty-nine Palms for secret missions. Only the best Marines get to go."

"Fuck you." After a four-hour drinking binge, it dawned on me that I'd been broke for three days. "Hey, who's buying the beer? Does someone have a rich uncle?" I asked.

One of the North Carolina Marines piped up, "I got paid two hundred dollars travel pay, and I have more money than I do sense."

That's fine with me, sucker! I thought and signaled the waitress for another round.

* * *

I knew I'd resumed a Marine's life when I re-turned to my barracks to grab some sleep before firing the next morning. There were fights going on right next to my bunk.

One asshole wouldn't leave well enough alone and started playing with my legs. "Get the fuck out of here!" I grumbled at him. All of a sudden he went for my balls. "You queer son of a bitch," I screamed and hit him on the head.

A fight ensued in the dark, with me, Charles, the queer and a bunch of other men. At some point I was sent flying through the air and slammed into a locker. *Shit! I think I broke my ankle!* The able-bodied man who'd thrown me over his shoulder like a rag doll turned out to be the asshole sergeant.

"What the fuck's wrong with you shitheads? What the hell is going on?"

I said, "That asshole over there was trying to play with my balls while I was in my bunk."

"Yeah," another Marine vouched, "the same guy wanted me to give him a blow job."

The sergeant grabbed the queer, slamming him into the wall as he knocked the shit out of him.

Yep, I'd missed Marine life.

* * *

"If you can't make it to the rifle range, you'll have to stay another week."

My ankle was swelling fast, and I knew if I didn't get my boot on right then, it would not go on in the morning.

The next morning it hurt like hell. I hadn't slept at all, and it was time to report to the range. I was hoping to catch a ride, knowing that, if I had to walk the mile to the range, I'd shit.

At the range my coach inquired about my foot, and I lied about having a sore on it. If he knew I was injured, I would have been kept back. It hurt so damn bad I could hardly stand to shoot. And I shot badly.

"What the fuck is wrong with you, Brandon?" the coach asked. "You hit the dirt with that last shot." (I only had two more lines to go.) "If you don't do better on the last two lines, you're not going to qualify."

I don't really give a shit, I said to myself. *My ankle hurts so fucking bad I can't wait until I'm done.*

Once again I was asked what the hell was wrong with me. I finally 'fessed up about my ankle and was taken to sick bay.

The doctor cut the strings to remove my boot; my toes were black.

"You dumb shit," the doctor swore. "You have a fractured ankle and we're going to have to cast it."

Certain that this was going to prolong my stay in Oceanside, I reported the injury to my sergeant—the same shit who broke my ankle.

Tough shit! You have two days to get to your base at Twenty-nine Palms. Get your orders and leave!" He was kind enough to send me to the bus station in a jeep, but after that it was up to me to make it there, cast and all.

Chapter 11
Twenty-Nine Palms

I was to catch a bus to L.A., then to Banning and finally to Twenty-nine Palms. Shit, I was wiped out before we even made Banning and fell dead asleep. The next thing I knew the sun was coming up.

"How long before we get to Banning?" I asked the driver.

"We left there two hours ago. We're near Indio now."

"SHIT! I HAVE TO GET OFF!" I was going to have to catch a bus back to Banning. I thought: *Shit, this is all I need. To check in late with a fucked up leg.* It took two hours to ride a hundred-year-old bus to Twenty-nine Palms.

"What's wrong with your foot?" the driver asked, when we stopped in a little town called Joshua Tree.

"I broke it."

"Did you do it in the war?" he asked.

"Yeah," I lied with a straight face. I thought I at least deserved a little special attention for all the trouble I'd been through.

"Let me go buy your beer for you."

"Great!"

* * *

I wonder why I always check in on Sundays. There's never anyone around, and I can never get sheets or blankets. No one gives a shit whether I have a bunk or not.

Twenty-nine Palms at least had a new building but that was about all. This must be the be the asshole of nowhere: nothing but sand and more sand.

"How far is the mess hall from here?" I asked a corporal.

"About a mile."

Jesus! I'll never make it, I thought. "What about the PX?"

"About the same, but I can get you a ride with the MPs."

Knowing how MPs could be, I asked, "Why do you think they'll give me a ride?"

"That's where you're going, Brandon. To be an MP in the infantry. Give them a call, let them know you're here."

* * *

"Military police, Sergeant Jackson speaking."

"Sergeant, my name is PFC Brandon, and I'm assigned to the company. I'm up here in transit with a broken foot. I was wondering if I could bum a ride to chow."

Sergeant Jackson picked me up in a jeep a few minutes later. Twenty-nine Palms was the windiest hellhole I'd ever seen.

"Does it blow like this all the time?"

"Shit, today isn't bad." Sergeant Jackson replied. Jackson was a Negro and had a typical New York accent.

"Do you have a military driving license?" he asked.

"Sure do, jeep and PC rigs."

"Good, we need more MPs on base patrol." The company had about thirty

MPs, including the office staff.

"What kind of duty do you pull," I asked, "besides the base and the gate?"

"We have town patrol; we ride with the police department. On payday weekends, we send Marines to town for shore patrol."

I'd done a lot of that in Japan and remembered how many fights we had to break up. "Had lots of fights in Japan, is there much fighting out here?"

"Not much, sometimes at the PX. We send everyone to Camp Pendleton's brig where they get the shit beat out of them. Everyone's too afraid of their old master sergeant, Carl S. Johnson. Not many Marines fuck up out here."

Shit! C.S. Johnson—old Chicken Shit Johnson!

"You're right," I said. "He's a mean son of a bitch." I remembered how he'd beat the shit out of the prisoners and knocked me on my ass for letting a prisoner step over a line without calling me sir.

The MPs stayed in an older barrack block down near the gate. It looked like something left over from World War II. I was told it was colder than a witch's tit inside; you could look right through the cracks in the walls. They had used their shelters to halfway cover their bunks to keep the sand from blowing through the cracks of the bunks.

I met PFCs Maynard from Nashville, Walker from California, Trijallo from Arizona, Corporal Comstock from Washington and Corporal Lee from Louisiana. The others were at chow.

"And this is PFC Hundesinger. He is a kiss-ass who works in the office. He is also a California queer."

"Fuck you, Maynard," Hundesinger said.

It turned out I was the only MP who'd "been around." Most of the men were just out of boot camp, or had never been overseas. They all thought I was rich, with my twelve dollars, and promised to pay me back, come payday, if I'd buy beer and wine. I was smart enough this time to keep a few bucks to have my uniforms pressed: they'd been in my seabag for a month.

We have this big, good old boy motherfucker from Oklahoma, Jack. He runs to town for us if we pay for his gas. Wait till you see this guy. He's about six-six and weighs in at around three hundred. Just don't piss him off or try to screw his old lady. Don't even joke about it." There was one other married PFC, named May, who also lived in trailer housing.

I was given a bunk under a PFC McCleary, a Marine from Washington who *had* been overseas and thought he was some kind of cowboy. He was mostly full of shit.

They were right about the goddamn sand. "Do you ever get used to this stuff?"

"Yeah, we just don't let it get up our asses."

"It does make cornholing hard on your dick, though," Maynard said.

"It sure doesn't hurt your dick, Maynard," Hundesinger said. "You're the one we all cornhole!"

"Fuck you."

"No, it's your turn tonight."

They were right about Hundesinger, too.

* * *

Shaking hands with PFC Jack was like holding onto a hamhock. He was one huge son of a bitch. The others were the most laid-back bunch I'd ever seen in the Marines. All they did was sleep, drink and stand duty. They never shone their shoes, as they wore their boots most of the time, and gave me holy shit every time I'd shine mine. They'd had no training or marching. *Hell*, I thought, *we were sharp in Japan. Some difference!*

I wasn't the only one who noticed. The first sergeant always sent me and Walker to stand duty in Palm Springs on payday. We were "the most squared away men in the company."

First Sergeant Foote liked to screw around with our paychecks. We'd pay a buck to get into a serial number pool. Whoever had the best poker hand, won the pool—after Sergeant Foote's cut, that is. No one questioned him about it, and he stayed off our asses.

It was so slow compared to my earlier tour that I hated every weekend that wasn't a payday. At least when I had that duty there was something to do.

I was at the gate one Saturday morning, talking with Trijallo, when a truck pulled up. The driver needed to unload the boxes of floor tile on his truck and offered five bucks an hour to anyone who would help.

"How many guys you want?" I asked.

"The more we have, the quicker we get done," he replied.

Shit, everyone was out and ready in five minutes when they heard "money." We were done in less than two hours. Everyone got ten bucks, and the driver gave me an extra ten for lining up the help. We had over a hundred dollars between us and, man, we thought we were living!

"Hell, let's have a party."

"Shit, no! Let's go to L.A. and get some fucking!"

"I have a better idea," said Harris. "You guys buy my gas, and I'll go to L.A. and bring the whores down here. Then we can get screwed all weekend."

Now Harris, being a colored dude and all, was questioned about his choice in whores. "Shit, man! Honky whores charge too much, and they don't fuck for shit."

In the long run, we agreed to put Harris in charge of getting the women, Jack in charge of getting booze from town, and Comstock in charge of bringing chow back to the barracks. We were damn lucky we were the military police, or we would have all gone to jail.

I'd been introduced to a new drink called Purple Delight: beer mixed with wine and gin. Shit, if you spilled any of it, it would eat a hole right through the floor. Most of us were drunk on our ass when Harris got back with the women. *Shit! They all have fat asses and, boy, are they dark! I'm going to have to get a lot drunker than I am,* I thought.

Maynard had made the same observation. "Damn, Harris! Couldn't you find any skinny whores? My pecker won't get past the fat," he said.

"How do you dudes screw with your little peckers? I can fill those holes and have five inches left over I haven't used!"

We didn't stop all night, and by noon on Sunday, we'd had enough.

And I thought I had some wild times in Japan.

* * *

On Easter weekend, I pulled duty in Palm Springs. We were bunking in the firehouse, when someone pissed off the chief, and he made us find another place to stay. Because I was in charge, I went to the police department; all they had available were two jail cells, no showers, and it was colder than shit in their building.

Well shit, I'll just ride with one of the guys on patrol. At least it will be warm in the car.

The man I rode with was one smooth talker and convinced a waitress into taking him home. He didn't show up the next morning for Easter-service traffic duty. I had never seen so many Cadillacs and limos in my life. We had set up roadblocks to control traffic.

"Absolutely no cars through the blocks," the police had instructed, and they meant it. I can't remember how many drivers tried to slip me money to let them through the blocks to park. I saw a few movies stars (anyway, I *thought* they were movie stars).

It was all over in three hours, and it was either back to the cold jail cell or the base. I opted for the base. My buddy bitched and whined all the way back. He had wanted to stay another night in Palm Springs. There was no way I would sleep in that cold cell.

* * *

Five of us got a three-day weekend and headed to Mexico, by way of Arizona. In a 1939 Ford Club Coupe, we headed across the desert away from Twenty-nine Palms.

"We better leave the car on the Arizona side of the border. It'll be safer that way in case we get into trouble in Mexico," Corporal Lee said. He'd been there before, obviously. The best way to have a good time is to get a taxi and have the driver line us up with the whores. If we go to their place and drink, our money will last longer."

"Sounds good to us."

We all chipped in twenty bucks, and Lee handed it over to a cabdriver. That was the last we saw of the driver or our money. We had about fifty bucks left between us: just enough for some chow and gas money back to the base.

We were all pissed-off, but Corporal Lee was downright crazy about it. He was hell-bent on finding the taxi driver and getting our money back. He was gone almost two hours. He came back screaming, "LETS GET THE FUCK OUTTA HERE!" He had recouped some of our money, and so we wanted to stay. "Fuck no, we have to get out of here," he insisted.

"Well," Maynard said, "how about giving us our share of what you got back."

Lee handed Maynard a wad of blood-covered money.

"SHIT!" Maynard screamed as he threw down a bloodied glob. "It's a fucking ear!"

Lee started laughing, "I didn't get all our money, so I took his ear instead! You guys had better not say anything about this, I'll cut *your* fucking ears off."

Good lord! If the Mexican police came after us or called the Arizona Border Patrol, we'd end up in jail for the rest of our lives. That crazy son of a bitch! I was never so glad to make it back to the base! I hoped he hadn't killed that driver.

We were all back on duty the next day and had just gone to chow. Hundesinger came over to tell us about the police officers who were at the Provost Marshal's office. They wanted to run a check to see who had been to Mexico over the weekend.

"Who did they talk to?" I asked, petrified.

"The first sergeant," he answered. "He told them there were several thousand Marines on base, but he'd check with each company. The sergeant also told them almost everyone at Twenty-nine Palms went to L.A., because we only had two-day leaves. So they left."

I went straight back to the barracks to tell Lee. "Keep your mouths shut about it. I just cut the guy's ear off, that's all!" We didn't hear any more after that, and Lee made sure we kept quiet. I still thought Lee was crazy. I wanted to get away from him.

* * *

PFC May had orders to go to Alaska. He was extremely upset about it: he didn't have enough money to take his wife and kids home before he left, let alone enough to get to Alaska.

"Why don't you ask if you can get out of your orders?" I asked.

"I did, but someone has to take my place."

"Shit, May, I'll take your place," I offered. "Let's go ask."

When we approached the first sergeant he asked, "What the hell do you want to go to Alaska for, Brandon?"

"To help out PFC May, sir!" Damn, I sounded good. "He's married, sir, and I'm not."

I had fifteen days before I was to report in Alaska.

* * *

I decided not to say anything to the rest of the group. I checked out, picked up my travel pay and orders and made sure I didn't run into Corporal Lee.

Trijallo and Maynard came into the barracks just as I was leaving.

"Where the hell you going, Brandon?"

"Alaska."

"Yeah. Sure."

"No shit. I'll write when I get there." I knew there were more orders for Alaska and told Trijallo and Maynard to check into it.

Jack gave me a ride to the bus station and asked, "How'd you get your orders so fast?"

I said, "I'm going in place of May; we just switched names on the orders." *Shit, they're going to think I'm one great son of a bitch!* I thought, so I added, "Besides, I want to get away from that crazy, fucking Lee. "

Jack chuckled, "Yeah, so do I."

"Well, shit, Jack, go tell them you want to go to Alaska." (No one in their right mind wants to go to Alaska, but I don't care. I just want the hell out of here.)

* * *

In a little over two years I had seen a lot, met a lot of great Marines and a few bad ones. I wondered what it would be like in Alaska. But first, I had to concentrate on getting out of Twenty-nine Palms.

In town, I barely had time to say my good-byes to Sam, the cabdriver and an old ex-Marine. There was only one bus leaving each day, and damn if it wasn't right on schedule this time!

"Look me up if you're ever in Oregon, Sam. I only have ten months left in the Marines, then I'm going home."

"They'll ship you overseas, sure as shit," Sam said.

"Yeah, when hell freezes over. "

Chapter 12
Warm Beer, Cold Feet

The old stageline didn't make great time. It stopped in every town, no matter how small.

There I was, leaving California, and I still hadn't looked up my two sisters. My sister Toni's father-in-law, Dr. Stoneman, lived in Banning. I thought he might be able to tell me where Toni lived now. I made a point to stop and look him up, but it was a waste of time. He didn't seem to give a damn where Toni was. So, in the long run, I headed for Palmdale where my other sister Jerry lived. I had almost all day to get to Palmdale, so I took my chances and started hitching rides. I was lucky: it only took me four rides to get there.

In Palmdale, I rode along with Robert, my brother-in-law (we called him "Lefty"), while he drove cement truck. I remembered him drinking a lot when I was a kid. Things hadn't changed at all. Every time we came to a store, he would stop and buy a six-pack of beer, and before we went home after work, he bought a case of beer and a jug of booze. Of course I paid: things were pretty tough for them.

Jerry was glad to see me and cooked a great meal. They lived with their four kids in a tiny house.

Every half hour Lefty would go outside for a swig; that's about how long he could last between drinks. Poor Jerry. If he didn't stop drinking, they would never get out of debt.

* * *

I headed for Oregon after two or three days. I wanted to see the folks before I went to Kodiak Island. When I hit Valley Junction, I was only a couple of miles from home. *And it isn't even the middle of the night this time,* I marveled.

I knew I could walk the distance but didn't want to lug my three bags around. Valley Junction was a one-horse town, and I knew I could probably find someone to give me a lift. At the only gas station in town I found Marvin. He used to live next door to me as a kid.

"You home for good now, Percy?" he asked.

"Hell, no. I'm on my way to Kodiak Island, Alaska, in the middle of the ocean."

"Damn, they have the biggest bears in the world up there," he said. "They're called Kodiak bears."

A picture of King Kong flashed through my mind. *What the hell have I done? Why did I ever ask for this duty?* At that moment, crazy-assed Corporal Lee was far from my mind.

Marvin happened to be between jobs, and I sweet talked him into driving me to Portland to pick up my pay. I had about two week's pay coming; that would buy us a few beers. We made a quick trip to the air force base in Portland and I had no trouble getting my pay—including an extra two week's salary. Damn, that was a lot of money.

"Hell, Marvin, let's get a case of beer and see if we can put a hurtin' on it!"

With the case of beer in the back seat and ready to head back, Marvin spotted a hitchhiker from back home and picked him up. This kid turned out to be a real churchgoer and lectured us on the evils of beer, warning us not to drink any of our case. He wanted to talk about all the good times we had in school instead.

Shit, this is all I need, I thought. The only hurting we did on that case was letting it get warm.

* * *

Marvin was to pick up a friend of his wife's and take her to Grand Ronde with us. I thought I knew the girl, then remembered Earl Homes' girlfriend Shirlie from the last time I came home on leave. She remembered me, too, and muttered something under her breath and gave me a dirty look.

In the car she asked if we'd seen Earl around.

"Well, yeah," Marvin hedged. "He was in Valley Junction when we left there."

That was where Shirlie wanted to go.

When she spotted Earl's car—with Earl and another woman inside—her eyes had fire in them.

Shirlie went to Marvin's house with us, after all.

"Boy, Earl's in the shithouse now," I said after she'd left the car.

"No shit," Marvin said. "That girl he was with has been known to screw anyone at the drop of a hat. Everyone knows her."

Earl was right behind us, with his tail between his legs. He and Shirlie went outside to "talk," and after a while, Shirlie came back by herself.

"Where did Earl go?" Marvin asked her.

"To hell—as far as I'm concerned," she said.

Tough luck for Earl, but this is my chance. I just hope Earl doesn't think we planned this!

* * *

Funny things happen to people who start out hating each other's guts. Shirlie and I became good friends and started dating during the next few days. I thought Earl was a fucking nutcase to let Shirlie slip away.

I promised Shirlie I would show up at her high school May Day dance, but for some reason, I got cold feet and didn't show. One thing Shirlie was good at was getting pissed at me. To make it up to her, I went with her to meet her mother. I must have passed muster, because she told Earl to go to hell when he tried to patch things up between them.

We were together every day and night. The night before I was to leave, she told me she loved me and would wait for me to come back—if I loved her, too. I told her I liked her better than anyone I'd ever met and would write her from Alaska. I know she wanted hear that I loved her, but I just couldn't make myself say it.

* * *

Once again my ride to the bus station turned out to be the shady character from school, Robert. He reminded me of my promise to go into business with him. He needed someone he could trust, because some of his deals were "a little outside the law."

Yeah, I'll just bet they are, I thought.

I told him I'd been thinking about staying in the Marines and wasn't sure if I could keep my promise.

* * *

I called Shirlie from Portland during a layover, just to say good-bye again. I didn't know why, but I was sure going to miss her. I was torn between getting out in nine months or staying in the Marines and trying to make corporal. I just couldn't figure out why I hadn't made the promotion yet.

Maybe I need to stop drinking and study the Marine Guide Book a little. That's what I'll do in Alaska, I promised myself.

* * *

We arrived in Seattle about four in the morning on a Sunday. I checked in early and found my way around the base.

Pier Ninety-One, a navy base, looked older than the hills. One old gray building was in serious need of a good paint job. You could tell where the Marines stayed: the grass was cut, everything was clean. Their barracks always looked good.

When checking in, the sergeant looked me over and said, "Don't I know you?"

Well, hell, it was Recola from my boot-camp days.

How the hell did he get stripes? I wondered. "How long you been a sergeant?" I asked.

"Just made it last week. What the hell has happened to you? You're still a PFC."

I didn't have any good answers. "Maybe I'll make corporal in Alaska," I replied.

* * *

Recola wasn't the only boot-camp buddy in Seattle. Arthur Bengen was now living in Seattle, was a sergeant, and got to go home every night! I was beginning to wish I'd been stationed in Seattle: it was only two hundred miles from home.

I met two Marines headed to Adak, Alaska, which was about four hundred miles beyond Kodiak. They informed me of our three-hour bus ride to Whidby Island Navy Air Station on Wednesday, where we'd catch our flight to Alaska.

"What do we do until Wednesday?" I asked.

"Chip paint, paint—all the shit details."

What did I expect?

"The best jobs are cleaning the barracks. If you get on painting detail, the asshole police sergeant won't let you quit until the job is done. Sometimes we've painted until the lights go out."

Seattle was a dry town on Sundays. The retired men usually came to the base to drink on those days, since that was the only place open with booze. If you shut up and listened to their old war stories and took razzing about

Arthur Bengen, fellow GySgt and boot camp buddy. Art died in Vietnam 15 years later.

"how easy we had it in the military these days," they would even buy a round or two.

It was kind of a run-down old club, but the beer was cold. We stayed until closing, letting the old-timers buy our beer. Most of them had worked at the navy base in Bremerton, riding the ferry across each morning. It sounded to me like they didn't have it so bad themselves.

I did get a good night's sleep. Strange: I was expecting to stay up all night thinking about Shirlie.

* * *

The next morning we reported to the police sergeant for work detail.

"You coming or going to Alaska?" the sergeant asked.

"Coming, sir. I just came from Twenty-nine Palms, California and Japan before that."

"How come you're still a PFC? You get busted?"

"No, sir. I have a clean record. Maybe it's because I've been transferred so many times," I said.

"You know how to run a buffer?" he asked.

Shit, what the hell is a buffer? "Yes," I lied.

I was given cleanup duty along with another man.

"I'm sure glad you know how to run a buffer," he said.

"Hell, I don't even know what a buffer is, but I sure don't want to paint all day."

A skinny little sergeant told me to plug the thing in and be sure to walk backward, so I wouldn't run over the cord. I figured if that skinny little guy could run the thing, it'd be a cinch for me. I flipped on the switch and watched the buffer plow into the lockers, then the bunks. Then the damn cord wrapped around my leg and pulled me all over the place, like a rag doll.

"SHUT THE GODDAMN THING OFF!" the police sergeant screamed. "Just what in the hell are you trying to do? I thought you said you'd run one of these before. "

I thought it better to lie rather than admit I hadn't wanted to paint, so I said, "I thought it was a floor sander."

In the long run, I chipped paint all that day till the lights went off, then finished chipping and re-painting the entire floor before I caught my bus on Wednesday.

Chapter 13
Alaska

Whidby Island Navy Air Base looked like a World War II base with lots of old buildings. I stayed at the Marine barracks because my flight didn't leave until nine the following morning. There were several Marines and sailors on the flight, but I was the only one headed for Kodiak Island.

There wasn't much to see from the air: just lots of mountains and plenty of ocean. As was my usual habit when traveling, I slept most of the way. It was sure a lot different from my flight two years ago, when I went to boot camp. I no longer suffered from motion sickness. *I must be getting tough,* I thought.

It looked like we were going to land right in the middle of some mountains. We had been following a channel for about a half hour. I saw an airplane hangar and wondered if that was the base. It sure looked small. The hangar had "Kodiak" painted on the side.

Boy, we're going down fast.

We were told to stay in our seats until the Marines came aboard to clear us: this was a top-security base. No one was allowed to leave the plane except the Kodiak passengers, and the plane would only stay to refuel. I was the only Marine who didn't stay aboard to go to Adak Island. *Shit, I hope this isn't a bad sign. What the hell kind of assignment did I ask for?*

The two Marines who accompanied me off the plane were boots. They spotted my overseas' ribbon and were surprised. Most of the Marines at Kodiak had never been overseas, except the NCOs.

I told them about how I had asked for Alaska to help out a married guy.

"You must be nuts or liked that guy a lot."

"I only have about ten months left, and I can stand on my head that long," I quipped.

* * *

The first thing I noticed at Kodiak Island was that all the barracks were connected by hallways. I asked why.

"The wind and the snow gets so bad in the winter months it isn't safe to go outside."

"How do they keep the base secure in the winter?" I asked.

They both laughed, and I was told that the Marines go out and stand guard duty.

I noticed the Marine barracks was adjacent to the mess hall. *Well, at least that's one good thing,* I thought.

I was let off in front of the barracks, and three or four other Marines came out to help me carry my gear. What a shock I got when they told me they were all from Lebanon, Oregon. They had joined up on the buddy system and all ended up in Alaska.

Good drinking…

That sure says a lot for the buddy system, I told myself.

I set my gear down in the hallway, and took my orders topside to check in.

The first sergeant welcomed me to the base and asked a lot of questions, including why I was still a PFC. He then took me to see the company commander, a major. The major looked over my record book. He, too, asked why I was still a PFC. I was beginning to get paranoid about this rank stuff. I told him my guess was that I had moved too much. I also said that I had always done my job the best I could.

What he said after that almost made me pass out on the spot.

"You'll be promoted to corporal on Friday morning at personnel inspection and assigned as squad leader in the rifle platoon."

Well. I'll be damned! That was great. And a job I knew, at that. Shit! I'm gonna be a corporal.

* * *

When I joined up with my platoon, there was only one man who had been overseas, a private named Garrad. Garrad was from Oregon, too. He had been wounded in Korea, and from what I'd been told, he always got his ass in trouble when he drank. (Great, someone I'd have to baby-sit right off the bat.)

The barracks were spotless. Almost everyone was a PFC, so it looked like my job was going to be cushy.

"Hey, Brandon, you asshole, did you get shit-canned to Alaska, too?"

I looked up to see Sanchez, a man I knew in Japan. Hell, the last time I'd seen him, we were both drunk on our ass and trying to screw the same girl.

"Hey, Sanchez," I said, "damn, are you still a PFC?" I just couldn't resist.

"Only for the last month," he said. "I got busted for fighting."

"Damn, you wetbacks are always fighting," I said. "How long you been here?"

"About four months now, I guess."

Well, how's the liberty up here?"

He started laughing, "Compared to what? Boot camp? Shit, man, there's nothing but cluches up here."

"What the hell is a *cluche*?" I asked.

"Man, those are the ugliest women God ever put on this earth. They're Eskimos with no teeth, and they're fat. The only thing that will screw a cluche is a Kodiak bear, so if you want to try to screw one, you have to whip a bear first."

"Well, what the hell do you do for puss up here?" I wanted to know.

"We screw sailors and pound our puds a lot," Sanchez said.

"Too bad. I'm in love, buddy," I said, thinking of Shirlie. "I'm making corporal on Friday, so it looks like I'll shape up."

"Hell, Brandon, you will shape up when hell freezes over."

I told him I might even make sergeant. Damn, did that make him laugh.

Hell, maybe I am a screw-off, I thought, but I'd made up my mind to do my best.

* * *

Our platoon sergeant, Sergeant Emery, called the platoon together to introduce me and told them that I was being promoted to corporal at Friday's inspection.

A red-headed kid from Montana said something smart along the lines of my having to prove myself a better man than him before he'd take orders from me. Then he started laughing, along with a kid from Michigan. It didn't take very long to pick out the wiseasses.

I could hardly wait to find the base laundry and take my uniforms in and have corporal's stripes sewn on. Getting ready for inspection was a breeze. We had our own pressing room and a Marine assigned to press uniforms. All we had to do was drop off our uniforms. I gave him two bucks, and he said that I didn't have to pay him. I said it was worth it. Damn! I was excited.

I shone my shoes the best they'd ever been, cleaned my rifle and washed all my belts. It looked like I was the only one spending so much time getting ready for inspection. Almost everyone else headed for the Marine Club. It was somewhere up on the hill by the Navy Club. But that was the least of my worries. I was going to be a corporal in the morning.

* * *

I met my platoon commander for the first time. He was a lean Marine, with big ears, who everyone called "Radar Ears." He had been wounded in Korea and seemed like a good man. He told me I that looked squared away and wanted to know where I'd learned to shine my shoes: they looked like mirrors compared to the rest of the platoon. I told him about being with the military police in Japan and how we had to be in shape there.

I was the only PFC making corporal. I can't describe the great feeling when the first sergeant called my name and called me front and center. My military record was recited, as well as what I had done for my promotion.

Hot damn! I'm a corporal.

* * *

Sanchez showed me around the base. It only took ten minutes, as most of the base was restricted. About the only places we were allowed in were the post exchange, the club, the gym and the weight room.

I sure liked the gym. There were lots of weights and punching bags and a full boxing ring. I saw the red-headed kid from Montana working out in the boxing room. When he saw me, he tried to impress me with his boxing skills.

"Do you want to do a little boxing one of these days?" he asked me.

"Sure," I told him.

"How about now?"

I wanted to start running and get into shape. It had been a while since I'd boxed, and there had been far too many beers. I sure didn't want to get my ass kicked by a smartass, now that I was a corporal.

"Maybe next week. After I get to see what my job will be," I replied, fudging.

* * *

Sergeant Emery liked to sleep and let me handle most of the squad's training. I was doing great. I'd been

Good fishing...

there over two weeks and hadn't even been to the club! I stood duty and took care of my squad. They began to look good and enjoyed learning what I showed them from my experiences in Japan.

I wrote to Shirlie almost every night about how I didn't have to stand duty and that I was saving money. *Shit, I can't believe I'm doing this.* I even went to the post exchange and bought her a necklace.

* * *

Being a corporal was great. So far, I hadn't had much trouble with anyone, but I knew it was just a matter of time before I would be tested. I was in charge of the hallways leading to the Marine barracks. We were getting ready for a major barracks inspection, so all the old floor wax had to be taken off and new wax put down.

Three of the worst shitheads were assigned to my work detail. I had to stay on their asses constantly to finish the floor. Only one more hallway was left when one of the men came up missing. I found him in one of the navy barracks, shooting pool. I ordered his ass back to work and took his pool cue away from him.

"If you weren't a corporal, I'd stick that cue up your ass," he snapped. The sailors started to laugh; I was pissed.

"Let's go out behind the barracks. There you can show me what you'd do if I weren't a corporal."

We headed for the side door; I made sure he went out first. As he stepped off the stairs, I hit him just below the ear, and he went down on his knees. I didn't stop there. I kicked him in the ribs and hit him twice in the face, before heading back to the barracks. He followed ten minutes later and didn't have much to say.

"Keep your fucking mouth shut about this, or I'll do the job *right* next time," I threatened.

Boy, things just went from bad to worse that day. Another man was missing after I went back inside the barracks. I found him in the head, reading a book, and I told him to get his ass back to work before I kicked it.

He laughed.

Wrong day to mess with me, buddy, I thought. I grabbed him by the neck and flipped him over my hip. He landed on his back; that knocked the wind out of him. Five or six men watched. As he pulled himself off the floor, I threw him out the door. He slipped on the wet wax and ended up with a huge knot on his head.

I was doomed to get my ass in trouble with Sergeant Emery. I did.

After cleaning was done, I headed for the gym to let off a little steam. I was working the weights when the kid from Montana came in.

"Hey, Corporal Brandon, you want to put the gloves on with me?" he asked.

"Not tonight," I told him.

"How about wrestling?" he asked. I could see that he was dead set to try me, so I got in the ring with him. In the mood I was in, it took about one minute to put him on his ass. Damn, all that Judo training was sure paying off.

"Well shit, man, you outweigh me by twenty pounds," he whined. "Come on. Put the gloves on with me." He wasn't about to give up.

He was a good boxer, but he didn't hit very hard and was out of shape. After five minutes he was done for, and I ended up beating the shit out of him. With his big mouth, I was going to give him something to talk about. That was the last time he ever asked me to box. I guess I should have told him that all I did in Japan was fight drunks, and with two years of Judo training, I got damn good at it.

* * *

I looked forward to mail call. There was always a letter from Shirlie, and my mother wrote a lot, too. I'd been in Kodiak two months when, one day, I received a letter from Shirlie that said Earl had been hurt in a logging accident. She was going back to him and they were going to be married. That was hard to take. *Maybe I should have told her I loved her,* I thought. But she should have known that, even though I hadn't actually told her. My mind was fucked up.

I went upstairs to find Sanchez. "Come on, fucker," I said to him, "Let's go to the club; I want to get drunk."

"What's the matter, Brandon?" he asked. "Someone die?"

"Hell, I got a Dear John letter," I said. "Piss on it. I'm gonna get drunk."

I'd never been to the club since I'd made up my mind to straighten up and fly right.

"Hey, Corporal Brandon. This is the first time I've seen you up here," Zemen said. He was in my squad and spent all his nights in the club. "What's up?" he asked.

"I just got a Dear John letter, and I'm gonna get drunk. Can we go in here and get a whiskey?" I asked, pointing to the bar.

"No," Zemen said, "you have to be twenty-one. But we can go over to the Navy Club and drink whiskey. They never ask our age there."

Man, did I pour them down. That was the most I'd had to drink in over two months, and I was on my ass.

After the club closed, we walked down the hill, and I started telling Zemen how I must really be in love with Shirlie. I'd been around a lot of women over the past two years, but most of them were whores, and I never had much feeling for them.

Until now, I had never been sure how I felt about Shirlie. "Why don't you write her and tell her you love her?" he asked me.

"I don't even know what being in love means," I said. "I only knew her for ten days, and I'm not sure how I feel. I do know I don't want to lose her."

"Well, don't get stupid and drunk every night. I did that and look at me now," Zemen said. "I should be a sergeant."

Zemen tried to get me to hit the rack, but all I wanted to do was stand in the head and cry. Lights were out and I was told to keep my mouth shut. "Go to hell," I muttered. Inside the head was a senior corporal, but rank didn't stop me from grabbing his head and shoving it in the toilet bowl. At

Bad Duty! (Two our of three ain't bad!)

that moment, Sergeant Emery came in and told me to get my ass in the rack or he'd take me down and throw me in the brig.

I woke up the next morning with a hangover and felt like an asshole, but I was still acting stupid. I didn't want to talk to anyone and told everyone to stay away from me. I wrote a few letters to Shirlie but that didn't help. I made a few threats to kick some ass when I got home, and I continued going to the club every night. I was drunk most of the time. Good old Zemen always went with me.

* * *

There must have been a full moon one night, because everything that could go wrong did. A Drum and Bugle Corps team came to Kodiak to put on a show. They frequented the club during their stay, and one of their sergeants must have taken a dislike to me. Every time he'd walk by my table, he had something smart to say. Once he flipped the back of my head.

"Too bad you're a young punk," he said. "You can't come in and drink with the big boys."

"I think you must have kissed someone's ass to get your stripes," I replied. "You don't look smart enough to have earned them."

He said my ass needed some kicking. It probably did.

We went out in the snow, and I nailed him alongside the head and once in the nose. He didn't even get to take a swing.

He stood up and said, "I guess you're not a punk." That was the end of that fight.

The club manager cut me off for the night, so I went to get my jacket. I asked Zemen to go to the Navy Club with me. Outside there were two Marines waiting for us. They were twin brothers and started kicking the shit out of Zemen. I plowed into them and was kicking the shit out of them, but old Zemen was no fighter. He was getting the beating of his life. The club bouncer came out to stop the fight and grabbed me. By then I was ready to tangle with anyone, and I knocked him on his ass.

"Fuck you, Marine," he said. "Go get yourself killed. See if I give a shit."

Finally the club manager, Corporal Johnson, came out and succeeded in stopping the fight. He was tough enough to get the job done. He'd been wounded two times in Korea, had earned a silver star and was tougher than shit.

All hell was breaking loose back in the barracks. The lights were on and it was eleven-thirty p.m. We were bloody as hell and needed to get to the head to clean up. Sergeant Emery was standing by the door. "What the hell have you been up to, Brandon?" he asked.

"Oh," I said nonchalantly, "me and Zemen got into a fight. But we're friends now." I sure didn't want him to know about the bouncer, the club manager and the other two Marines we'd tangled with.

Emery couldn't understand why I would hit a little shit like Zemen.

* * *

"How come all the lights are on?" I asked, forgetting there must have been a fall moon.

Emery said, "The shit hit the fan. Three guys were found drunk on their ass in the supply room. They were screwing PFC Sanchez in the ass."

"Oh shit! Who was it?" I demanded.

"The same guys who run the supply room: two corporals and a sergeant."

Damn, I always thought Sanchez was a little sissy, but I never thought he was a queer.

The OD came in and ordered us into the racks. We were threatened with doing drills out in the snow, if he heard any more shit going on that night. We talked half the night, anyway, about what was going to happen. The consensus was that "the goddamn Navy will be in our shit for this."

We were cleaning up the barracks the next morning when a captain came in asking for me. I reported to him. He just stood there looking at me. Then he left. I looked at Sergeant Emery and asked him what that was all about.

"I heard you were in a fight with a sergeant last night, not with Zemen," he said.

"Well the fight with the sergeant was a little earlier," I lied. *I'm getting good at covering my ass,* I thought.

"You dumb shit," Sergeant Emery said, "the man you beat the shit out of was Captain Lange's son!"

"Oh shit. My ass is in trouble now."

"You are not shitting," Emery said. "Captain Lange will have your ass before you get off this island."

Shit, I only had a few months left, and knew I had better start watching my ass. I stopped going to the club and started working out in the gym more.

* * *

I was on cleanup detail and had the same PFC from Montana who'd tested me before on my work detail again. Once again he split and went to the gym to screw off. I would have kicked his ass again, but I was already on thin ice.

I put him on report for leaving his duty. Shit, he was pissed. He got office hours and they gave him a suspended bust. For some reason, the PFC thought he had been busted down to a private, so he had all his stripes cut off his uniforms. When he came back he was ready to kick my ass and asked me to go to the gym with him so he could try. I asked him why the hell he cut off his stripes, since he'd only been suspended, and that all he had to do was some extra duty at night. God, the look on his face was dumbfounded.

"Shit! What a shit I am," he said. "I'm sorry, Corporal Brandon."

"You still want to go to the gym?" I baited him.

"Fuck no, sir!"

* * *

One thing about Alaska: there was plenty to do if you liked to fish or hunt. We checked out trucks from the motor pool and spent entire weekends driving around on the back roads. We could get all the C rations we needed to last us while drove to the end of the island. Then we'd shoot the hell out of everything and catch fish. It was a good way to keep away from Captain Lange.

One weekend, three of us decided to climb the highest mountain in the area. I would never do that again. Half the mountain was frozen ice and made descending pretty dangerous. We had a hell of a time getting back down.

I had checked out a .300 Savage rifle, so I could do some shooting. We had an old mongrel dog as our barracks mascot and took him with us. We were ten miles from base, in Kodiak bear country, and stopped to eat chow.

"Simmons, you hear that train?" I asked.

"Hell, there aren't any trains up here," he said.

"Well, it sure sounds like a train," I insisted.

"Can't you hear it? It's getting louder. The wind must be carrying the sound up to us."

"Shit. It isn't even coming from town," he said.

By now we were both listening. Then I noticed the hair on the back of the dog standing up. *Shit, maybe it's a bear!* I thought. Hell, it *was* a bear, and it was running full out. "Shit, I hope it isn't coming this way," I said.

"Hell, shoot it, shoot it!" Simmons screamed.

I could see it now, but there were two bears, not one. One was chasing the other.

"Grab the dog and hold him. Don't let him bark," I said. "Goddamn! They are big sons of bitches! I hope they don't see us."

"Fuck! Let's run," Simmons said.

"No! Lie still. They've been fighting. Look at the blood."

We must have lain there five minutes or more. When we took off running, I think I passed the dog twice. Damn I was scared. I had never seen anything so big that could move that fast.

*   *   *

I only had two and a half months left and hadn't screwed up yet. I got a letter from Shirlie's mother telling me to keep writing to her; at least I had her mother on my side. I wasn't sure what to do about staying in or getting out of the Marine Corps. I knew one thing for sure: I'd be glad to get the hell off this base. It was snowing a lot by then and the cold was crippling.

I had the honor of lowering the flag—not the most pleasant thing to do in those temperatures. The wind blew a hundred miles an hour, or close to it. One evening there were three of us on color detail; I was in charge. We only had a small flag but had to wait in the cold for ten minutes before the flag could come down. We would watch the navy officer in headquarters; he would let us know, with a wave, when he would start the music. That was our cue to lower the flag. We were shooting the breeze when the Marine holding the rope let go. The wind had caught it for a second and pulled the rope right out of his hand. Both flag and rope went flying. Shit, there we were, looking up at the flag forty feet in the air at the end of the rope.

"Damn it, you shithead!" I said. "Why the hell did you do that?" I ordered him off color guard and told him to tell the sergeant of the guard before the duty officer called. About ten minutes later he was back.

"What the hell have you been doing?" I asked. "We are freezing our asses off out here! What did the sergeant say?"

"He said for you to stay out here, wait for the wind to stop blowing and catch the flag when it comes down," he answered.

"Your ass!" I said. "I'll freeze to death!"

"Yep, that's what he said. Captain Lange was there. This was his idea," he said.

Those two assholes left me standing out in the freezing cold.

Shit, he had to be kidding. I looked at the duty officer. *Shit, maybe he'll tell me to come over and watch the flag from his window.* Fat chance. That dumb fucking swabby just stood there, and I knew I would never make it. Soon my nose was ready to fall off, and I wasn't watching the flag anymore. I was jumping up and down, running around, trying not to freeze. When I felt the rope hit me, I grabbed it. My hands were so cold I couldn't feel to unhook the rope. I finally got if off but couldn't hook the rope back to the pole. *Hell with this,* I thought, *I'll come back later.*

"Damn it, Sergeant Luke," I said, once inside. "I almost froze out there. What the hell did I have to do that for?"

"You know the rules. The American flag never touches the ground," he said.

Damn, I would be glad when I got the hell out of there.

* * *

It was still cold when I reported for patrol at midnight, but at least we were inside a truck. I would have hated a walking post after my incident at the flag pole. I was on post with PFC Thornton. He was a good Marine, a bit of a kiss-ass, but we got along well. And our post wasn't so hard. We drove around the warehouses making sure they were locked and that no one came near them.

Thornton had orders for Alameda Naval Air Station in California. He was due to leave in a few days and talked about what he wanted to do. He planned on getting married and was thinking about staying in the Marines.

About a half hour before our watch was over, we got permission to leave our post to service our vehicle. I was filling out the trip ticket, and Thornton was putting gas in the rig when the OD pulled up.

"What are you doing off your post?" he asked me. It was Captain Lange.

"I radioed for permission to service the truck. We got the okay, sir," I explained, hoping that would be good enough for Lange.

"I just came from the guardhouse and you did not call in. You are off your post without proper authority. You are relieved of your post, and I am putting you on report. Get in the back of my pickup, NOW!"

He had Thornton return to our post, then he drove around the base for forty minutes with me in the back of the pickup. The wind was blowing and it was twenty below zero. I was almost frozen by the time we got to the guardshack.

I went to the corporal on guard and asked to see the logbook. There was no entry of my radio call. I asked why there was not an entry. He said I had not called in. "Captain Lange was here during the last hour and said no one called in."

"Well, someone returned my call and gave us permission to service that truck," I countered.

I was told to hit the rack; I was on report. I would have to tell my story during office hours the following day. I caught up with Thornton and asked if he knew we had called in. He said yes.

In the first sergeant's office, the next morning, I had to sign papers stating that I acknowledged I was on report and restriction until I could report to the commanding officer. I was on restriction for over two weeks and my only witness, Thornton, had received his orders and left the base. He had not told anyone the truth about my radio call. I knew I'd been set up and could only hope the commanding officer would see it that way.

I didn't know what was taking so long to hold my office hours, and we were about to go into the field for a week.

* * *

The Navy set up a training operation between us and their frogmen. They were going to make a landing on the base and plant fake bombs. We were to defend the island and try to capture them.

Clarkson and myself were sent two miles out on point to watch for a landing. There was no way to keep from freezing. The wind, as always, was blowing, and we couldn't see a thing. We moved to a flat spot, out of the wind, and dug a hole in the snow. I remember telling Clarkson that my nose and fingers were half-frozen, and I was sweating. I thought I was going to pass out. That was the last thing I remembered, except that I could hear people talking. It was Clarkson. He had called in on the radio, reporting that I had passed out, and he could not wake me.

I was taken to the hospital with a fever of a hundred and four degrees and a mild case of frostbite. I stayed in the hospital five days before I was released.

* * *

I got a letter from Shirlie. Earl had been killed in a logging accident, and she was moving to California soon. She wanted to know where I would be stationed next. As well, I learned that Captain Lange had received orders and was leaving the island. Boy! This was turning out to be a red-letter day.

I was finally to see the CO the next morning for my office hours. This was the first time I had ever been in enough trouble to actually stand in front of my commanding officer. I didn't like it; everybody treated me like shit. I reported at 0800 hours; Captain Lange was there. *Damn it! I thought he was gone!*

He and the CO called me in. Captain Lange told the major I was a real screw-off and left my post whenever I felt like it. He also said that, when we went on the field operation, I faked being sick to get out of the field.

I almost shit. I could not believe what he was saying.

When I was asked what I had to say, I just stood there. I was busted to PFC, lost half my pay and was put in the brig for twenty days.

Under guard, I took all my things from my locker, along with all my gear, and stored it in the supply room. Then I was put into the brig.

One of my buddies PFC Kidd was the brig guard. I'm sure he knew I had just gotten screwed, but he didn't give a shit. He made me do jumping jacks and push-ups and clean up whatever he threw around the place. I couldn't believe what was happening to me. The next few days were hell. That damn Kidd was the worst asshole I had ever seen. He loved screwing with the guys in the brig.

I'd been in the brig six days when my platoon leader, Lieutenant Garrett, came by. We went over my office hours, and I told him my version of what had happened. I also told him that I suspected the fight I'd had with Captain Lange's son was the reason I was in all this trouble. Soon after, Kidd took me and my gear to my platoon leader. Lieutenant Garrett agreed there were too many things that hadn't added up. He decided that part of the charges against me would be dropped. I had put myself in a spot, however, and would not get my stripes or my pay back.

"I think I'm getting a bad deal," I told the lieutenant.

* * *

I was going to do some serious ass-kicking once I was out of the brig. I was going to look up that lying corporal of the guard and PFC Kidd and kick them all the way to Seattle. No such luck. Both of the assholes had received orders and left the island.

That didn't stop me from being a real asshole in the barracks. I was looking for trouble, and whenever I looked for trouble, it never took long to find it. I was told by the corporal whose head I'd stuck in the toilet to get a broom and sweep all the hallways. I told him to get screwed and was getting ready to punch the man when Sergeant Emery came in. He put me on thirty days of mess duty. I had to stay in the cook's barracks. The only people who pulled mess duty were the real screw-offs, and now I had to live with that bunch for thirty days.

I got along with them pretty well during the first two weeks. I kept to myself and cleaned all the garbage cans. I worked for an air force sergeant on the salad line. He made all kinds of fancy carrots and radishes, which I promptly ate before anyone got to see them. He put me in the scullery to count silverware.

I hated breakfast: the eggs stuck on the trays, and I had my hands in the dishwater all the time. Most of the men would slap their used trays on top of the water in order to splash me. Well, not being the happiest of Marines, I ended up in some kind of fight at least once a day. I usually stayed late to clean up, because I got in trouble.

One night, pulling late duty paid off. A navy commander shot a moose and needed help cutting up the meat. I didn't know he was the mess officer, but I stayed. I knew from my deer hunting days how to clean a carcass. The commander and I got along so well that, for the next three nights, all I had to do was cut and wrap meat. On the last night, he cooked a steak the size of a trashcan lid for me. He also gave me three days off and twenty dollars. I was drunk the entire three days and nights. I only had two days left of mess duty after that.

Chapter 14
Going Home

My orders were in and I was going home by ship.

Ten of us were leaving, all PFCs, except for Corporal Johnson. I couldn't fathom how he got off the island with his stripes. He'd spent all his time in town fighting the sailors, but I only saw him get his ass kicked once: by a colored kid who was screwing off on work detail. Johnson had tried to grab him to throw him outside. This scrappy kid punched Johnson, and when Johnson had tried to punch back, this kid was too good for him. He damn near got killed.

This was the first time I had been on a MSTS, and I wasn't sure what that meant. I just knew that the ship was run by civilians and the chow was supposed to be good.

We were to pick up some army troops along the way, and a pretty big deal was made about the stop being at a top-secret base. No pictures were allowed, and no one was allowed on deck. That was okay with me: it was colder then hell out there.

I thought I would look out one of the portholes on the mess deck instead. But when I got there, someone else was getting his ass chewed out for trying to take a picture from one of the portholes.

All the cameras were opened to expose the film.

* * *

Seattle looked great. In three weeks I would be out of the Marines. We took our gear and left the ship. I had three bags, and it was a long way down to the docks. We carried our bags ten blocks to an old navy building, the same one I had stayed in on my way to Alaska a long ten months ago. We had liberty for the night.

I met a few Marines returning from Adak, Alaska. Adak was the shits; they had it a lot worse than we did at Kodiak. One said that the first thing he was going to do was get laid. That sounded good to me.

"Well, where do we go?" I asked him.

"Down to Skid Row. The beer's cheap and so is the pussy."

We jumped in a taxi and headed for town. I had never seen so many bums in my life. Most of the women looked just as bad.

"Maybe we should find a better part of town," I suggested.

"Hey this place is okay," a man on the street said. "We have women in our apartment. You buy the beer and wine, and we'll fix you up."

The bartender told us we were just looking for trouble if we went with them. I was the only idiot who decided to go.

We were headed up the stairway when one man offered to carry the wine for me. I was carrying the beer. Halfway up, the guy ahead of me stopped, while the one in back tried to run past me up the stairs. All of a sudden, I was being kicked from the front. I dropped the case of beer and grabbed for a leg, then jerked it as hard as I could. The man attached to the leg flew over me and landed on the one behind us, who had tried to run up the stairs. I grabbed two or three beer bottles and threw them at them as they retreated down the stairs. "You son of a bitch!" I yelled. "If you want to fight, that's all I've been doing in Alaska." I went crazy for about five minutes, kicking the shit out of both of them. Almost every bottle got busted, and my uniform was soaked with beer, but I was okay.

I returned to the same bar, and the two men I had come in with were still there. One of them looked me over and said, "What happened. Did you get laid?"

"Almost." I told them about the fight and how it was almost more fun than getting laid.

It was only nine o'clock at night when the bartender, a heavyset woman, told me to stick around until she got off. I lied to her and said that I'd come back for her. All I managed to get done that night was a good drunk and return to the base.

* * *

I felt good the next morning, but my hands were awfully sore. I headed in to shower and clean up, but there were four or five guys ahead of me. I looked around and damn if there wasn't PFC Kidd, my old buddy from Kodiak Island, standing there. He looked like he had seen a ghost.

"Hey, you asshole! I forgot to thank you for the way you treated me in the brig," I yelled at him.

He took off and tried to crawl out a window. He was trying to jump to the roof of the second floor. He missed and fell all the way to the ground. *Oh shit,* I thought. *You're going to jail now, Brandon.* Two sailors saw him fall and ran to see if he was hurt. Kidd didn't return to the barracks, and I guessed he must have hurt his leg. *Shit, I didn't even touch him. I just scared the shit out of him.* I had the weekend off and decided to take my liberty before someone came looking for me.

* * *

I had hoped to catch a bus to Oregon, but the bus station was packed. There were too damn many people waiting; the only thing I could do was take a taxi to the interstate highway and start hitchhiking.

It was raining like hell, and I thought I was going to drown. Luckily, it only took me three rides to reach Portland. Once there, though. I didn't think I was ever going to get through town. After my last ride dropped me off, I grabbed a cab to get back over to the interstate. The damn taxi driver took me to the wrong side of town. I ended up in a suburb called Beaverton and had to hitch back through town before I could get a ride to Willamina.

It must have been around midnight when I finally got to Willamina. A bar was still open, and I heard a western band playing in the backroom.

I was greeted by Marvin. "Hey Percy. Are you out of the Marines, yet?"

"I still have about a month left. I'm just home for New Years." After discussing the work situation in Willamina and what my prospects might be, I finally got around to asking about Shirlie.

"What do you see of Shirlie? Is she still around?"

"She works in Grand Ronde," he answered. "She should be on shift now, I guess."

I grabbed a ride home with Marvin and thought about getting a place of my own and a job. Shit, I wished I had saved a few bucks in the Marines, but it was too late now. It was three o'clock in the morning when I got home, and everyone was in bed. Mom thought I was nuts: always coming home in the middle of the night. She got up long enough to let me know she was glad I was home.

The next morning I got up and went for a run. I needed to clean up my brain. Now that I was home, I had better learn to watch my mouth and keep from swearing around my family.

* * *

That morning run took place on New Year's Eve (1955). Almost three years earlier I had left to join the Marines and had grown up a lot. But there I was, still just as stupid as ever. I looked over toward The Manor where Shirlie worked and thought I should go see her. I needed to know if we were going to get along and, damn, I didn't even know what to say to her. I ran back home to get cleaned up, unpack my seabag and press my uniform. I thought that I might wear my uniform when I went to see Shirlie.

The Manor looked a lot different than it did when I was a kid. It had been a hotel, and only the loggers working for Long Bell Logging stayed in it. I used to sneak down and use their showers because we didn't have indoor plumbing at home. Whenever I needed a bath, it was the old tin tub in the winter and the swimming hole in the summer.

One of my cousins met me at the door of The Manor. She worked in the kitchen. Over a cup of coffee, I found out The Manor was now a care home: a kind of hospital for invalids and older people. Marie went to find Shirlie.

"That's who you came to see, anyway," she said, laughing.

Shirlie looked awfully good, but was cold towards me. I guess I was the same. We talked, and I eventually asked her if she wanted to go for a ride. She turned me down, saying she had to work late. I didn't give up. I asked if we could go the next day. Finally, she agreed.

Happy with the promise of seeing her again so soon, I left and went to Valley Junction. I felt like stopping for a beer, but the bartender had known me my entire life and knew I wasn't twenty-one. She wouldn't serve me. I gave her some shit about being old enough to serve my country but not man enough to get a beer. Even my speech didn't work; she just told me to get the hell out.

I proceeded on to Fort Hill, where everyone was glad to see me. No one asked for my I.D., and my brother Gary (who happened to be there) didn't even squeal on me. Gary promised to take me in his log truck with him the next day, but after I found out he left for work at five o'clock in the morning, I said, "Screw you, come get me about noon."

The next morning, bright and early, I rolled over in bed and heard a god-awful racket outside. *Who the hell is making all that noise?* I thought. It was Gary, blowing his air horn.

"You better get up," Mom said, "or Gary will throw water on you."

Into the truck and we headed into the mountains.

"How far up in the mountains do you go?" I asked. I was going to make sure Gary didn't make me miss my date with Shirlie.

"About twenty miles." I told him about taking Shirlie for a ride later on, and how I didn't know what to say to her.

"Well, don't let your pecker do your thinking for you," he said. "You'll end up married and never have a pot to piss in or a window to throw it out of."

I wasn't even sure if we would even get along. We both had a chip on our shoulder over Earl. I was sure Shirlie thought I didn't give a damn about Earl getting killed and that all I wanted was a piece of ass. Well, that part was true, but I did feel sorry for Earl. We were good friends until a woman got in the middle of us.

Gary and I talked about New Year's plans, but I still wasn't sure if mine would be with Shirlie. I wanted to go to the coast, but I didn't think she would trust me that far. We Brandons—when we have a hard-on—can't be trusted.

I had Gary let me off at the pond and walked home from there. I wanted to see how much things had changed around town. I stopped at the restaurant for a burger, then went home to get my dad's car. It was still too early to pick up Shirlie, so I went to the mill to talk to Dad for a while. I wanted to see if there would be work when I got out of the Marines.

Dad was running the pond, making sure the logs were cut for the mill. I stood on the bank watching him work. I thought: *Damn, he sure looks old. He must be about fifty-six now. I hope I don't have to work that hard when I get to be his age.*

He looked up and flagged me over.

"What are you going to do when you come home for good?" he asked. I thought he had read my mind.

"Maybe working in the mill, if I can get on."

"It will be slow here until April," he told me. "You may have to sign up for unemployment for a few months."

"That fourteen dollars a week won't go far. I better find something quick." I didn't think I could stay in the Marines after the trouble I had gotten into in Alaska.

"I'll talk to my boss, then. Maybe you can work on the green chain, pulling lumber for awhile. Do you still remember how to do that?" he laughed.

* * *

The date I'd been looking forward to with Shirlie started on the awkward side. We talked a lot, but not about much. I knew something was going on and wasn't sure if it was with her or with me. I knew I was letting her and Earl's situation get to me. We ended our drive, still unsure about each other, but made another date to go see a movie.

At the movies we stayed together until early morning and made up for lost time. We went out. again the next two nights.

I was drinking and being an asshole after two nights; I knew I was still thinking about her and Earl. I couldn't leave it alone and brought the subject up—none too tactfully, either. Shirlie pointed out what an asshole I was being and got out of the car. I went to Fort Hill to drink beer without her.

The next morning I walked to The Manor to see Shirlie. She was right when she told me I had no right to hold anything against her about how I'd screwed up in Alaska. I had done that on my own, and it had nothing to do with her. Still not realizing how deep I was digging myself in, I left. To hell with her. I didn't need her shit.

* * *

As I walked up to the house, some Marine buddies from Sweet Home drove up. They were going to have a big New Year's dance and party all night.

"Come with us if you want to, Brandon."

"Do you have any women over there?" I asked.

"Hell, yes, and they love Marines."

"Well, shit, I'll get my uniform and let's go," I said. "You don't by any chance have a car full of beer, do you? New Year's won't be here for another seven hours. By that time, you'll be in bed sleeping off what you drank before the party ever starts!"

"Your ass, Brandon," Tracy said. We have been known to party all night!"

We ended up at Tracy's long enough to change into our uniforms, then headed for the dance. Hell, there must have been four hundred people there. As usual, drinking was not allowed in the club; between every dance we headed for the cars for a beer. Everyone I'd known in Alaska was there. They'd been out of the service for two weeks.

"I still have twenty days left. I get out on the nineteenth. Because that's a Friday, I'm going to get drunk on my ass that night. Maybe I'll even come see you guys."

We stayed at the dance until three o'clock in the morning and then headed back to Tracy's house. About daylight, we conked out and got some sleep. After a few hours, we resumed drinking "hair of the dog" and all, but by then no one really felt like it. We sat around falling in and out of sleep most of the day.

I made my excuses, saying that I had better be getting ready to get back to base; not to mention that, by now, I would surely be in the shithouse with Shirlie.

It was just getting dark when I got home. Shirlie had been by to see me while I was partying. I was in a bad mood and said to hell with it and went to bed.

The next morning I went to Valley Junction and caught a bus north to McMinnville. I met a girl at the McMinnville bus station that I had gone to school with. She was working for a doctor there. We talked until my bus came, and I knew what was coming next. As she walked me to the bus, she gave me a big kiss and promised more when I came home the next time.

What I'd like to know, is how do I get myself into these messes? I asked myself.

* * *

At the base in Seattle, I met another boot-camp comrade, now a corporal. He was also waiting for a discharge, so we spent the next few days together. Corporal Bryant was originally from Washington and planned on returning to the family farm to work. He was a corporal and had had enough of the Marines. Everyone awaiting a discharge had to go in front of the company commander to state why he chose not to stay in the Marines.

When my turn came, I said, "I think I got a bad deal while I was in Alaska."

"You had a good record before that. Don't let one thing like that change your mind about staying in. Just forget about it," he urged.

I thought about how I'd been told what to do and how to do it for the last three years—I wanted out.

"I'm going to state in your record that I think you should stay in the Marine Corps. If you change your mind later, it will be there," the major promised. He seemed like a fair man, but my mind was made up.

* * *

On the morning of January 19, 1956 my time was up. I turned in my records at the navy base in Bremerton and took my final check up. I got my final pay; it wasn't as much as I had hoped. *Hell, it should last me a few days,* I thought. Maybe, by the time my pay was gone, I would have a job and all kinds of money.

I got back to Pier Ninety-One just before four in the afternoon. The major gave those of us awaiting discharges our papers. Everyone received a Good Conduct Medal. At first you could have knocked me over with a feather: I never thought I would get a Good Conduct Medal after Alaska. But then it made me feel good. Anyway, I was done.

Corporal Bryant and I took a taxi to the bus station, bought a fifth of whiskey and headed for the back of the bus. We both felt lost, no longer Marines. We took turns drinking out of the bottle until we reached Portland five hours later. The whiskey was almost gone, but as seasoned as we had become over the last three years, we were holding our booze.

"Let's go downtown and see what's happening on a rainy Friday night," I said. Neither of us were adjusting well to being a regular Joe.

Nothing much was going on, and I think we were both hoping to feel better. After a few drinks, Bryant called his brother to come get him. I stayed long enough to say good-bye and then went out to find a room for the night. I probably should have gone home, but I just wanted to be by myself.

* * *

It was January 20, 1956: time to go home. I walked to the bus station. There was a three-hour wait until the bus for Grand Ronde left, so I walked around town for a while. I ended up buying some clothes. I had always wanted a Stag jacket, but never had the money to buy one. *Hell, now is the time. I might be broke but I'll have a nice jacket.*

I got home around two in the afternoon. I remembered the girl in McMinnville and asked my dad if I could use his car. On the drive north, I kept thinking about how I *should* be going to see Shirlie. I rationalized that I wasn't sure where she was and that she was probably still mad at me.

I ended up dating the girl from McMinnville several times (I tried to make out with her every time, but she had more will power than I did). Other dates with yet another girl from my old high school soon followed the McMinnville girl, but I still kept thinking about Shirlie.

* * *

Hell, I had been out of the Marines for twenty days and had been broke for ten of them. I sold about everything I owned, signed up for unemployment and waited a week to get fourteen dollars. What a life!

Hustling pool at the pool hall in Willamina for extra money seemed like a good idea to me at the time, and so I headed up the road. In the pool hall, damn, I had another surprise. There stood a Marine sergeant playing pool. I told him I had just been discharged.

"Why the hell did you get out?" he asked.

"By now, I'm not too sure," I replied despondently.

"Do you have a job?"

"Hell no. I'm about to go nuts looking for one."

"Why don't you go back in?" he suggested. "You get one hundred dollars for every year that you sign up for and any duty station you want."

"Shit, I didn't know that!" I said. I hadn't been this excited in weeks.

"You think I could get duty in San Francisco? Hell, I'm ready now. How long do you think this will take?" I shot question after question at the sergeant.

I went home to tell my mother I had decided to go back into the Marines. Gary said, "Hell, don't do that! Work will open up soon, and you can have all you want."

I lied to them about "just checking it out." I didn't want Gary trying to talk me out of it. The money sounded too good.

* * *

The next morning, back in Portland, I signed up for another six years. I was given seven days to reach the Marine barracks at Treasure Island, San Francisco. I was promised a three-year stay in San Francisco.

I bought a 1950 Ford Saleman sedan. It didn't have a back seat—a huge drawback—but I took it, anyway. I was told to come back the next day, and my car would be ready, seats and all. I went back the next day, and my Saleman had new red seat covers and had been all shined up.

Pretty impressed with myself and my new car, I thought: *Well, I'll go see Shirlie and tell her I am going back into the Marines. Maybe we can be friends now.*

Shit! She had gone with her parents.

Still hell-bent on showing off my car, I went instead to see the girl in McMinnville. I was told that I was too pushy and not to come see her again. Damn, I was all worked up and there was no one to go out with. Shit. I went home and packed to leave the next morning.

Afterward, I went by The Manor one last time to see if Shirlie was there. She was. I told her I was leaving and thought maybe things were going to be all right between us after all; we could be friends again. When she left to go back to work, I told her I would write once I got settled.

Shirlie, too, was headed for California. She wasn't going to be working at The Manor much longer and was going some place not too far from San Francisco. After all the grief we had caused each other, I still remember the stupid grin I had on my face when I heard she would be near my base.

Chapter 15
San Francisco

I left early the next morning, only three weeks after my discharge. I had only been on the road three hours when it began to snow. Damn. It snowed all the way to the California border and then some.

I picked up two hitchhikers going to San Francisco. Hell, I was driving straight through, and I offered them a ride all the way down. They had no money, so I bought milk, bread and lunch meat at a store along the highway. I thought, *This should get us down the road.* I was serious about getting to Frisco. I didn't intend to stop except for gas.

We reached Frisco around eleven o'clock that night. After dropping off the hitchhikers downtown, I decided not to check into the base at night. I felt like hitting the bars to see what the women looked like. The last time I had been in Frisco had been eighteen months ago. I visited a few places I'd remembered in Chinatown. *Shit, I must be lonesome. I'm looking at the Japanese women. I never thought I'd think about them.* I ended up having a beer in a female-impersonator bar. *Well,* I thought, *they're really girls!*

Damn they were friendly. They blew kisses at me and acted like they were hot for me. One kept asking if I wanted to feel her tit for a dollar. I was short on money, so I told her I would come back later, when I got paid. I fully intended to go back and pick up that big-titted woman, after checking into the base and getting my money.

The next morning I put on my uniform and headed for the base. I got lost on the freeway and ended up in Oakland and had to turn around to find my way back to Treasure Island.

At headquarters I was sure surprised when the staff sergeant turned out to be Shannon, the older bald guy who had been in the Navy during World War II. He had also signed up for six more years. He'd been at Treasure island for six months and told me how a lot of men were re-enlisting in the Marines.

I was assigned the 2nd Guard Company in charge of the navy brig. *Damn, I am going to hate that!* I thought. Because I had been overseas and worked in the brig before, it was my best chance to make corporal. Most of the men at Treasure Island were new, and I had the advantage.

My headquarters were in the new barracks, but when I checked in, I found out I would be staying on the other side of the brig. *Shit, old wooden barracks from World War II.* I checked in at the brig with the first sergeant, a tough looking gunnery sergeant named Wolfe. He talked to me for a while and then took me to meet the brig warden. The warden was the greatest-looking Marine I had ever seen. He had snow-white hair and a mustache and his office was spotless. He smoked a pipe and looked like someone out of a story book. The gunny introduced me to Warrant Officer Stone.

"PFC Brandon reporting as ordered, sir."

"Welcome aboard, Brandon," he said and went on to tell me about his thirty years in the Marines, most of it as a brig warden. There wasn't much he didn't know about what went on around Treasure Island.

"You do a good job for me and we will get along fine. Anything less, and you will be a guest in my brig. Do I make myself clear?"

"Yes sir!"

As we left the warden's office, the gunny said, "He means every word." The gunny was going to make sure I didn't screw up. If I did, he'd kick my ass. I would have one week to learn the duties before standing duty on the port duty section. I was also told that I would stand a day on and a day off and get every other weekend off.

Back at the brig, the gunny called in Staff Sergeant Price. He was just a short little guy, but tough. He had three rows of ribbons, including a Purple Heart. Price took me to the barracks where I was assigned to Corporal Hartcell's section and told that Hartcell would show me all I needed to know.

"Boy, for an old barracks, this place sure is clean," I said.

"One good thing about the brig: we use the prisoners to do all our cleaning. We make them do a damn good job of it," Price explained.

* * *

Most of the men were laying in their bunks. They got up for introductions and seemed like a friendly bunch. There must have been twenty guys from Oregon there in our company. The first thing they asked was how long I had been a PFC, and I entertained them with the story about my demotion in Alaska.

"I was a corporal in Kodiak, Alaska, and I pissed off a captain," I started.

"How the hell did you do that?"

"I punched his son in the mouth," I answered. That got a hoot out of them. They were all laughing, trying to imagine the scene.

"What the hell was his kid doing to make you punch him?"

"Well," I said, "he was a sergeant in the Marines and wanted to kick my ass. I don't know why. He just didn't like my looks, I guess."

Staff Sergeant Price warned, "Don't try punching anyone here or you'll get your ass thrown in the brig…after *I* get done kicking it." He said it like he meant it. But that was one thing no one had to tell me. I had learned my lesson.

I made friends fast when they found out I had a car. "Shit, now I *know* we are going to be buddies. I can show you where all the pussy in San Francisco is," one guy said to me.

* * *

PFCs Gilmore, Hanson and Loranzen walked me to the brig to pick up my car and showed me around the base.

Damn, this looks like a good duty station," I said.

They all agreed it was. As long as we did our jobs, we were left alone, and the only training we had was three days a week, four hours a day.

"There are sure a lot of WAVES on this base. Do they like Marines?" I asked.

"Yes, but the assholes in the first guard have most of them taken." The first guard stood the gates and had base patrol, so they met most of the WAVES before anyone else.

"We have four WAVES working in the brig office, but they are snakes," I was told.

"Hell," I said. "They all look the same in the dark."

"Not these. They glow in the dark. Just ask Gilmore. He's been screwing them," Hanson chuckled.

"Your ass, Hanson," he retorted as he and Gilmore threw punches at each other in the car.

Loranzen was a tall, good-looking redhead who laughed a good deal of the time. "Don't believe these guys," he said. "They are full of shit most of the time."

* * *

The next day I checked on my pay.

"Six years is a lot to sign up for at one time," the Marine taking care of my pay said, when he saw my papers.

"Well, I was out for a few months and I didn't like it. Now I'm glad to be back in," I said, not believing I'd just said that.

"How do you want your pay?" the pay officer asked.

"Cash. I have to buy new uniforms."

The pay officer started counting twenty dollar bills. I must have looked stunned by the six hundred dollar pile of money in front of me. I hadn't been told I would get the entire amount at one time. It was the most money I had ever seen.

"Well," he said, "don't get stupid and drink it all up ."

Still stunned at the wad of cash I was carrying, I called my mother and told her to expect a money order to pay for the car. After sending the money order, I bought more uniforms. I wanted to be ready when it came time to stand duty.

* * *

I had a three-day weekend to check out San Francisco before standing duty. Hanson and Gilmore headed out with me the minute liberty call went out. It was a Friday night *and* payday. Everyone was in town.

After beer and sausages in a Polish tavern, Hanson said, "Okay, Brandon, we are going to take you to a place where the best-looking women in town can be found."

We parked the car in Chinatown and walked to the female impersonator bar I'd visited the night I drove into San Francisco. *Hell, I've been here before, but I'm sure as hell not telling these guys that!* I thought my little secret would be to my advantage in case they tried pulling a fast one on me.

There must have been twenty women working the floor and just as many female impersonators. I wasn't sure who was who. Hanson called over a good-looking woman to meet "the new guy." We shook hands and she promised to come back as soon as her number was over.

"We'll fix you up with her, if you buy the drinks tonight," Hanson offered.

"Okay," I said. "But I don't want one who has more balls than I do." Then I started laughing. Damn! I just couldn't keep it to myself.

"You asshole," Hanson said. "You've been here before."

"Shit, yes," I said, "two weeks ago, before I checked into the base."

Well, shit, I'd screwed up all their fan. The tradition was bringing the new guys in and setting them up with a "girl," then watching the fan when they found out half the women were men.

"Most of the guys actually buy them a few drinks, then try to grab a feel. You should see the looks on their faces when they get a handful of balls."

We never did get laid, but we sure got drunk. How the hell we ever made it back to the base, I'll never know.

* * *

The next day I picked up Staff Sergeant Shannon and went to town. He wanted to buy a car, and I needed a change.

I was learning my way around town, and after a while, Shannon found a place to buy a car. I dropped him off and spent the rest of the day looking the town over.

One thing about San Francisco: it doesn't lack for bars. Around midnight, I picked up a woman, but was so drunk I forgot where I had parked my car. We took a taxi to her place. I stayed with her half the night drinking and screwing. When I left, I was still so drunk that I called a taxi to get back to the base. *Thank God tomorrow is Sunday and I'll be able to sleep in.*

* * *

I got up around noon and showered. I didn't remember much about the night before and asked Hanson and Gilmore if they wanted to run into town and see what was going on.

"Where in the hell is my car?" I yelled. I was damn sure they'd put one over on me after all.

My memory finally came back, and I confessed about returning to the base in a taxi.

"What the hell did you do that for?" Hanson asked me.

"Hell, I forgot I even owned a car. I was screwing around, and when I left, I just called a taxi."

"Well, where did you leave your car?"

"I think at some parking lot in town."

"Do you know how many fucking parking lots there are in town?" Gilmore exclaimed. "About a thousand or more. Shit, you will never find your car."

I might have been stupid the night before, but I had a pretty good idea that I had gone to Market Street and must have turned into one of the first parking lots I came to. I convinced them that the only thing we had to do was go down Market Street until we came to a parking lot.

"Hell, sounds like a plan to me," Hanson said. We decided to take the base bus. Its route went right down Market Street.

One thing was for sure. Not many guys went to town on Sundays. The bus only had two sailors and the three of us on it as it headed up the hill and over the bay bridge to San Francisco. Twenty minutes later we were in town.

"How shall we look for the car?" I asked.

"Let's split up," Hanson said. "We'll each go one way and meet back here in an hour."

"Fuck no," said Gilmore. "Let's stay together. We have all day and can drink a few beers while we're looking."

"Yeah, right," I said. "If I get drunk again, we will never find the car. Let's look first, *then* get some drinks."

We got lucky and found my Ford in the first lot we went to. There it sat, all by itself. The parking lot had been washed down and my car had been sprayed with shit. It was filthy.

"Hell, let's just go," I muttered. "We can find a place to wash the car later."

We hit the beach around noon, just as things were opening up. Gilmore wanted to go swimming first; Hanson wanted to go to the zoo.

"The zoo sounds good to me," I said. "Anyway, we can get some chow there."

At the zoo, we came to a cage with a pissed-off gorilla. I thought it must have been because of the kids who were throwing shit at him. The gorilla jumped at the bars. *Damn, I hope they are strong enough to hold him,* I thought. The gorilla started taking a dump—then threw the shit at everyone standing outside his cage! It didn't take long before everyone cleared the hell out of there. Swimming sounded like a better idea after all.

It was great. We stayed at the pool on the beach until sundown, got some chow and headed back for the base.

What a weekend!

* * *

Monday was a big day for me: my first day on duty. I spent two hours getting ready. I didn't know why; I was only going to be guarding a bunch of shithead sailors, who had screwed up enough to land themselves in the brig.

We stood guard mount, getting checked out to make sure we knew our orders and what post we were to stand. I was new, and so I got to stand the front gate: in case I needed to ask the desk sergeant any questions. It was an easy post, checking anyone who came through on their way to the brig. I remembered this same duty from Japan. Four hours on and eight hours off. *Damn, I hate that kind of duty,* I thought, *but I better get used to it because I'm going to be here for three years.*

Things were quiet until 1600 hours when all shit broke loose. Everyone brought their prisoner working parties back to the brig. I was to make sure the right number of prisoners returned with each chaser and that all the chasers were sailors. The chasers were in such a damn hurry to get rid of prisoners and go on liberty that they tried getting their groups through the gate like a bunch of cattle.

"Walt a fucking minute," I said. "I want one group at a time. Take everything out of your pockets and lay it down in front of you. Spread your legs, put your arms over your head and lean toward the wall. No one goes into that brig until I've checked each prisoner. Chasers, stay put until I have cleared your prisoners."

Matches, cigarette butts and bottle caps came out of the first four prisoners' pockets.

"What the hell are you shitheads doing with bottle caps?" I asked.

"We use them to play checkers."

"Well, you assholes are not here for fun and games," I said. Man, did that get them pissed at me. They had been used to slipping by the gate guard.

They won't slip by me, I thought, and made them stand at attention inside the gate until each one was checked. Those with shit in their pockets, I made do push-ups and jumping jacks and any other shit I could think of.

My name got around the brig fast. The word was that the new guard was an asshole who had worked the Middle Camp brig in Japan. (Middle Camp was known as the meanest brig in the Marine Corps.) Shit, this was great! One day on duty and they were all talking about me.

After post, at chow, the prisoners sat on their benches laughing and talking. I asked the other guards how come the prisoners got so much slack around here. Hanson told me that once the guards were off duty they went back to the barracks. "No one wants to stick around and mess with the prisoners," he said.

"That's bullshit," I said. "No wonder those assholes keep coming back to the brig; they have it made here! You go ahead and go to chow, I'm going to fuck with them like we did in Japan." I was going to have a heyday.

* * *

"All prisoners get your asses in the center of the compound and line up in four ranks.

"If you assholes want to sit around on your asses and shoot the shit, then you're going to have to earn it. When you learn to be military, and that's what you are, you might get to sit on your asses.

"No smoking will be allowed. Anyone found with cigarettes or matches will be thrown into the hole with only bread and water, and ten more days added to your brig time.

"Talking will not be allowed. Anyone talking without permission will clean out the grease pit after chow. No more leaving chow hall and sitting on your asses. You leave the hall and form four ranks. You will stand at attention until a Marine guard tells you to do otherwise. You will not talk to any guard unless you call him by rank and ask permission to do so."

Well, I thought. *Not bad for starters.*

The sailors were pissed as hell, but I had scared the shit out of them with the threat of bread and water and ten more days brig time.

For the next two hours I marched them around the compound and punished anyone who screwed up with push-ups and jumping jacks. Working their butts off was bad enough, but no cigarettes on top of that, I knew, would make it even worse on them. After the two hours, it was time for them to shower and be counted into cells for the night.

"Where did you learn to handle prisoners like that?" the desk sergeant asked.

"That's how we were taught to treat the prisoners in Japan. They never wanted to come back once we got through with them. These guys are just sailors, they aren't used to this kind of shit, and we should be able to scare the shit out of them," I said.

* * *

I had watch again the next morning, and I was right back in those sailors' shit. I made them sound off for everything. The first time an officer walked through, and the prisoners shouted, "OFFICER ONBOARD" and "ATTENTION," it scared the shit out of him: he had never heard that before.

The brig warden came through as the prisoners were lining up for work parties. When two hundred sailors all sounded off at the same time, the warden looked at me and smiled. That was my ticket; I was going to make those prisoners shine. I stayed at the brig every day, even on days off, and screwed with them. The other guards thought I was crazy.

"Damn it, Brandon, you eat this shit up, don't you?"

"Hell yes," I said. "If those asshole sailors think they can come in here and screw off, I'll make them pay."

"Hell, he thinks he's great," Gilmore muttered to the guy sitting next to him. "The prisoners jump now when he tells them to do something. What the hell you gonna do, Brandon, if the prisoners decide to test you and see if you really can add ten days?"

"Hell, I don't have to do anything. See," I explained, "you just keep switching them around in their cells so they get confused. Then you take away their calendars: that makes them *totally* confused—they don't know if they are coming or going. Don't let them buddy up with anyone; keep mixing them up and around; make lots of noise at night, so they don't get any sleep. Hell, If we have to be up all night, let those assholes go without sleep, too."

"You know, Brandon, you're a real asshole."

Not compared to old C. S. Johnson, I wasn't. I told them how he used to kick the shit out of the prisoners *and* the guards, and how he didn't give a shit but that he damn sure got the job done.

"The prisoners don't know what you can get away with; just keep them in the dark," I told them.

Soon thereafter, I was called to the brig warden's office and told that I would be in charge of the brig chow hall. Shit, that was great: that meant I would have every night and every other weekend off.

* * *

Gunny Wolfe, the brig gunny, told me I had thirty days' leave to take whenever I wanted. I thought a little about going home to see what had happened to Shirlie, even though I was now dating a Navy WAVE. This WAVE had also been seeing another Marine, and I was sure this other guy was getting more screwing than I was.

Because my duty stand allowed me more liberty time, I thought I would get to know some of the guys in other duty sections. I had heard there were a bunch of nurses from one of the hospitals these guys were screwing. I talked to PFC Skidmore and asked him if I could go with them the next time they went to visit the nurses.

"Hell yes, Brandon, if you have wheels you can go with us all the time."

On my next Thursday night off, Skidmore, Fitzgerald and I headed for the nurses' place. On the drive over, they introduced me to a drink made from white port wine and lemon juice. Man, was it good. Two jugs of wine later, we were feeling no pain. We showed up at the girls' door with four more jugs of wine.

There were six nurses and three guys. Damn, it looked like a good deal to me.

It *must* have been one hell of a night, but I couldn't remember shit. The only thing I did remember was waking up in the shithouse puking my guts out. I learned that lemon juice lets the wine sneak up on you, and I was paying for it.

"Hey, Brandon, the nurses loved your act; they want to know if you can come back and do it again."

"What the hell are you talking about?" I asked.

"You know, the one where you pull your cock out while you're sitting in a chair and piss all over the floor," Skidmore said.

"You're shitting me," I said. "I didn't do that."

"The hell you didn't. Suzy took your picture," he said, laughing.

"Goddamn, you asshole, why didn't you stop me?"

"Shit, man, you *had* to piss! Why else would you have pulled it out?" He laughed again.

The next day everyone knew about my pissing act.

"Hey, Brandon, how about doing your act for us?" I heard this every time I turned around. Even the goddamn sailors gave me shit. I couldn't think of a better time to get the hell out of here and take my thirty days' leave.

Chapter 16
Thirty Days' Leave

I loaded up the old Ford and headed out of San Francisco across the Golden Gate Bridge. I wanted to drive up the Coast Highway, but it turned out to be a big mistake. At ten o'clock that night it was both foggy and snowing. I could only drive ten or fifteen miles an hour but kept at it until I found a motel.

"To hell with it. I'm stopping for the night."

I wasn't sure how far I had driven in those conditions, but the next morning I figured out I could make it home before night. I hoped to pick up a hitchhiker, someone to shoot the shit with, but I never saw a one.

I pulled into Grand Ronde about five o'clock that evening and went straight home. Hell, I had only been away for two months, but I had thirty days on my hands. I knew I had come back to see if Shirlie was still there.

After supper, I told my mother that I was going to look up a few buddies, and I would be home late. I headed straight for The Manor but only saw my cousin, who still worked there. Shirlie had left with her parents for Fort Jones, California, near the Oregon border. *Shit,* I thought, *Oh, well, what the hell, I'll just go get drunk and forget about her.*

I headed towards Willamina but saw several cars around the tavern in Fort Hill, so I pulled in to have a beer. I must have been in my magic uniform; everyone who knew me wanted to buy me a beer. After three or four beers, a man asked if my name was Brandon. I told him it was and asked why he wanted to know. He pointed me to the door and said someone outside wanted to talk to me.

I walked out to see who it was and felt my jaw hit the ground when I realized it was Shirlie. She had been driving around hoping to find me.

"I thought you went to California," I said.

"My dad is sick, so we're staying in Sheridan till he's better," she said.

"Where are you going from here?" I asked her.

"Sheridan."

"Would it be okay if I gave you a ride?" I asked.

She grinned at me.

In the car we talked about how most of the kids from school were married or were going to be soon.

"Let's get married now," I said, somewhat surprised at myself. "Do

Gunny and Shirlie. We fell in love and...

you want to?"

"Are you asking me to marry you?"

"Yes," I said. "We can get married in Washington State."

Shirlie was only seventeen years old and would need a parent's signature. Knowing the next day was a work day and that we would need two witnesses and our birth certificates, we decided to ask for her mother's permission. I sure hoped her mother would give her permission; I didn't want to have to ask her father while he was in the hospital. We visited with her mother for a while before bringing up the subject of marriage. At almost the same moment, Shirlie and I said we wanted to get married.

My soon-to-be mother-in-law stared at us and asked, "When?"

"As soon as we can find someone to go with us as witnesses," I replied.

Shirlie's mother must have known we were dead-set on getting married and said she would go with us, if we couldn't find anyone else. The three of us looked around at each other, and after an awkward silence, I stood up and thanked her.

We decided to look for someone to witness our marriage the next morning before we left.

* * *

Shit, I can't believe I'm doing this, I thought, after I had left the house. I went home early that night and didn't say a word to anyone. Mom asked me if I was all right; I told her I was just tired.

We spent the entire next day asking, but couldn't find a single person to come with us to Washington.

"Hell, let's just take your mother and take our chances," I said.

Shirlie's mom seemed glad we asked her to go along, so we made plans to leave the next morning at eight o'clock, getting to Washington before noon.

Maybe I should just load up my car and take off for San Francisco before it's too late, I thought as I headed home.

Driving through Fort Hill, I spotted its tavern. It was still open. *I better have a beer. I'm all nerves.* I went inside. Helen, the bartender, was getting ready to close.

"Can I have a beer?" I asked her. "This is my last night as a free man; I'm getting married tomorrow."

"Who in the hell would marry you?" Helen asked good-naturedly.

"Well, Shirlie Bird would marry me!"

"Hell, Brandon, let me close up, then we'll go in the back and have a few to celebrate."

We stayed in the back drinking until it started to get light. I finally told Helen I had to go.

"Well, let me give you one last kiss as a free man," she said.

"Damn, I have butterflies. I hope I'm not screwing up."

* * *

Mom was up when I came home, getting Dad ready for work. I went straight to the bathroom to shower; I smelled like a beer wagon. When I came out of the bathroom. Mom asked what I would be doing for the day.

"I'm going to get married today." She started to cry. "I'm going to marry

Shirlie Bird. Her mother is going with us to Washington. I just know I want to marry her, and one thing the Marines has taught me is how to get when I want."

My mom was still crying as she gave me a hug and said, "Please think about what you are doing."

"I'm trying, Mom. All I know is: I want to be with Shirlie."

I headed for Sheridan, and I'll be damned if it didn't start to snow. That was all I needed, along with the hangover I was sporting. *I hope Helen has a hangover, too. Maybe if she'd have given me a good screwing, I would have turned chickenshit and run. I hope she is puking her guts out.*

Shirlie was ready and waiting when I got there and was wearing a blue suit. Her mother wanted to hurry so she could get back in time to go to the hospital that night. As we walked to the car, Shirlie said, "I wasn't sure if you were coming."

I wished I hadn't worn my uniform. I was starting to sweat out the beer, and the damn snow was falling down in big flakes. We crossed the bridge into Washington and were about twenty miles from Stevenson when I saw a car with two old ladies, stuck off the road in the snow. I couldn't leave them there, so we stopped to help them, and I got my own car stuck in the process. Shirlie drove while I pushed. She gunned the motor and sprayed mud and snow all over me. "Take your foot off the gas!" I yelled at her. By the time we got out, I had shit all over my legs. (At least we got out.)

We pulled into Stevenson, Washington right at noon, and the damn court house was closed for lunch.

Maybe if I have something to eat I'll feel better.

After lunch, we filled out our papers at the court house and headed up the road to the office of the local justice of the peace.

The JP happened to be a lady. She offered to have a carpenter, who was working on the house, stand in as our second witness.

"That's okay with me," I said.

In less than five minutes it was over. We left, and I was so nervous I hadn't even paid the justice of the peace.

* * *

My new mother-in-law suggested that, rather than drive back on the Washington side of the Columbia River Gorge, we drive on the Oregon side and cross the Bridge of the Gods. It was the first time I had been on this road since my family moved to Oregon in 1942.

"Would you mind stopping in

...were married March 9, 1956

Portland on our way through?" Shirlie asked. "I'd like to see my sister and her son."

Her sister was a tall blonde and was glad that Shirlie had gotten married. After a million questions, Shirlie's mom finally said we had to leave to get back in time to see my father-in-law.

Shirlie and I dropped off "Mom" in Sheridan, on our way to my house in Grand Ronde. I went in to get my clothes.

"Did you get married?" my mom asked.

"Yes," I answered. I told her everything had gone well, and that we were going to spend our wedding night at the coast.

"Can we have a party for you, before you head back to San Francisco?" Mom asked. We told her to go ahead and make plans for the party and that we would be going to California in a couple of days.

We headed for the coast and, with Oregon being Oregon, it rained. It poured all the way. We found a small motel right on the beach. Hell, married or not, we acted like two kids trying to screw for the first time. There we were, trying to get it done all in one night.

* * *

Back in Grand Ronde, after our one-night honeymoon, my mother had invited over friends and family. That was the first time I had ever known my mother to allow beer in the house.

One uncle showed up with a fifth of whiskey and started singing old Indian songs. Gary started laughing at him, which pissed my uncle off. Uncle Harry wanted to kick Gary's butt, but my mom settled them down by threatening to do the butt kicking. The booze was soon gone and the party broke up early.

Shirlie and I went to Willamina and got a motel. I was on my ass from all the partying and passed out as soon as I hit the rack. I didn't wake up until the sun hit my eyes the next morning.

I was sitting on the bed when Shirlie woke up.

"What's the matter?" she asked.

"I want to go back to California," I replied. Man, I had the strangest feeling about the whole affair.

"Let's go get my things at home and take off," she said.

* * *

What the hell have I gotten myself into? I don't even have a place for us to live when we get back to California, I kept thinking to myself on the drive south.

Shirlie asked why I was so quiet, so I told her. "Shit, we have a lot to think about. We don't have anything to start out with, not even a place to live," I said. She could tell how worried I was.

"We may not have a place to live," she said, "but I have a hope chest and a few other things to get us started."

She was right; our little old car was loaded down. Her mother had given us a lot of things to get started.

We pulled into the base just as liberty call was going out. I had hoped to get there sooner, so I could ask some of the married guys where I could find a place to stay. I went to the barracks first. It was payday, and my section was just leaving on liberty.

"Brandon! You're just in time; we're gonna get drunk and get laid. You want to come with us?"

I couldn't see any point in beating around the bush. "Hell, I got married while I was home." I sounded braver than I felt.

"Your ass," Hanson said. "Who the hell would marry you?" (Where have I heard that one before? These guys just aren't original!)

"I'm not shitting you, go look in my car."

"Hey, there is a broad out there!" Hanson said, as they all raced out the door to see. It must have scared the hell out of Shirlie to see a bunch of sex-starved assholes running at her.

One of the men from another duty station was heads up enough to ask where we would be staying and to say that his apartments had some openings. He said, "Maybe you could stay there. PFC Harris is the manager." Harris ran the brig mess hall and was a real prick. Well, it was better than nothing.

The apartment building was located on a street, I knew, where most of the colored people lived. We were happy to find the apartments at one end of Turk Street. Maybe that was far enough away to stay out of trouble in the neighborhood. Harris met us at the door. "What do you want, boy?" he asked.

Oh, shit, I thought, *a damn Texan.* "I got married while I was home, and we're looking for a place to live."

"Get your wife and come on in. I'll show you around. I'll tell you right now, Brandon, I don't like niggers or wetbacks. So don't bring any of those shitheads up here from the barracks."

The apartments were the smallest living quarters I'd ever seen: they only had three rooms. It was so small you could reach through the kitchen into the bathroom.

"Where is the bedroom?" I asked.

"Don't let your pecker do your thinking for you," Harris said. "You want the place or not?" He then pulled out a Murphy bed from a set of double doors on the wall.

We spent that night in our new apartment by the light of a flashlight.

* * *

Shirlie and I carried our things up the stairs. We were almost broke, and I wasn't getting paid until noon the next day. Shirlie wasn't happy at all when I told her she would have to stay at the apartment while I went to the base to get my pay.

"Get used to it, I'll be gone a lot." I knew Shirlie didn't have the slightest idea about living with a Marine, and things had happened so fast that I hadn't told her yet. I ran to the snack bar for poor-boy sandwiches and milk to tide us over till the next day. It wasn't much, but it would have to do. I was stone-cold broke.

"Damn," I said to Shirlie when I returned, "this is our first meal at home and it's horse-cock sandwiches."

"What kind of sandwiches?"

I laughed to myself. Shirlie would have a lot to get used to being around a Marine, let alone being married.

* * *

The first thing the next morning we headed for the base commissary. There was a long line already forming by the time we got there. I had been told it was always like that on paydays.

Shirlie wanted to know what kind of a store it was. I'd never been in a commissary, but I thought it was like a grocery store. One thing for sure, the prices were real cheap. We filled our cart and went to check out. As Shirlie unloaded our cart, she piled stuff all over the counter. "Stop!" I yelled. "Line everything up in order. Don't just pile it up." Everyone was looking at me. I just kept lining our items nice and neat on top of the counter, You better get used to doing things in order." I knew I had hurt her feelings. She was quiet all the way back to the apartment.

We spent the next two days getting settled and pulling the bed out of the wall. Shirlie got her kicks by throwing cold water on me through the window of the bathroom, while I was laying in bed. It wasn't far to throw. We had a lot of water fights.

We lived on Turk Street a couple of months before I could apply for military housing and get the hell out of those apartments. Harris did too: mostly because of an incident after a colored man rented one of the apartments. Someone chased the man onto the roof where he fell off. The shit was really starting to hit the fan on Turk Street, and it was time to get out.

Those first four days, though, went by fast. Then it was time to get back to the base for duty.

Chapter 17
Treasure Island

I worked the prisoners' compound, and I was on their asses constantly. Those who didn't go out on work details worked for me. I knew I was doing a good job, and only three weeks later, the gunny asked me to work the brig mess hall.

Man, that's good duty. I'll get every night off, I thought. I was pleased as punch and couldn't wait to tell Shirlie.

I hadn't even made it through the door, that first Monday of my new duty, when the desk sergeant said, "The gunny wants to see you."

I reported in, and he said, "Why are you late?"

"It's only six-thirty," I said. "I report in at seven."

"It is now seven-thirty," he said. "Didn't you set your clock ahead last night?"

"No…why?" What the hell was he talking about? I'd never heard of changing the time of day! You don't just change the time of day!

"Don't you watch television? Don't you read the newspapers? It's Daylight Savings Time."

When I answered no to both, and still didn't have a clue about what he was talking about, he rolled his eyes.

"Well, what in the hell do you do? Lay up there and fuck all night?" Shit, my face was red. "I've only been married three weeks," I told him.

Well, goddamn it, you can't wear it out." Then he warned me about getting my ass kicked the next time I showed up late for duty.

Damn, what a way to start my new duty! Daylight Fucking Savings Time? I took out a subscription to the base newspaper that day. *You never know when these shitting Marines are going to pull one over on you.*

* * *

I assigned a prisoner to run the mess-hall store room. One day I caught him smoking and put him in the hole with only bread and water for seven days. He turned out to be from the south where everyone knew how to make homemade corn liquor. He had saved the juice from pineapples and peaches, then mixed it with yeast, sugar and rice. It was hidden in a five-gallon coffee can, stored in the bottom of a fifty-gallon drum under some old greasy rags. After sitting under all that pressure for seven days, it blew up. At two o'clock in the morning, no less.

The explosion sounded like a stick of dynamite going off and scared the tower guard so badly that he fell through the hole in the floor and landed twenty feet below on the ground. (He must have been half-asleep because he didn't break anything.) The guard was so embarrassed that he tried to convince everyone that the explosion had blown him out of the tower.

Harris and I lost our job over that one and were put back in the duty section.

* * *

At least once a month we formed an Honor Guard: every time some big shot came through on his way to Washington, D.C. First Guard, one of the two companies, was the base military police and stood guard at the main gate. Those assholes always had all the women.

Second Guard was made up of Marines who formed the brig guards. Anyone in the off-duty section had to stand Honor Guard inspection. The best man was selected, and the rest sent back to stand duty. The best part of being selected for Honor Guard was getting liberty when it was over. We spent a lot of time making sure we were squared away so we would get picked. Because our barracks were several blocks away from where we formed up for inspection, we had to be careful on our way over not to screw up and make a mess of our uniforms.

One day Corporal Higley walked with me to inspection. We must have had invisible targets pasted on our heads; a seagull flying overhead let one loose. Goddamn, it hit both of us with shit. We tried our best to clean it off. but we were toast. We were off the detail.

At the E-Club Higley and I got drunk and made plans to kill every seagull on the island. We devised a somewhat elaborate, but stupid, plan involving string, meat and colliding seagulls.

We even made up a song about our seagull woes:
Seagulls, seagulls in the sky, dropped some shit into my eye.
But I'm no sailor, we won't cry; we're just glad that cows don't fly.
First Guard, First Guard, you ain't shit: all you assholes eat seagull shit.

We sang our song once to the gunny. He wasn't impressed and told us to clean it up. Higley and I always sang it in its original version, even after cleaning it up some for the gunny. We were so damn proud of that song. We planned to write more songs, but never got drunk enough to try again.

* * *

Once we moved into military housing, Shirlie got to know some of the sailors' wives. That meant trouble for me. I had been having Shirlie come to the base with me on my days off to help clean my rifle and shine my shoes. The other wives told her that I was scamming her; that she didn't have to go. She was also told I was playing pool while she'd been cleaning my rifle. Naturally, Shirlie stopped going to the barracks with me. I knew there was something I didn't like about those sailors.

It was 1957, and I had just made corporal. It was my first stripe since I had been busted in Alaska two years earlier. Shirlie was pregnant. I guess we pulled that bed out of the wall one time too many.

* * *

I hate Monday mornings. Always have. One Monday all hell broke loose when a sailor named Henderson beat up another sailor on a ship moored at the docks. That was just the beginning. He then shot two ship's officers and held yet another sailor prisoner.

Word went out for the top rifle experts to report for sniper detail. I turned out to be one of the top shooters in my section and was sent to the adjacent ship. We had orders to get Henderson in our sights, then wait.

Henderson was a local boy, and the authorities were able to bring his mother to the base. Damn, that lady must have weighed three hundred pounds; she could barely walk. It worked, though. She talked him into surrendering.

We sharp shooters had been lying on our bellies for over four hours on a steel deck before it was over, and my ribs felt broken.

The military police were at the brig with Henderson. He was giving them nothing but shit. I was assigned as one of five special guards to stand watch over him. The five of us took psych tests before the assignment, to make sure we weren't crazier than he was. We were to stand four hours on and twenty hours off until he was court-martialed. We were lucky if we got ten hours off.

Two guards had to be present every time Henderson was taken out of his cell. During the second month, three of the special guards were taken off duty. This guy was hell to deal with. He never slept and raised hell all night long in his cell. He spit on us and tried to kick us. It took two guards and a driver whenever we took him out of the brig.

One day I took Henderson to the doctor. The doctor asked me to leave the room, while he checked the prisoner. I told him that my orders were to stay with the prisoner at all times. "I'll take responsibility," the doctor said and sent me out.

I had only been out of the room a few seconds when I heard all hell breaking loose in the doctor's office. Henderson had jumped the doctor and had his handcuffs around his neck, choking him. I have to admit I was glad to beat the shit out of Henderson, while I was getting him off the doctor. He'd been such a pain in the ass. From then on he went for me every chance he got.

Henderson was so crazy we fed him his food on paper plates and made him use plastic spoons. One night he called for me to come for his plate; he was finished eating. He had pissed and taken a crap on the plate and threw it at me when I opened the door. Shit was all over me.

I went crazy. I grabbed him by the neck and threw him on the floor. "I'll kill you, you black son of a bitch." It took four guards to get me out of his cell. I ran to the barracks to shower. That was one time none of the guys tried to kid me. I swore that I would kill him before he got out of here.

The next day Henderson was transferred to Oakland Naval Hospital. We accompanied him and stood guard in the mental ward. Damn, they had some bad cases in there.

One day, at noon chow, there were eight patients at one table. The tables were picnic style with benches attached. One patient had on a restraining belt and handcuffs and suddenly went crazy right there at the table. This man stood up, table and all, and walked across the room with seven other patients still sitting at the table. I never knew a person could be so strong.

He was taken to a padded cell in the same area where I guarded my prisoner. He'd been banging around inside the cell for quite awhile, so when it got quiet, I looked in the little window to see what he was doing. He had taken a shit and was writing all over the walls with it.

* * *

They had a good club on the base, and once we got off duty, the only way we could get any sleep was to get smashed. One of the guards got drunk one night and went nuts. He refused to stand his watch because the prisoners drove him crazy. I had to return to duty and stand his watch. Man, was I pissed. I felt like kicking the shit out of him when I got off.

The next few weeks, during Henderson's court-martial, we were on television and in the local newspaper. I was famous—everyone knew me!

Henderson was eventually sentenced to life imprisonment and sent to Port Smith, New Hampshire, a federal prison. At last we were getting rid of him. But I still wasn't quite free of him; I had been assigned as one of the guards to take him back East. The Navy had a special plane that would hold just Henderson, the guards and the crew. We were to have him at the air station in two days time.

During the Henderson guard duty, I was lucky if I got to see Shirlie once a week. I asked the gunny if I could have the day off to go see her; the baby was due anytime. Taking the prisoner back East was going to take a week or more. Shirlie was, of course, worried about me and what she would do if the baby came while I was gone.

"Hell, I don't know," I told her. "Ask one of the wives to take you." I had to do what the Marines told me to do. "I'm going to go get a beer," I said as I walked out the door. This Henderson thing was getting to be pretty miserable.

* * *

I had just started on my first beer when an air force sergeant offered me ten bucks to drive him to Oakland. He had orders for Hawaii and needed to turn in his car. I remember telling him I could make it over there and back in an hour, but we stopped at every bar we passed. Shit, at one o'clock in the morning we were still trying to turn in his car. I knew I'd better be getting back and drove wide open through town. I got pulled over and ticketed for doing ninety miles an hour in a thirty-mile-an-hour zone. I sent the sergeant back in a taxi (it cost me my ten bucks) and headed home.

Shirlie was one mad mother-to-be. I had made myself late and had to get back to the base. I took off and left her with no money.

* * *

When I arrived for duly I had a hangover, and Henderson was raising hell. He wanted to see his mother before he left, and she was nowhere to be found. I was handcuffed to him, and he was jerking the shit out of my arm. I was also carrying his bag, and he gave me shit about his eyeglasses being inside it and not to break them. I told him to shut the fuck up, and he slammed his head into mine. He hit me so hard my ears rang.

His lawyer told us we could not handcuff the prisoner to the plane. Shit, I knew what that meant. I would have to sit next to this crazy asshole all the way back.

Once we were airborne Henderson raised hell—again.

The officer in charge said, "Fuck that lawyer. Chain his ass to the seat and leave him."

Thanks to the noise of the C-130 Hercules transport, we couldn't hear Henderson's shouts and screams. Every time he looked at me, I gave him the finger and laughed. I could see his mouth moving, but I couldn't hear a word he said.

There were plenty of people in New Hampshire to meet us. They'd heard that our prisoner was a real badass. I was once again handcuffed to him, while putting him in the paddy wagon. He tried spitting on me, but I pushed his face away. I "accidentally" dropped his bag and stomped on it. You could hear his glasses break.

"You no good motherfucker," he said, "I'll get out and come kill you."

We had a three day layover in Washington, D.C. The other chasers and the brig officer lived in D.C. I was left by myself in a strange place with five bucks in my pocket.

* * *

Four days later I was back in California, just two days before the Marine Corps birthday ball. On the day of the ball, I got poked in the eye playing football and had to wear a patch over my eye with my dress blues.

Shirlie wanted to know why she had to stay home.

"Because you're going to have a baby, and you don't need to be out running around," I said. And then I left.

Most of us got drunk on our asses, and after the ball, went to my place to finish drinking. That made Shirlie even madder.

The next day was Veteran's Day, and there was always a great parade in downtown San Francisco. Damn, my uniform looked like a mess from the night before, and I was trying to hurry to catch the base bus. Shirlie tried to

Marine Barracks, San Francisco, Nov 1957: Four Team Members from 12th Naval District All Star Football Team

help me, but I was still drunk and stupid enough to say, "Do it right." That was the last straw for her. She left me to finish cleaning up by myself.

I got my ass chewed out but good by the officer in charge. I had candle wax all over my hat. I had no idea how it got there, but assumed it must have happened the night before with the guys.

Unfortunately, Shirlie was mad enough at me to let me leave looking a mess, knowing I'd get an ass chewing.

* * *

A few days later I was standing duty when the desk sergeant called me and told me Shirlie was in the hospital having the baby. I was given four hours liberty to go see her and the baby.

I found the maternity ward and asked, "Is there a lady in here having a baby?" God, how stupid could I get?

The nurse curtly informed me there were several ladies having babies there. She finally took me over to a window and showed me a tiny little baby.

When I asked if it was a boy or girl, she said, "Ask your wife. "

"Did you see the baby?" Shirlie asked me. After she told me it was a girl, I teased her about calling the baby Jan Marine.

"No, we are not! She's Jan Marie," she said. I was laughing but Shirlie wasn't.

Before I left, I promised Shirlie I'd get a few days off as soon as she was released from the hospital. I also promised the woman in the bed next to her that I would tell her husband they now had a baby boy. He was in the brig.

I headed back to the base and started shaking. I thought: *Damn, I'm a dad. Now I HAVE to stop screwing around.*

* * *

I made myself shape up some. I wasn't getting drunk all the time. I played football for the station team and was picked for the all-star team. And I was selected to make sergeant in May of 1958.

Almost all the prisoners were sent out on work details during the day. Most of the time there only were four prisoners to one chaser with a shotgun. One day a prisoner jumped the navy guard and took away his shotgun. He tried to get off the is-land. The escape alarm sounded. Ten Marines were always on standby in case of an attempted escape. They were taken to the bridge to close off both ends. One Marine in the back seat of the truck was loading his shotgun. He jacked a round into the chamber and pulled the trigger. He blew a hole the size of a basketball through the roof.

I could hear "Goddamn you, Cunningham!" as they drove away. It wasn't funny then, but we sure had fun with Cunningham afterward. At least it wasn't me who had screwed up!

* * *

I'd only been a sergeant a few months when I received orders to join the 1st Marine Division at Camp Pendleton. The shit was hitting the fan in Cuba and the 2nd Marine Division was on alert. I knew, sure as shit, that I would be going to war: every sergeant on the base had orders. We had parties every week for someone who was leaving.

Shirlie didn't like the prospect of going to stay with her family while I was gone, but that was what Marines did: they left their families behind. I took her and Jan to her folks. That was the first time I had ever seen her cry.

I had a week before reporting. That gave me time to look up some old buddies who were on the drill field. It made me feel good to see the real Marine Corps again, after almost three years in San Francisco.

San Francisco, May 1958: Making Sergeant

Chapter 18
Camp Pendleton

I checked into division headquarters and was assigned to 1st Marine Regiment, 3rd Battalion. They were stationed up north at Camp San Mateo. I hadn't been out there since I left boot camp in 1953.

At battalion headquarters I was told I would be joining H&S Company, 81st Mortar Platoon.

I reported to my platoon leader. He was a boot lieutenant, fresh out of officer's school.

"You've never been in Eighty-one Mortar, have you?" he asked me.

"No, sir," I answered.

"Well, as a sergeant you're expected to know every weapon in the battalion. We are field Marines, here. Get rid of those salty uniforms and get some new ones."

I thought I'd gotten off on the wrong foot with the guy. I guess I did look a little salty.

My platoon sergeant was a gunny from the south and had a real thick accent. "Where you from, Brandon?" he asked me.

Not understanding his question, I said, "Marine barracks, San Francisco."

"No! What state are you from?"

"Oh, I'm from Oregon."

He asked about my new rank and what I thought about being a sergeant.

"Shit," I said. "I'm not sure. We have acting sergeants, corporals and sergeants, E-5 sergeants. I guess it will be okay, once I'm used to it."

"You ever been in mortars before?"

"Nope, this is my first."

"Well, me too. We can learn together," he said.

I told him about Shirlie and Jan up in northern California.

"Hell, Brandon. They need to be down here."

"But I heard we would be shipping out soon."

"Bullshit. We will be here for three years, so get them down here."

* * *

I was in Sergeant Shipman's section. He was a good sergeant but had a reputation for drinking too much. I was warned not to let him lead me to the watering hole.

I need to save my money to move Shirlie and Jan back down, anyway, I told myself.

Shipman told me we had the best sergeants' quarters in the Marine Corps. He had counted the twenty-six steps from our front door to the coldest beer in the world, the NCO Club.

Camp Pendleton, 1960

"Do you drink beer, Brandon?"

"Do wild bears shit in the woods? Is the commandant a regular? You bet!" I said enthusiastically, briefly forgetting about my family.

"Happy hour is from 1630 hours to 1730 hours; the beer is twenty cents a bottle. We try to get over there first, before the grunts do, or those assholes drink all the cold ones."

"I have to save a few bucks," I explained. "I have to get my wife and daughter down here and find a place to stay. But I will be staying in the barracks for a while."

"Shit, Brandon," he countered, "at twenty cents a beer you can afford a few. I take twenty-six steps over and twenty-six steps back, so I don't get drunk. Anyway, it's almost time. Let's move out."

We were the first two in the NCO Club.

"Give us ten beers each," Shipman ordered. The bartender removed four bottles from a case and gave the case to us.

"Hell, Shipman, I can't drink that much," I said.

"Don't worry. Drink what you want and I'll drink what you don't."

We were on our third beer when the troops from the line companies came in. The place filled up in just a few minutes.

"See why I got my beer first?" Shipman asked. "You won't get near the bar for an hour."

Gunny Felts, our section gunny, came over and had a beer with us. "Don't let Shipman lead you down the wrong road, Brandon. He thinks he has to drink beer every night." Shipman had really earned his reputation; it seemed everyone knew about his drinking.

Gunny Felts told us a story about his joining the Marines: "Hell, coming into the Marines was a move up in the world. We had to get up at two in the morning to a milk a barn full of cows, feed pigs and then walk five miles to school. After all that, we had to eat goddamn lard sandwiches for lunch.

"One Saturday, my old man took me to town on the wagon. He told me to load it and headed for the bar. I saw a man in what looked like a monkey suit, and I asked him if the circus had come to town. He said he was a Marine; I asked him what the hell a Marine did. He said that they are the best fighters in the world. Then I asked him if he got paid and he said, 'Hell, yes, plus three meals a day, clean sheets once a week and brand new uniforms.'

"Well, hell, I done crawled down off that wagon, jumped in with the Marine and left. I wrote my old man when we landed at Guadalcanal. He wrote back to me and said, "Hurry home, Son. I need you to help milk the cows." He told me not to be telling him lies about all the things we got as Marines, there ain't nobody got that much."

"Have you been back home yet?" I asked. "Hell, no, and I ain't going back. I done got me a home away from home."

* * *

My first week off, Shirlie and I met in Bakersfield. She was going to stay with my brother's family until we found a place closer to the base. Bakersfield was a little over a hundred miles from the base, and I could make it there on weekends.

We had a full training schedule back then, and I was having a hell of a time trying to keep my mind on my job and worry about my family. I had a shitty outlook on our training field, and I still wasn't hitting it off very well with my platoon leader. He was a self-proclaimed know-it-all who really didn't know shit and never listened to anyone.

Finally, Shirlie and Jan moved closer to the base. We tried to work things out, but I let my drinking get in the way. I was spending too much time at the club, going home half-drunk every night, and doing a piss-poor job at the base. We couldn't make ends meet, so Shirlie moved to her sister's. That gave me too much time to myself.

The next two weeks on rifle range gave us every night off. Shipman and I spent every night at the club. We bet a dollar each day for best shooter. I was shooting great, so I won the pot everyday...and drank it up every night.

The weekend after firing for the record, Shipman and I headed for San Diego. Shipman drove and got picked up for speeding and drinking. I was passed out in the back seat. The cops left me there sleeping and hauled Shipman off to jail. I woke up along Highway 101 wondering where in the hell I was. I couldn't find the keys to the car but had one hidden under the hood. I was headed back to the barracks when the MPs pulled me over for speeding. Shit, now I was in trouble. My car would be removed from the base, and I would have to go in front of my commanding officer to explain why I was speeding.

Shipman got back to the barracks late the next day. He was kind of pissed at me for not coming to get him. I hadn't even known where the hell he was.

Word must have gotten out about me hanging out with Shipman. I got a phone call from my old gunny from San Francisco. "What in the hell is going on with you, Brandon?" he said. "I see you're fucking up. And where in the hell is your wife?" He had me transferred to the military police. He'd told the battalion commander I was a good football player and that I had better get ready to play some football when I got there.

I called Shirlie and told her I was in a military police company, and that as soon as I was settled, I would come and get her. I was going to get my head on straight and get off the shitlist.

* * *

Playing football was great, and I was definitely an asset to the team; we were seeded to make the playoffs. Thank God for that, because my speeding ticket had caught up with me. I had my ass chewed out good, my car was kicked off the base for one month, and I got a fourteen-day restriction. But it didn't go on my record; they needed me to play football.

The very week I was given base housing, I tore my arm open on duty, and it required an operation. By the time I got out of the hospital, I only

Camp Pendleton 1960: 287-lb Nose Guard. Even tried out for the Chargers (then in LA; later San Diego). Jack Kemp was a quarterback here before he was a Senator.

had two days left to pick up Shirlie, Jan and all our furniture. By the time we made it back, I had only two hours to unload and turn in the U-Haul trailer, or I would be charged for another day's use.

Hurrying like hell, I reopened the arm injury trying to move all our shit and was twenty minutes late with the trailer. The asshole charged me for another day. Damn, I was pissed.

Shit, there were cockroaches all over the house. I remembered them from Japan. They were hard to get rid of. And on top of that shit, Shirlie was pregnant again.

* * *

My buddy Dutch, from Treasure Island, was on the drill field at San Diego. Shirlie, Jan and I went to spend a weekend with Dutch and his wife. He worked the receiving barracks and the base was going crazy. The Everly Brothers had just joined the Marine Corps. They were going through boot camp, so everyone was trying to get on the base to see them.

We told the girls I needed new uniforms, and Dutch and I headed for the base. We ended up at the club and went home drunk. His wife had made a big pot of stew. She filled it with

Dutch and me at Camp Pendleton

peppers and made us eat it until we sobered up. God, it was nasty tasting stuff!

On our way home Shirlie asked, "How come you always go get drunk when you and Dutch get together?"

"Hell, we don't plan it. It just happens that way."

* * *

I had hoped to pick up another stripe, but the Marine Corps was going through another rank change. Even if I did make another stripe, I still wouldn't be a staff sergeant. I would only be a Sergeant E-5.

We had a lance corporal, a corporal, an acting sergeant, a master sergeant and a master gunnery sergeant.

Shit, at this rate I will never make it to the staff club, I thought.

There was a special pay, called "pro pay." If you were good at your job and could pass a test, you would get thirty dollars extra pay per month. I had put in for the pro pay and passed the test. Boy, that money came in handy.

Monday, after the weekend with Dutch, the first sergeant asked, "Do you want to go to water-safety school?"

"If I say no, do I still have to go?" I wanted to know.

"Hell, yes!"

"Okay, I want to go."

Damn, that was a good school. We swam all day and had liberty every night. I came out one of the top three in my class. The master sergeant asked me to work for him during the summer, training people to swim. I would have every weekend off.

I only stayed until football season. The battalion commander would have been on my ass, and I would have lost my pro pay if I missed the season. But I was shaping up!

* * *

On September 12, 1959, around two in the afternoon, Shirlie said, "I think it's time we go to the hospital."

I dropped her off at the hospital and took Jan over to a friend's wife.

"Has she had the baby yet?" Betty asked me.

"I don't know yet. I just dropped her off before I came here."

She gave me the phone, and we called Shirlie.

"What's going on," I asked. "What are you doing?"

"Nothing, I just had a boy. What are you doing?"

Betty watched Jan, while I went to see my new son, Russell Allen.

* * *

I finally made Sergeant E-5. That was a big jump in pay. Along with my pro pay, we were finally doing okay.

Riding the bull instead of pitching it! Long Beach, CA, 1963. Photo © Foxie

A buddy of mine rode the rodeos, and I let myself get talked into riding. I didn't get very good, but I tried it every weekend. On one weekend, I signed up to bulldog a steer, ride a saddle bronco and a Brahma bull. I missed the steer, caught my foot in the stirrup, and got dragged around the arena by my horse. The horse fell and broke its flank, and I broke my tall bone. Damn, I could hardly walk.

The next day the officer in charge gave me hell. He teased, "You rode that horse so bad that you broke its back; they had to shoot it." I was in no mood for a joke; my butt hurt so bad, it was all I could do to stand up.

That year I competed in the wild-horse race. Twelve horses were turned loose in the arena, and we had to catch one, saddle it and ride it across the finish line. I got beaten to rat shit. I'd also played eighteen games of football: nine on a semi-pro team in Los Angeles and nine games on the base. Every bone in my body was broken or dislocated at least once during that year. It took me an hour to tape up before games.

My XO was pissed-off at how much I'd been playing around.

He said, "You have been screwing off. If you don't get back here and do your job, I'm going to transfer you and take your pro pay." He made me company police sergeant and gave me every shit detail he could come up with.

* * *

Camp Elliot was closing, so I checked out a truck and asked to go on a "com-shaw" to get things out of the camp's supply system. I took three troops with me. After finding the chief in charge, I asked if I could trade him for some of the base's supplies.

He said, "You get me some fishing gear and golf balls and you can clean this base out."

We loaded up with paint, potted plants, banana trees, peach trees and palm trees. We even found a Marine Corps emblem that was three feet across. It took a forklift to load it. but we took it anyway. We made two trips to get everything back to Pendleton.

I thought the XO was going to shit when he saw all the supplies I'd come up with.

"Goddamn, Brandon, we'll go to jail if we get caught with that stuff!"

For the next two weeks we planted trees and flowers on both sides of the road leading to our company. We painted anything that didn't move. Our barracks looked like a flower in a pile of shit, compared to the other barracks. We had more plants in our company than the entire base had.

Our battalion adjutant was a tough old mustang of a captain. You didn't pull much shit when he was around; he scared all the officers shitless. Somehow he'd heard about our barracks and grounds and came to visit.

The XO saw him coming and said, "Goddamn you, Brandon, you get out there and explain to him where all this shit came from."

I saluted the captain and said, "Good morning, sir!"

"Damn! You must have the goddamnedest com-shawing police sergeant on the base. This is the best-looking area on the goddamn base. Who is your police sergeant?"

I puffed up and said, "I am. I made a good find when they closed Camp Elliott."

"What did it cost you?"

"A few golf balls."

He walked into the supply room and saw all the extra supplies and the big Marine Corps emblem.

"Jesus Christ! Now I have seen everything. What the hell are you going to do with that?"

"We're still looking for a place to put it," I said.

"Hell, that needs to go down in front of the general headquarters. That okay with you?"

"Yes, sir," I said.

The captain told me to follow him. We went to my commanding officer.

"I think your whole damn company should have a ninety-six hour pass for all this work on your area starting now."

Hot damn!

* * *

Man, did me and the boys get drunk. We ended up at my house again and pissed off Shirlie. (I seemed to do that a lot back then.) She was pregnant for the third time and got pissed at all my screwing off. She drove me back to the barracks, opened the car door and pushed me out. I crawled under the clothing wash rack and went to sleep. I woke up sometime in the middle of the night. *Where the hell am I?* Damn, it took me an hour to figure out I was at the barracks, and why. I may have been the best com-shawing sergeant, but I was sure a shithead otherwise.

* * *

I'd joined a club called the Water Spouts, a group of master swimmers and scuba divers. One night, after coming home, a buddy's wife was in my house watching my kids. Shirlie was in the hospital. I only got to see her for a few minutes. She had a miscarriage and was hurting real bad.

"Gene, will you please try to help me?" she pleaded. "You are never home, and when you do come home, you're drunk, and you never help me with the kids." I'd never seen Shirlie like this. She touched a nerve, and I knew she was right. I promised I would help more.

Things got better until I started riding in the rodeo again. All the guys were party-goers. After we rode, we would head for Ethel's Tavern outside the rear gate. It was a shit-kicking bar with lots of fights. One night, the bunch of us stopped to buy beer, and I was stopped by a group of Mexicans when we came out. One took out a knife and demanded a beer. I gave him one, then he wanted all my beer. I hit him in the face with the six-pack I was holding. The rest of them took off, while the man I'd hit tried to figure out what had happened to him. I hit him a few more times, and he took off running, too. I chased him in my Volkswagen bus, jumped out and beat the shit out of him one more time. This time I took his knife away.

By that time, me and my buddies were wound up and went looking for trouble. Luckily we didn't find any. We stayed in San Diego until the bars closed, then headed over the border into Mexico. About six in the morning, we started back to Pendleton, still drunk on our asses. We stopped at Ethel's again on our way to the base. A San Diego sheriff was there with a warrant for my arrest. I turned over the knife the Mexican had pulled on me. Ethel backed up my story: I hadn't picked on the Mexicans; they had jumped me first. I was let off with a fine and two years' probation. If I got into trouble again, I would go to jail.

We had to get back to the base and get ready to ride the rodeo. We were still drinking and I kept falling asleep. A kid gave me some pills called "No Doz." I took two or three. Damn, in about an hour I was wound up like a top. I rode the shit out of the bull that day, and when I jumped off him, my spur hooked his side and cut him wide open. I was duly chewed out and got kicked out of the rodeo club. I still hadn't had enough trouble and headed to the swimming pool. I was only going there to get some beer money, but we ended up jumping off the thirty-five-foot tower, clothes and all. At least it sobered me up.

* * *

Shit, I'd been on a three-day drunk when I got word that Shirlie was looking for me. I went home, still soaking wet from jumping into the

Guarding the Marine payroll

pool.

There were boxes piled up in the front room. "What's going on Shirlie?" I asked.

"I can't take this shit anymore," she said. "I'm going home. "

"What do I have to do to get you to stay?"

"Get me out of this cockroach-infested place, stop drinking and act like a husband."

* * *

Damn, I was in trouble. I'd not only gotten in trouble with the law and been kicked out of the rodeo club, but the XO was tired of my fucking off. I was being transferred. I was sent to a supply company, and a week later I was back working at the swimming pool.

I took a week off and found a small house in Vista, a little town outside the rear gate. We bought enough furniture to get by and moved in. Shirlie was pregnant again and stayed on my ass to clean up my act. The colonel let me come back to the rodeo club, and I slowed down on my drinking. I did a little work on the side to make a few bucks. Things were a little better.

Shirlie woke me up about midnight, November 1, 1961. "Gene, it's time to take me to the hospital to have the baby."

One hour later, on November 2, she had a baby girl, our third child. Shirlie brought Rita Kay home in just two days.

* * *

The next day was Sunday, and I was off to ride the rodeo. It had rained like hell, and I was the last rider. The colonel wanted to stop the rodeo because of the wet ground, but I was ready, so they let me out. The bull slipped and slid all over the muddy arena and bucked me off. I forgot to spit out my chew and got sicker than hell. I went home to bed and woke up the next day with the flu. Shirlie was not happy with me.

* * *

"You have orders to Hawaii."

"My wife just had a baby," I said. "I want to stay in Pendleton one more year."

I was told I'd been there too long and to start packing.

"My enlistment will be up in two months," I said. "I'm getting out of the Marines." The first sergeant made me sign a statement to the effect that I was going to get out, and if I ended up coming back and shipping over, I would lose a stripe.

I got out in February 1962 and headed for Oregon. We had no place to live, and I had no job. We were going to stay with my parents until I found work.

I found work logging in the woods, setting chokers behind a cat. It took a three-hour ride to get to work, then I worked nine hours a day. Fifteen-hour days, six days a week—and I made barely enough to live on.

Damn, I wish I were back in the Marines.

* * *

I went to see the Marine recruiter. He told me I had ninety days to re-enlist or it would be too late. I was overweight and had to lose twenty-six pounds. I started running ten miles a day and cut back on what I ate. I was still six pounds too heavy when it came time to report back. My doctor gave me water pills and told me be careful because they could make me lose too much water.

When I got home, my mother told me my sister had been in a car accident in Washington. She wanted Gary and me to go get her kids and make sure she was okay before I left to report.

It was after midnight before we could start back and my body was cramping up. I had forgotten about the water pills and hadn't drank any water. I passed out and scared the hell out of Gary. He got me back to Portland two hours before my deadline.

The doctor said I had an off heartbeat. It was much too slow, and I was going into shock. I was put on an intravenous hookup, but it still took almost six hours for me to come out of it.

The officer in charge of recruiting said, "You must want back in pretty bad; you almost died." He let me sign up for six years.

This time I was determined to stay in until I retired.

I left Shirlie with her parents: we didn't have enough money for her and the kids to come with me.

I joined the 1st Marine Division again, but this time I asked to go back to the infantry. I was not going to screw off again. I was going to be the best damn Marine I could be.

Chapter 19
The Third Time Around

I joined the 5th Marine Regiment, 1st Battalion. They had made a name for themselves as a gung-ho outfit. They were just reforming when I joined up and most of the troops were fresh out of boot camp. Most of the NCOs were from sea duty—real sharp guys, but they didn't know much about the infantry, and I had been away from it over seven years.

I stayed away from the clubs and ran in the hills every chance I got. I never walked anywhere; I ran everywhere I went. The troops hated it when I took them on a run, because I ran the shit out of them.

I didn't know what was happening to the new Marines coming out of boot camp, but they were sure salty. You'd have thought they had been in for years.

I had told the PFCs to knock before coming into the NCO quarters. I was shining my boots one day when one walked in without knocking. I jumped up, grabbed him by the neck and threw him back into the barracks, so all the troops could see. "That's what you can expect if you come in without knocking!" I yelled. I was going to be one mean son of a bitch.

* * *

The next week a colored sergeant, fresh off the drill field as a DI, joined us. Sergeant Wells said nothing but swear words: every word out of his mouth started with "motherfucker." He was six foot four and quick to grab someone if they pissed him off. He helped shape up those salty troops in a hurry and backed us up whenever we needed it.

We also got a new lieutenant, right out of officer's school. He, on the other hand, didn't believe in swearing or grabbing the troops.

"Anyone using cuss words will lose one hour of liberty for every cuss word he speaks," he ordered.

On the first day of the new edict, the lieutenant asked Wells what was for chow.

"Pork motherfucking chops, sir."

Shit, poor Sergeant Wells was thirty days in the hole the first week.

* * *

I was able to get a place in Vista again and brought Shirlie and the kids down to be with me. Things were going great. The battalion sergeant major took a liking to me. He said I was the most gung-ho corporal in the battalion. I didn't get to see Shirlie much because of our tough training schedule, but she came to the base to see me a lot.

Camp Pendleton, 1962:
The day before I left for two years at sea.

We passed a general's inspection with flying colors (the best the sergeant major had seen in a long time we were told). I was rewarded with a three-day pass.

The sergeant major patted me on the back and said, "Come see me when you get back. The base can operate without you. Take the time off." He did, however, want to see me first thing after I returned.

When I reported back, he said, "I have good news: you will be going to sea school. That division wants a squared-away corporal, so I'm sending you."

"What am I going there for?" I asked.

"After school you'll have sea duty. It'll be good for you. I had sea duty and made rank fast. As gung ho as you are, you will do fine."

* * *

I checked in early and had two days to get squared away and learn a little about the school. Most of the students were right out of boot camp. There were only a few NCOs in school. There were two classes going through sea school. My class had only one other corporal besides myself. The other class had four. The two classes were very competitive. At times it was damn near cutthroat. Even with four corporals, the other class was a bunch of real shitheads, and our class did great. We passed all areas. Our class commander had to look pretty hard to find anything we'd screwed up.

We finally received orders for the *USS Columbus CG Twelve* and *the USS St. Paul*. My entire class went on the *St. Paul*, except for myself and the other corporal. We were heading out with the other class on the *Columbus*. It had been rebuilt from the keel up and was basically a new ship. We would be plank owners: the first ones to sail on the newly commissioned ship.

I told Shirlie the *Columbus* was in Bremerton, Washington, and she would have to stay in Vista, until I found out where we would be home-ported.

"We might even come back to San Diego," I told her.

I had seven days travel time and knew it would only take me two or three days to get there by bus. I had time to stop by Grand Ronde and spend a day.

My brothers gave me hell about being sea-going; they had both been in the Navy and had spent time in the brig under the Marines. My older brother John was in the Bremerton navy brig during World War II. They were off work for a few days, and John wanted to see the old base again, so they offered to drive me the rest of the way up.

The three of us took off Saturday morning. Between stopping to piss and drink beer, it took us nine hours to drive a hundred and eighty miles.

Most of the other Marines were already checked in and at the Marine Club drinking beer. John wanted to go to town and see if any of the old bars were still there. He could only remember the Crow's Nest and the Pink Pig. We asked the club bartender if the two bars were still around. They were, and he told us how to find them. There were only two other corporals, besides me, who were old enough to drink, and they came along. Damn, we drank until the bars closed and had to get a motel for the night. We had to be in by 0600 hours.

Damn, I had a hangover that would kill a horse. John and Gary dropped us off at the base gate, then headed back to Oregon.

* * *

Formation was at 0800 hours; everyone's presence would be verified at that time. I was wearing my battle jacket, double-soled shoes and my pockets were sewn up. All that was a no-no, but it was too late by then.

My new commanding officer was a 1st Lieutenant, a Korean veteran who wore a Purple Heart.

Our ship gunny was a staff sergeant, just off the drill field, and our XO was another lieutenant who did all the talking.

The XO said, "We will be staying at the Marine barracks one more night before moving aboard ship; troops secure until morning formation; NCOs meet in one hour in the barracks."

In the barracks, once again, the XO did all the talking. Our CO just hung his head and listened. We were introduced to each other and were told about the ship. We were going to have to do everything for this new ship: write ship's orders, set up guard, and be ready to work long hours without liberty, until things were set up properly. That night would be our last liberty, but we weren't allowed to leave the base.

Shit, what kind of liberty is that? I wondered.

As we were leaving, the CO asked how I got so salty for only being a corporal. I explained my past, and he said, "Well, I don't like salty Marines."

"Yes sir," I said. "I'll get rid of the uniforms."

* * *

We boarded ship the next day. Our compartment was a mess. There was dust all over the bunks. We were only one deck below the mess decks, though, and that wasn't far to go for chow. Our supply room was four decks below. That put it almost to the bottom of the ship.

We worked day-in and day-out cleaning and trying to set things up. Damn, we had some of the worst 782 Field Gear I had ever seen. Our rifles had nicked stocks and the wood was dry. If this was seagoing gear, it was a mess.

We were having a hell of a time trying to get the ship ready to be commissioned. The weapons system would not pass inspection, as the weapons were all missiles. We could not go to sea. We spent almost four weeks without leaving the ship except to go running.

* * *

Man, the Marines must have been nuts when they put the troops together for this detachment. I had never seen so many mismatched personalities in my life. Nobody in the troop was gung ho; we had to be on their asses to do anything and everything. I didn't think any of the corporals had ever had to kick ass before, by the way they stammered around these lazy-assed

In full regalia for my 2-year on a Navy ship

troops.

The staff sergeant, our gunny, stayed in the chief's quarter most of the time, never coming down to shape up the troops. Our first sergeant was a born-again Christian and a good Marine, but he was far too easy on everyone.

Shit, Christmas came and we still hadn't sailed. The Navy let seventy percent of their men go on Christmas leave. We were only allowed fifty percent at Christmas and fifty percent at New Years.

I lucked out and got seven days leave for Christmas, but Shirlie and the kids were almost sixteen hundred miles away. There wasn't enough time to take a bus, so I started to hitchhike to Oregon. I caught a ride with a man going to Sacramento. Hell, that was almost halfway. That was the only easy part of getting to Vista. It took me two more days to get the rest of the way. I only had time to stay overnight, and Shirlie had to take me back to the freeway to start hitchhiking back. She stayed with me until I got a ride.

* * *

At last we got commissioned and headed to sea for the first time. There were nine decks above the main deck, and the damn ship rolled from side to side. Shit, I was seasick. Almost every Marine was. I wondered how the hell were we going to stand duty if we were all sick. We weren't the only ones, though; half the Navy was sick, too.

I went to get a cup of coffee. The mess deck was empty. I saw a sailor and asked, "Is the water rough or what? Most all the Marines are seasick."

"The damn ship is top-heavy," he said. We have to go back to dry dock until they fix it."

"Shit," I swore.

We got word the next morning that we would be moving off the ship and staying in some old navy barracks. The barracks had been empty for years and, Oh God, what a mess. We spent a week just cleaning. The rest of the time we spent in classes and marched. Our morale was getting low, and fights were breaking out almost every day.

Our CO called the NCOs together and asked, "What the hell is wrong with the troops?"

One of the corporals said, "The morale is low, and the troops have no pride in what they are doing."

He gave us the job of keeping morale up. As to just how the hell we were to do that, I didn't have a clue.

* * *

When we moved back on the ship, there were two huge gun mounts installed. Hell, they were two, old five-inch, thirty-eight gun mounts, just like World War II: all manual operation. They sure looked funny on our missile cruiser.

Two Marines got caught sleeping on post. I was sergeant of the guard. The CO called me to his quarters and chewed me a new asshole. "Get those fucking troops shaped up. I don't give a shit how you do it, but I better not hear of another Marine sleeping on post, or I will have every goddamn stripe you have." He yelled at me for over an hour.

My mood was so bad that, when I got back to the compartment and caught the standing corporal of the guard laying on his bunk, I knocked the shit out of him. He was wearing his uniform, duty belt and pistol and was obviously supposed to be on duty.

"I had better not find you in your bunk again while you are on duty," I warned him.

Two or three other troops were in their bunks with their boots on. I jerked every one of them out and choked the shit out of them. Shit, everyone ran for cover. I wasn't done. I raised hell for the rest of the day.

I found PFC Walker on post with his hat off and his head down on the desk. I grabbed him by his tie, pulled him out the door and busted him in the mouth. Blood flew all over the place.

Then I found the corporal of the guard and said, "Relieve that man of his post and bring him to the brig."

Walker's mouth was busted open, and his lip was still bleeding. I threw him into the brig, slamming him into the wall. "If I ever catch you out of uniform and sleeping on duty again, I will lock your ass up in the brig forever."

Then, to the lance corporal, "If my ass is grass because of your troops, then so is yours. If I ever find another man on your watch screwed up again, I will kick your ass."

I stayed out of the compartment and only went in to change clothes and sleep. The men never knew what I was going to do next. I took the troops out on the pier for a run and one of them fell out of formation. I dragged him by his neck until he got back in sync with the rest.

I warned the rest of the corporals that they had better start kicking ass, or I would be sending them to the CO. Then they could go through the same shit I had gone through.

"What the hell did he do to make you turn so mean?" they asked me.

"Fuck up...and you can find out for yourself."

* * *

That was all the troops needed; they snapped out of their shit pretty damn quick. They still weren't very gung ho, but at least they had stopped screwing off.

The damn ship could not pass shakedown cruise. A shakedown cruise is when all departments must pass their operation tests. My department did fine, and we ended up manning the two five-inch, thirty-eight gun mounts. We did great at firing, but we all ran around with smashed fingers from dropping the shell casings on them when we loaded.

Our CO was selected for captain and turned into a worse asshole than he already was. He was on everyone's ass. He decided we needed to take a fifty-mile hike one day. None of the troops had been doing much marching or running because we couldn't get off the ship. He took us off the ship that morning at 0500 hours. By the time we had gone fifteen miles, our legs were cramping, and it was raining cats and dogs.

We stopped for chow: cold sandwiches and milk. After sitting down for an hour, almost no one could get back up.

The CO went crazy. "Get up! Get up, NOW!"

After two more miles, he started limping. As we passed one of the base gates, he disappeared for a while.

We were doing better by the time he caught up. We had gone about thirty-six miles, and it looked like we would make it after all.

Two buses came, and he ordered us on board, calling us quitters.

I said, "Sir, we can make it."

"Shut up and get your ass on the bus." He was hell-bent on making us take the rap for him not being able to finish the hike.

He sat in front of me on the bus. He turned around and said, "You were hurting too much to finish the hike."

"I would rather kill myself than quit," I told him. "You ordered us to quit. It was not my choice. Those goddamn sailors are going to ride our asses, and we'll pay hell trying to make them do their jobs."

The next day no one could walk, and the sailors knew how we felt. Nobody dared say anything to us. We didn't see the CO for over a week.

* * *

We had to off-load in Long Beach for repairs, so we were to go to Camp Pendleton for a week of training.

An hour before we were due in port, the CO called me to his quarters. He said, "We need to unload smoke grenades and ammo for training. Have them ready when we come into port, because they'll take us and the ammo in first."

I ran to the compartment and got as many troops as I could. We ran like hell to get ammo lockers open and ammo ready to off-load.

Shit, why did that asshole take so long to let me know about this?

We were nearly ready but had a few smoke grenades left to get. I sent a corporal and two men to the fourth deck for the rest of the grenades. They ran with them and dropped a box; three or four smoke grenades fell out. They picked them up and kept running. We got all the ammo unloaded, and by the time I got back to the ship, we were tied up and everyone was ready for liberty.

I had not seen Shirlie and the kids for almost six months and was excited to get liberty. The officer of the deck said that my CO wanted to see me as soon as I returned to the ship. I told the sailor who I had caught a ride into town with that I would be ready momentarily.

"Reporting as ordered." He didn't look at me for over twenty minutes.

I said, "Sir, some men are waiting to give me a ride home."

"Did one of the Marines drop some hand grenades?" he asked.

"Sir, they were smoke grenades, not hand grenades, and they were still in the box." He didn't say anything for another ten minutes.

"Sir, may I go now?" I finally asked.

He looked at me and said, "Why did they drop them?" I told him again. He took out an expert shooting badge that had my name on it (for shooting the highest score on the range and for shooting expert six years straight).

"How many people saw that Marine drop the grenades?" he asked.

"I don't know, sir. I was getting the boat loaded."

"Were any officers watching?"

"I think so."

"How many?" This went on for two hours. I had been standing at attention the entire time.

"May I stand at ease, sir?" I asked him. He just kept looking at the badge. I said, "I have not seen my wife and kids for over six months. Will I be able to go on liberty this weekend?"

"You don't deserve this medal," he said and put it back on his desk. "Get out of my sight."

My ride was gone. I started to leave the ship, to hitch a ride, when the officer of the deck said, "The CO said he wants to see you again in the morning at 0600 hours."

Goddamn that son of a bitch. He was going to make me come back to Long Beach when he knew this was my first liberty in over six months. I got home about midnight and stayed with Shirlie until four a.m. I took our car and drove back to Long Beach. Maybe I would get the rest of the weekend once he was done with me. *Why didn't he fuck with the gunny?* I wondered. *This was his job. Shit, I'm only a corporal.*

I went to his quarters and knocked at his hatch. I waited for over an hour for the CO to return from chow. When he did come back, he told me to write a report about what happened and turn it in to him.

When I finished the report and took it to his quarters, he was gone. I left it and went on liberty.

Fuck him. If that isn't good enough, he can hang my ass on Monday.

* * *

Monday we took the bus to Pendleton for a week of training. We only saw the CO once during the entire week.

The next week we were back aboard ship, waiting on the repairs. A big rodeo had come to the Long Beach arena, and some of the cowboy sailors teamed together and challenged the Marines from Pendleton. Word had gotten around about my rodeo days, and I was asked if I would be on the sailors' team, riding against the Marines. I was given free tickets to attend. As my luck went, I sprained my ankle playing baseball before the rodeo. I decided to buck up and offer the tickets to my CO. That was the first time I ever saw the asshole smile.

"You are going to be promoted to sergeant and awarded a six-year shooting medal," he told me, with a smile all over his face.

Shit, you could have knocked me over with a feather. I still don't know if it was because I backed down first with a peace offering, or if it finally just got through his thick skull that I deserved it.

* * *

No one gave a shit about my ankle at the rodeo. I was told that I was going to ride—come hell or high water. Because I'd ridden some of the bulls in the pen, I went to check on the bull I had drawn. Shit, it was a bull with a reputation for goring and gouging its riders. I knew he was fast and would probably dump me just as fast. *Shit, that's okay. I won't have to run very far to get away,* I thought.

The Marines were racking up points fast, beating the hell out of the Navy, but we were having a great time. We drank lots of booze in the chutes, and I was half-plowed by my ride time.

I'd guessed right; in only a few jumps the bull dumped me. Shit, was he fast. He got to me before I could even get off the ground. He hit me in the side at a full run, threw me into the air and nailed me coming back down.

Oh shit. I didn't think the clown was ever going to get that bull off me.

After I made it out of the arena, I went behind the chutes and famous rodeo rider Casey Tibbs came to see if I was all right. I acted tough, saying, "I'm okay."

But I kept right on drinking until the pain went away.

I made it back to the ship and hit the rack. I woke up an hour or two later in a lot of pain. In sick bay I was told I had broken ribs and a dislocated shoulder.

Shit, I have to make ship inspection in the morning. I'm being promoted to sergeant.

* * *

Oh God, I hurt bad. I had to be helped getting dressed. At least I didn't have to take my rifle. We stood at parade rest, and my arm was stuck behind my back. When someone behind me pushed my arm down, I almost threw up, it hurt so bad. Still, I was excited at my promotion and had to get home to tell Shirlie.

Shit, I almost died of the pain that weekend. It told myself that would be the last time I ever rode. That was May 1963.

* * *

A few Navy officers and both Marine officers received orders to leave the ship. Our new CO was a Captain D.D. Dorman.

The ship went on alert: everyone was in shock at the news of President Kennedy's assassination. Liberty was canceled, and we went on standby, holding a military service for the President aboard the ship.

My two years of ship duty were up, and the ship was due to go on a world cruise. I had the option of extending another year on ship. I chose not to.

During my last weekend duty, I was being a little slack with the troops for gambling. The troops also thought that, since I was a short-timer, I would let it pass. I started to leave when one man mouthed off. "Why don't you get the fuck out of here and leave us alone?"

Well, so much for letting things slide. I replied, "We don't allow gambling because of cheaters like you. I just saw you deal off the bottom."

He jumped up, shouting, "You're lucky you're a sergeant, or someone would have kicked your ass a long time ago. "

I threw a punch at his neck and tossed him around the compartment for a while, then said, "When you grow up to be the size of your mouth, then maybe you can kick my ass." I left him lying on the deck.

When I checked out, I didn't have a big gathering of troops standing on the rails to say goodbye.

1964: Coming into San Diego for the last time: my tour of duty was up!

Chapter 20
North Carolina

My orders read: 2nd Marine Division, Camp LeJeune, North Carolina. That was clear across nine states. On the map, it looked like over three thousand miles. I had seventeen days allotted to travel time and thought I could make it in under seven.

We packed up the car and the kids and headed east.

We made it in just over six days. We must have eaten the entire time: our food bill was bigger than our gas bill. Shirlie and the three kids were beat by the time we got there. We had no housing, so we stayed in base temporary housing for a few days. By the time I checked in, however, we were able to get housing. I also got another week off, enough time to settle the family in, at least.

* * *

I had never seen such a slack command. You could tell when weekends came up; the men started getting ready by Thursday mornings and by noon on Fridays the place was empty. Almost everyone stationed there lived in the area. I found very few of my Marine comrades from the West Coast on the base.

I was assigned to H&S Company, 81st Mortars, a company where everyone actually held the rank their job called for.

Doing my job seemed hard for me: there wasn't anything to do. I guess I had been used to the tight training on the ship. After a while, I told the supply sergeant how tired I was of not doing anything, and he said he wished he could trade jobs with me. It seemed like a good idea, so I offered to trade.

The supply job was great. I worked all I wanted, and I was my own boss, reporting only to the gunny. He gave me all the troops I needed to work. We repainted my supply and anything else that wasn't nailed down.

The first sergeant commented one day, on the job I was doing. "Everyone is talking about the gung-ho supply man in H&S Company."

"Shit, I'm just doing my job. Glad for a change and something to keep me busy."

"I have a colored corporal who is a first-class fuck-off. I want you to work the shit out of him. If he screws up kick his ass."

Now, I'm no small fish, but this corporal, Corporal Willie Reed, was as big as I was and looked mad at the world.

I began with, "You're going to work your ass off for me. To me you are a corporal, you are in charge of troops, and your job is to make sure your troop does its job. I'm here to see that you do just that."

He worked for me for a few days and damned if he didn't shape up. I was even able to take every noon hour off to swim, without checking up or worrying about the guy.

"I never did learn how to swim." Reed told me.

He started coming to the pool with me. I taught him swimming the same way I worked his ass off in the company, and I made a damned good swimmer out of him in the end. So good, that he qualified as a lifeguard.

Eventually, he became one of the best corporals I'd worked with. When he was given a job, it got done. Once again, I'd made a name for turning things tip-top. Corporal Reed ended up staying in the Marine Corps, retiring as a sergeant major.

* * *

We were finally assigned a battalion commander who made everyone get off their asses and, man, the battalion started to look good. We were waiting for deployment to the Caribbean on an island called Vieques and Guantanamo Bay, Cuba. Originally, we were to be stationed in Guantanamo Bay for nine months, but we stayed on standby during hurricane season and stood inspection every week.

One Friday, during a general inspection, all supply sergeants were competing for the best-looking supply. Because of the size of my company, I was allotted more gear than the other supply sergeants.

It was always hot and muggy in North Carolina. I thought of a nice touch to add to my inspection and made up large ice tanks filled with Kool-Aid. I was going to be ready for inspection with cold drinks. The inspection lasted more than two hours, and we received word that our supply rooms would be passed up.

I wasn't the only one who thought we were finished with inspection and that nothing had come of it; our battalion police sergeant, a salty old World War II veteran, brought and dumped a gallon of vodka into my Kool-Aid tank. Just as we were starting our impromptu social gathering, the general's inspection team arrived: the general, a colonel, two sergeant majors and ten Marines were in the group. The general said, "Damn, sergeant, do you have something cold to drink in that tank?"

"Yes, sir, Kool-Aid." *Oh shit!*

He took one drink. "Either that's the best Kool-Aid I have ever had, or else I'm awfully dry." He drank three or four cups and asked for the recipe for his wife.

I have never seen so many Marines trying to keep a straight face. The general was about the only one who didn't know what caused his throbbing headache the next day.

* * *

Rebels in Santo Domingo had tried to overthrow their government and were killing the government's leaders. We were on standby, forty-eight hour alert, so I reported in early each morning in case the word came to leave. The 6th Marine regiment was loading up and heading for Santo Domingo; our Catholic chaplain was requested to go with them. As I was the only one ready to leave, I loaded up to go with the chaplain.

I was just about ready to leave when the sergeant major asked, "Where in the hell are you going, Brandon?"

The Six Marine needs a chaplain, and I'm going as his assistant."

"Your ass you are! Get the hell out of that jeep. They can get their own assistant."

At chow that morning he told the company, "Brandon wants to go to war so bad, he tried to pass himself off as a Bible salesman."

Goddamn, for a while everyone folded their hands and bowed to me.

We finally got our marching orders and were moving out, getting ready to leave. The general and the division sergeant major saw us off.

I was loading a truck when the sergeant major said, "The general and I might come to see you. Have some of your Kool-Aid ready but leave out the booze. The general never figured out why he had a hangover the next day."

* * *

It was sure difficult getting used to lazy Marines. We spent half the time kicking them out of their bunks.

In order to keep an eye on the company supplies, I slept in a gear locker that had room for two bunks. The back of the gear locker was part of an old shower room that had been closed down. I traded a navy boatsmate some Marine supplies for the plumbing parts I needed and spent my extra time re-plumbing the old shower room. I had three of the showers working when I made the mistake of opening a hatch leading to the rear of the off-duty NCO's sleeping quarters.

The gunny from 81st Mortars came to see what was up.

"Whose showers are these?" he asked.

"I got the parts and fixed the showers," I told him. I was pretty proud of the "new" shower room I'd made.

"Well, I have some news for you," he said. "These are now the staff NCO showers. Get your ass out of here."

Goddamn asshole. After I did all the work, he kicked me out.

I fought two thousand troops to get a shower.

* * *

We pulled into Guantanamo Bay, Cuba for a two-week stay and to relieve the previously assigned battalion. We were only going to leave one company. The rest of the battalion would go to Vieques Island, Puerto Rico. We stayed on the ship, going ashore each day to train and hike the lines between us and the Cubans.

The temperature was in the hundreds every day, and the troops dropped like flies. So many troops out of shape! They paid for all the times they laid around on their asses, while we worked our butts off onboard the ship.

At the end of the second week, the battalion commander ordered a party to one side of the island. The Navy Seabees had built a cove and dumped rocks to break the ocean waves. It made a great swimming hole. We'd been warned about sharks and barracudas getting trapped in the cove during high tide and not being able to get out. Someone had to check the water each time to make sure it was safe for swimming.

The sergeant major knew I was a qualified lifeguard and assigned me to find three or four good swimmers to check out the cove. I might have been qualified, but I wasn't stupid. I went to the ammo bunker and talked them out of a case of M-23 fragmentation hand

Vieques Island, Puerto Rico, 1964

grenades.

I put on my face mask and looked for sharks. Shit, they were all over the place. I placed men on both sides of the cove, and we threw hand grenades into the infested waters. Shit, it was like shooting fish in a barrel: they started floating to the top by the hundreds.

"Damn, Brandon. What are we going to do with all these fish?"

"Drag them up on the bank. Maybe when the cooks get here they can use them. Or, we can carry them to the seal wall and throw them over. Hell, I didn't think there would be that many fish in there. Anyway, it's too late to hide them now. The truck is coming."

The company commander was first off the truck. "Where the hell did all these fish come from?" he asked.

I explained to him how we had gone about blasting the cove from both sides. "I guess I killed all the fish," I said.

"Goddamn, Sergeant Brandon, one hand grenade would have done the job. Well, start gutting them. Maybe the cooks will fix them up for us. If not, we have one hell of a lot of fish to dig a hole for."

Well, at least no one was scared to go swimming. There wasn't a fish in sight for a mile, and we had more chow than we could eat. The colonel didn't even ask what happened; I don't think he wanted to know. He just shook his head. The sergeant major, however, chewed my ass out good and wanted to know where the hell I had gotten all the hand grenades.

* * *

We got underway and headed for our next landing. I sure wanted to get off that damn ship.

Boy, it was hot. So hot, that we trained in the middle of the night rather than during the day. Most everyone spent their days at the beach, coming back in time for chow and ready by the time the club opened.

It didn't take long for the troops to get bored each night at the club. It was like a war zone, and the smart guys kept their backs to the wall. I never saw so many fights, not even in Japan. It didn't do any good to shut the clubs down: so much booze came over the fence that no one could control it. The battalion commander kept us in the field as much as possible, but it seemed like everyone always had booze.

I weighed in at two hundred and seventy-eight pounds, but it was coming off fast in that heat. I had made up my mind to put in for drill-instructor school after this cruise, so I had to get the pounds off. I got to where I could run up to ten miles a day in the heat, and I swam in the ocean everyday. My goal was two hundred and ten pounds.

Vieques Island, Puerto Rico, 1964

I had a medical checkup every ten days to make sure I stayed on track and was physically all right. I did over two hundred sit-ups and ran eighteen miles a day. I decided to train for the battalion's eighteen-mile marathon.

A fifty-mile hike was on our training schedule, but the CO made me stay behind. To entertain ourselves, while everyone else was getting ready to leave, another sergeant and I challenged for the most sit-ups. I beat him, completing four hundred and twenty sit-ups in twenty-seven minutes, but my ass was dragging.

The CO came in just after I'd finished. The gunny wasn't feeling well, and I was to take his place on the fifty-mile hike. I hiked, all right, but I was almost dead by the time we got back.

December 5, 1964: 501 sit-ups in 27 minutes! Followed up 10 minutes later with a 25-mile hike.

* * *

The eighteen-mile marathon started at three o'clock in the afternoon, and only eighty Marines entered. It was still over a hundred degrees outside. By the time we crossed the ten-mile mark, only a dozen runners were left in the race. At the fifteen-mile mark, there were only three of us. I was doing fairly well and was in the lead by about three or four hundred yards. We were a mile or less from the finish line, the remaining distance all downhill. Because of the ruts in the road, I ran on the side of the road in the grass. Damned if I didn't trip on some wire halfway down the hill and fall, twisting my knee and ending up using a stick for a crutch.

After all the training I had done, and all the weight I had lost, one Marine came up awful fast and beat me by a few hundred yards. He was a good sport: he told everyone the only reason he won was because I had fallen down.

I went to the club to celebrate that night for the first time in over five months. I was over sixty pounds lighter, and my uniforms were four sizes too large. I also wasn't able to keep my booze like I used to. Boy, did I get drunk. I was so sick the next day that I couldn't even get out of my bunk. I just rolled over and puked occasionally, The CO just laughed and let me stay in the bunk.

* * *

We loaded the ships and headed for San Juan, Puerto Rico around Christmas time 1964. We had liberty every day and the chance to take cruises once a week to the outer islands on the weekends. Vacationing cruise ships came to port in the Dutch Islands, and picking up women from these ships

Cabaria, Puerto Rico, 1964

became the new pastime. Most of the women, however, were old and retired. Our battalion XO hooked up with one and ended up onboard her ship which sailed the next day with him on it. He managed to get himself off at a nearby port and found a ride back, but he still caught hell from the CO. He must have had a great time: he took his ass chewing with a smile.

* * *

I was put on shore patrol to keep the Marines out of trouble. The Dutch Royal Marines had their own whorehouses, and it was no easy task to keep all our Marines out of them. Shit, that was putting our lives on the line, keeping a Marine away from a piece of ass.

I thought the Dutch Marines had a good idea, though. They contracted the women to work as prostitutes. They stayed for six months at a time, making money and taking care of the Dutch military. Even a few of their married men came, while I was standing guard. I never could speak their language, so I couldn't ask them if their wives thought it was a good idea. One thing I did know—most of them thought it was.

When I returned to the ship, my company commander told me I was assigned to the advance party headed back to North Carolina and Camp LeJeune. Two men would accompany me home to help get the area ready for the troops. We would be opening and cleaning the barracks.

It took only a few hours to fly to North Carolina, and I sure surprised Shirlie. She hadn't expected me back for two more weeks. She was even more surprised that I was only half my size. I had lost over seventy pounds, and in the middle of winter, I had a dark tan…even for an Indian.

My CO surprised me with a treat: when I went to ready the area, it had already been done. I didn't have a thing to do except make sure he had a ride back to base and to meet the ship two weeks later.

Everyone got leave as soon as their gear was turned in. We were told that, when we returned from leave, anyone who had been in the battalion would be on orders.

* * *

I was put in charge of battalion recruiting. The Marine Corps wanted to re-enlist as many men as possible at the base in Bangor, Washington. They needed over two hundred Marines of all ranks, mostly lance corporals and below. All anyone had to do was re-enlist or extend their duty for one year.

Somewhere along the line, division headquarters screwed up and cut orders for over a hundred Marines, sending them to Bangor, *Maine*, instead of Bangor, *Washington*. I would have hated to be the one who screwed up or the one who had to tell the Marine Corps how it happened. Maybe they'd heard that old song about Bangor, Maine and didn't know of Bangor in Washington State.

I remember battalion recruiting as the best duty I had. I was my own boss most of the time and saw all the quotes coming in for the specialty schools. No one said I couldn't go, so I attended all the courses I could in Bridgeport, California, at the Cold Weather Training Center: mountain-leadership school, escape and evasion school and more mountain-climbing school. Finally the sergeant major told me to get my ass back to Camp LeJeune.

Chapter 21
Drill Instructor Brandon

Back in North Carolina, inspectors from Parris Island were coming to hold interviews for drill-instructor school. Candidates had to pass the inspection board through battalion, regiment and division headquarters before they could apply for the school. I made it through the boards and thought everything (almost!) was fairly easy. After having been in cold-weather centers and running in elevations over seven thousand feet, my lungs were as hard as steel. I could do seventy-five to a hundred push-ups and not break a sweat, and I could run forever.

The DI board wasn't so easy. In fact, it was downright tough. Over three hundred Marines showed up; less than fifty of us made it past two days. The board of officers and senior staff NCOs raked us over the coals. Most of the men couldn't take the bullshit and opted out. But I knew other Marines who had made it, and I knew I was as good as they were.

When my turn in front of the board came, one master sergeant started to say things about my mother. "Are you fat because of your mother?" he wanted to know.

"I may look fat, but I can match or beat any Marine in fitness," I told him. I tried not to get mad. I knew he was trying to piss me off.

"I'll bet you're too fat to even do push-ups."

Without saying a word, I jumped out of my chair and did a two-handed handstand in full uniform, came down on my finger tips and the toes of my shoes and pushed seventy-five push-ups while counting as loudly as I could. I stood up, took a swipe across my forehead (making damn sure the master sergeant saw I hadn't broken one drop of sweat), and sat back down.

The captain in charge said, "I think you can pack your seabag. You're dismissed."

After thinking about what I'd done in front of the master sergeant, I was sure I'd blown it. I was afraid he would blackball me from getting into DI school after I'd made it. I was wrong. Only twenty Marines were picked, and I was the only one from my battalion, other than a staff sergeant who had previous drill-field experience.

I told Shirlie about attending DI school in Parris Island. She would have to stay at Camp LeJeune until I finished, but I would have some weekends off. The school was eight weeks long, and if I made it through, my chances of making staff sergeant would come up fast. DIs also got special pay and extra-

Parris Island, SC, 1965

clothing expenses. I knew I'd also have a chance to make gunny by the time I got off the field.

* * *

The drive to Parris Island took six hours. The island was out in the middle of the bay, just like they said. The base was spotless and everything looked immaculate.

School began on a Monday. We were Class 565. There were a hundred Marines in my class. *If the others had to go through the shit I did to get here, they must be the best from wherever they came from,* I thought.

I found out one thing fast: This was a cutthroat school; the top three students would have their pick of duty; the top Marine would receive an NCO sword and, possibly, a promotion to the next rank. We were allotted starting "points," and if or when we screwed up, points were deducted. However, we were also awarded points for passing.

I had never been through a school like this. They were on our asses for every little thing. If you weren't running, you had better be marching or counting cadence, and if a button or piece of string was out of place, they had us by the ass.

Fifteen hours was a short day in DI school. If we grabbed four hours of sleep, we were lucky. I was paying for not staying in high school. I didn't know how to study and couldn't take notes fast enough to keep up. And I had a lot of trouble remembering everything about drill. We were expected to know everything word-for-word and be able to explain it and teach it. Page after page after page of material.

We had as many as three inspections a day. Half the time I missed chow so that I could press my uniform. Everyday was over a hundred degrees, but I wasn't going to chance looking like shit. Out of air-conditioned classrooms and into the hundred-degree heat. God, no wonder the drill instructors were so crazy. I didn't know if I was coming or going.

We ran two and three times a day, sometimes in full uniform. We messed up at least two or three uniforms a day. I was going broke trying to keep my uniforms clean. We had to instruct at least two classes a week, some only three minutes long and others half an hour. We lost points for not hitting the exact time.

As many as five Marines a week dropped out of class, and these were the best Marines I had ever seen. At the end of the sixth week, I was in seventh place in my class. Things got tougher every day. Only one or two points separated first to tenth place. One fuck-up could cost you the running.

* * *

I held my own on the runs. If anyone fell back, I gave them shit. I knew I was in good condition and most of the time those who fell out were ahead of me in points.

One day I shoved around anybody who fell out. Three of them decided I needed my ass kicked. During hand-to-hand practices in the sawdust pits, they ganged up on me. I got punched a few times and ended up fighting with two of them later that day in the barracks. One of the class instructors broke up our fight. The five points he took off my grade dropped me to sixteenth place. We only had one week left, and I couldn't rebuild my grade to come out in the top three. I ended up with a chip on my shoulder, acted like an asshole and didn't get along with the others.

The pugel-stick course (obstacle course) was our final drill before graduating from DI school. The same instructor who had caught me fighting put me up against two of the biggest men in the class. They might have been two of the biggest, but they were a long way from being the toughest with a pugel stick. I beat the shit out of both of them and had to be pulled off of one of them. I was almost put on the shitlist, but after a good ass chewing, I managed to get off with only a warning.

* * *

I ended up finishing sixteenth in a class of fifty-three. I was sent as a DI to B Company, 1st Battalion.

Shirlie and I were getting good at moving, but this time the Marine Corps moved my things, so all we had to do was clean the house and take off. No more U-Hauls or boxes in the car. We got a small place, just two miles outside the main gate of my new base.

I reported for work during my platoon's last three weeks of training. Most of the time, another DI worked with me.

The senior DI had warned me about another DI, Sergeant Peters.

"You will be working the first night with Sergeant Peters. Don't pick up any of his bad habits. Do just like the school taught you, and you'll stay out of trouble.

"There's a wiseass in the platoon who makes a quacking sound when Sergeant Peters has the duty. That pisses Peters off, so walk away if he starts screwing with the platoon."

Sure enough, as we brought the platoon back to the barracks after chow, Peters began giving commands.

"LEFT FLANK!"

"Quack...quack."

Peters went crazy. "I'll find that motherfucker, or I'll kill the whole fucking bunch of you." He took them into the barracks, overturned bunks, dumped

DI School • Class 5-65 • M.C.R.D. Parris Island S.C. • Graduated 30 Jul 1965

footlockers, made them crawl on the deck—all kinds of shit. He screwed with them until it was time to go down for the night. The platoon didn't have time to shower or straighten up the barracks before he switched off the lights and told them it had better be clean when he turned them back on in the morning.

Once we got to the office, Peters and I talked about what happened. He said, "This shit started about three weeks ago and it happens about once a week." He laughed about it. "Someone will slip and we will catch them." I didn't think Peters was as bad as I'd been told, after all.

I had the duty a few days later and was bringing them back to the barracks after drill when I heard: "Quack…quack.*

In the barracks, I made them all get down in the duckwalk position—all night. They showered duckwalking, walked the halls duckwalking, hit the head duckwalking—everything they did was done duckwalking. Of course quacking goes hand-in-hand with duckwalking, so all night they were ordered to quack, over and over, until it was time to hit the rack.

I'll always think it was the quacking that got to them, because I never heard it again. Not so for Peters; they still tested him over and over. I never told Peters how I'd handled the problem, and when he asked if they ever quacked me, I said no!

* * *

I think every drill instructor on the island knew about the quacking. Those recruits had guts for keeping it up. They knew they would pay hell for quacking, because Peters would screw them good.

Once a platoon finished boot camp, we gave them their orders the night before shipping out. The next morning we would load them onto buses, and they would be gone by 0600 hours in the morning.

It was the custom for the drill instructors to shake hands with the troops as they boarded the buses and stay until they pulled away. As the buses pulled out, one of those green kid Marines opened the window and yelled, "Hey, Sergeant Peters! QUACK…QUACK!"

Everyone busted a gut laughing. All except Sergeant Peters. He ran after the bus yelling for the driver to stop. "Stop that fucking bus. Stop! I'll kill the son of a bitch. I'll kill him!" I didn't think we would ever stop laughing.

* * *

Once we got over Peters chasing the duck quacker off the base, we turned in our gear to supply. We had three series in each company. Each series had four platoons; each platoon had three drill instructors: mainly sergeants and staff sergeants, with maybe one or two corporals. Once we had the platoon equipment returned to supply, we checked out another issue for another series.

I would be working with Staff Sergeant Scribner again and a Sergeant Cody, a young boot-ass sergeant who thought he was God's gift to somebody.

Scribner said, "If we're lucky, we may have a week off before we pick up a new platoon."

"What do we do while we wait to pick up a new platoon?"

"I don't know what you do, Brandon, but I go fishing. The best fishing in the world is right here. Why don't you come with me?" he asked. "Come on over to my place tonight, and we can go do some shrimping."

Scribner had a small flat-bottom boat. "This is my special shrimp boat," he said. "I'll show you how to throw a shrimp net."

Boy, the goddamn bugs were everywhere. "How the heck do you stand the bugs?" I asked.

"Smoke a cigar and they'll stay away from your face. You get used to them after a while."

I spotted a snake that had to be the size of a cruise missile on the bank and made Scribner pull over so I could look it over.

"It's a bull snake," he said.

I watched it crawl up the sand and walked right up to it. I almost shit when it struck at me. "God-damn it! It's a rattlesnake," I screamed.

He threw me a boat paddle, yelling, "Hit the son of a bitch!"

I kicked sand on it and tried to get it to move, but there it lay. I took a swing at it with the paddle and hit it.

"Did you kill it?" Scribner asked.

I thought it was just playing dead, so Scribner took a swing at it. It didn't move. I stomped on it near the head; it still didn't move.

"Shit, it's dead," he said. That is the biggest damn rattlesnake I have ever seen."

All we had with us was a beer can opener, but I gutted the snake anyway. I was going to cut off the head, skin it and take it back to the house. It wasn't any wonder the snake hadn't coiled before he struck at me. Hell, he had a rabbit and three frogs inside him. His belly was full!

We took home a bucket full of shrimp and a bucket full of snake. When we got to my place, Scribner asked Shirlie if she wanted some shrimp.

She looked in the bucket that carried the snake. "Oh, get that shit out of here!" She was thoroughly disgusted with us.

Scribner took out a shrimp and kissed it. "Boy, you don't know what you're missing."

* * *

I was called the next morning and told to pick up our platoon by 1100 hours. We went in early and got the barracks ready. This was the first platoon I had ever had that would be my responsibility right from the beginning of its training.

Scribner told us how he wanted us to handle the platoon. "I do not allow the drill instructor working with me to hit a recruit. Grab them and push them around, but do not hit them. All of us will stay with the platoon during the first three days, from sunup to sundown. I will stay with them the first week. Then we will stand one night on and two nights off. We all work everyday."

We picked up the platoon at eleven o'clock sharp. Boy, what a strange smell. Brand new clothing, mixed with sweat, made for a strange odor.

Scribner kept dishing out

Rifle Inspection, Parris Island

orders; Cody and I kept giving them hell. We pushed, we shoved, we yelled, we threatened. Shit, I had a hard time keeping from laughing. I didn't know a bunch of human beings could be so scared. I didn't remember being that chickenshit in boot camp, and if I had been, I sure as hell wasn't going to admit it.

* * *

Within a matter of minutes we had them in shock.

"Close it up…pick it up. You seabag! Who told you to set it down?" We yelled at them all the way across the parade field.

We took them to chow before taking them back to the barracks.

"Look at the number on your seabag," Scribner said. "Remember that number when you come out of my mess hall. You will come back out here and stand by that seabag, at attention, reading your little red book until everyone is present. DO YOU UNDERSTAND?"

"YES, SIR!"

"What's your fucking number?" I asked a recruit. Hell, I scared the boy so badly, he didn't know what his name was, let alone his number. "The number on your field jacket and the number on your seabag are the same. Match them up. That's where you'd better be when I get out here." Tears were running down his cheeks. I stayed on his ass until he went through the mess hall doors.

We took turns walking through the tables, giving the new recruits hell. "Sit up straight…don't look around…get that food down." We pulled the old jumping-in-and-out-of-tables trick a few times and gave them twenty minutes to eat before we ran them out, giving them hell all along the way for not eating all their food. Shit, some had food running out of their mouths!

What we were taught in DI school was only the tip of what we really needed to know about teaching a boot-camp Marine. God have mercy if we taught them something wrong. They never forget. Everything had to be by the numbers. With seventy-five recruits, that meant teaching it seventy-five times. That seemed to be the only way to get it right.

Goddamn! Outside the mess hall they could not find their seabags from their backsides. Take one mistake, and multiply it seventy-five times: that's how many times they would fuck up. At that stage of boot camp, we were lucky to get them to walk a straight line, let alone march.

Each drill instructor taught one subject. It was our responsibility to follow up, making sure the recruits understood what we were teaching them. When seventy-five recruits do something wrong, you know it's the instructor's fault. The drill instructors' motto was: Excuses are like assholes. We all have one. If we screwed up as a DI, we were expected to accept it and try to make it right.

It was tough telling Scribner when I screwed up. At least the recruits didn't know, at first. But when you started to think the recruits were too stupid to know, that was when you got into trouble.

My first screw up was when I forgot to tell them to keep their thumbs along their trouser seams. Every day was a rehash of the day before, "…get your thumb along the trouser seam when you stand at attention!"

* * *

Halfway through training, the training schedule was changed. Eleven weeks training was cut back to eight weeks, and we were required to make up the extra time on Saturdays and Sundays. Most of the time, that took two or three DIs for each day of the week. My wife and kids became strangers. Sometimes I was gone all day and never saw my kids. I was finally going to get base housing and move my family to the base. Then I would be able to go home for an hour or two during the day.

I had gotten mad at Shirlie, after the shrimping trip, for not bringing my snake skin in from outdoors where I had hung it. All the salt washed off during a rain storm, and the skin dried up. I had thrown it in a closet and forgotten about it. Until, that is, the movers came to move us onto the base. A moving man was cleaning the closet when the snake skin fell out on him. He almost had a heart attack. Shirlie had to throw it in the trunk of the car before the movers would come back in the house.

* * *

The war in Vietnam was picking up. The Marine Corps was building up and wanted more troops. We would put one platoon on the bus and pick up another the same day.

"Try to forget what you just taught the last platoon and start all over again." Yeah, right.

Each time we picked up a new platoon, our company commander would change the DI teams. We had to get used to each other's habits all over again, and with all DIs from different Marine backgrounds, we had more than a few conflicts.

If training would have been run my way, I would have had DIs from the infantry only: Infantry was used to putting up with a lot of bullshit and worked hard.

I bitched at the air-wing DIs nonstop. They were used to screwing off and it showed. But the air-wing Marines thought the same about the infantry Marines. Regardless, we were a team, and the bosses stayed on our asses to make us work together.

Competition to turn out the best platoon was tough. Most of the DIs had worked around each other at one time or another and knew each other's secrets. With all the cutbacks in training, we found ways to get the job done and turn out good Marines. The general never wanted to hear excuses. We got in the habit of teaching full time. Between classes we taught new drill movements. While waiting to go into the mess hall, we reviewed classroom subjects. Time was tight; personal friendships between the DIs almost went by the wayside.

* * *

In March 1966, after working four platoons as a junior DI, I made staff sergeant. I had become a senior DI and would have my own platoon. I'd been in the Marines over thirteen years now,

Parris Island, 1966: Hold that rifle tight!

and this was the first time I had the chance to become a member of the staff NCOs. It was a big change from being a sergeant: staff NCOs have their own club and barracks; staff NCOs stay away from junior NCOs; staff NCOs must have fitness reports, and their careers are controlled at Headquarters Marine Corps in Washington, D.C.

The downside of my promotion was having to pass right by the staff club on my way home. The first few times I got off early, I made it a point to stop and have a few beers. It didn't take long to see my performance change before I stopped.

To make matters worse, the build up in Vietnam was reaching a climax, and the Marine Corps cut boot-camp time once again. Now we were expected to turn out Marines of the same high caliber as before in only six weeks. The recruiters in the towns and cities were pushing to meet quotas. Several of my new recruits came from gangs off the streets of big East Coast cities. We received recruits with little or no schooling. More than a few weren't even sure how they ended up in the Marines.

But train them we did.

One of my first platoons had several Puerto Ricans. They'd been through a language platoon with a Spanish-speaking DI until they learned enough English to attend boot camp. These Puerto Ricans were pretty hot-blooded. One of the new recruits came out of the head, scared to death. He'd watched one of the Puerto Ricans break open the razor blade box. I yelled for everyone in the head to come out. The Puerto Rican was the last one out, and his hands were behind his back. "Drop whatever it is you have there, or I'll kick your ass," I warned him. That was the wrong thing to say; he came at me with both hands full of razor blades. I grabbed a metal ashtray made from shell casings and hit him alongside the head as he came at me. He went down and didn't get up.

During those first few days we *carefully* picked out the crazy ones.

* * *

Some of the senior DIs doubled up with platoons. We sometimes had two platoons going at the same time. One platoon would be in their first week of training, and another would be nearly ready to leave.

A lot of the new DIs were just back from Vietnam and had seen a lot of combat. Just a year or two before that, they had been in boot camp themselves. They knew nothing about the Marine Corps, other than what they had learned in combat, whereas it had been eleven years since the Korean War, and many of the seasoned DIs had never even seen combat. We spent as much time teaching these new DIs about the Marine Corps, as we did the new recruits. Several resented being told anything. Some wore combat decorations: Silver Stars, Bronze Stars and Purple Hearts.

We underwent a change of command and received a new battalion commander. He was a colonel, fresh back from Vietnam, and he was very much in charge. He conducted all information programs passed on to the DIs and held school for us as well. If he disagreed with any part of the training we conducted, it got changed. All training percentiles had to be improved. We had to look good on paper at all costs. DIs worked seven days a week, and the commander was there everyday to make sure we did.

I turned on the lights many mornings to find him sitting in my barracks, checking on my training. He rode a bike and would come up alongside the platoons as we marched, stopping what we were doing to correct us.

One week, Colonel Parrish decided he didn't like the way that we handled our swords and held a special sword-drill school. All DIs drew swords from supply and reported for the drill. By the time I got to supply, they had all been checked out; I was issued an old 1890's cavalry sword. All the DIs laughed as much as I did when I showed up for the drill. Colonel Parrish was pissed that we were having fun for a change, but knew better than to say anything because I looked so damned funny.

* * *

By this time, as a senior DI, I had several platoons under my belt and held one of the top records on base for turning out the best platoons. I had been selected twice as outstanding DI in my battalion. Regardless of my record, I couldn't get passed on to regiment because Colonel Parrish would change his mind, sending another DI instead of me.

Once again, I turned on the barrack lights, and there he was, sitting there waiting for me. He took me out to the hallway and said, "You are the best DI in my battalion, but you don't look impressive enough in your uniform next to other DIs. I want to win the award for my battalion, so I picked Staff Sergeant Terry to go in your place. He looks better than you do."

I could not believe he was telling me this. I had always worked my butt off for the battalion. All I could say was, "Yes, sir."

That same day, I had just marched my platoon to chow when a group of DIs approached me. One asked, "Did you hear what happened to Terry's platoon? The officer of the day walked into the barracks and found one of Terry's junior DIs hanging the recruits by their arms from their bunks. Terry and his whole team of DIs have been relieved of duty for maltreatment."

Platoon 1034, First Recruit Battalion, MCRD Parris Island SC
Sgt. R. Ghilon • SSgt. P.E. Brandon • SSgt. C. Venegas • Graduated 2 Nov 1967

"Oh shit," I said. "The colonel just picked Terry to represent us at regiment, in place of me." Hell, Terry was going to be on the shitlist now. We were still talking about it when I spotted the colonel coming toward us.

He walked up to me and asked, "Have you heard what happened to Terry's team of DIs?"

"Yes, sir."

"I want you to accept my apologies for what I did."

"Well, maybe next time," I said. I still wasn't feeling very forgiving. Shit, his face turned as red as a beet. He left me standing there.

"Goddamn, Brandon, are you crazy?" another DI said.

"I didn't mean I wouldn't accept his apology. I meant maybe next time he would let me go for DI of the quarter."

"Well, I don't think he took it that way."

Sure as shit, he didn't. The CO came to fetch me to the commander's office. As we walked down to battalion, my CO asked me what I had said. "I think he misunderstood me," I explained.

I reported as ordered. Nearly every officer and staff NCO in my company was in his office.

He stood up, slammed his fist on his desk and shouted, "Who the hell do you think you are, turning down my apology in front of the men in my battalion!?"

No matter how hard I tried to talk, he kept right on yelling at me. At last I was able to tell him what I meant. I was ordered to tell every DI in the battalion that I had accepted his apology.

* * *

I was finally going to get the chance to go up against the other DIs on base and see just who really *was* the best. I did well and got good marks. I had been on the island longer than any other DI and had a good record. If I made top DI on base, I also had a chance to make gunny.

By the time I took my platoon out for final drill, I had won every award. I was far ahead of the others in drill; all I had to do was show up and not miss any moves. The three DIs closest to me in points knew it. This happened to be one of those windy days, so I decided to up the sound of my voice so my platoon could hear me. (We were not being graded on our commands.) I raised my voice to make it carry over the wind, and my command came out as, "Righhhhhht face!"

For some reason that pissed Parrish off, and he had the judges take fifty points off my score, because of my voice command. The senior judge informed him that it was not part of the drill, but the colonel won out. I lost top honors by only one point and should have won by forty-nine easy points.

As pissed as I was, on the way back to barracks, I jammed a recruit's rifle into the back of his head. The OD saw me and made a recommendation to the colonel that I be relieved of duty as a maltreatment risk.

I was taken off the drill field and put into the battalion as the training NCO. I made the DIs keep up with their off-duty training and trained all personnel who were not DIs within the battalion. The company had a good deal of trouble with the DIs coming home from Vietnam: they lacked Marine Corps knowledge. I had to set up classes for these men to learn from the ground up, after they'd already served time as a Marine in combat. I was miserable and wanted so badly to get out of the office and back onto the drill field, or else try for orders to Vietnam. After two years as a DI, the only good part of this new duty was having every night off.

* * *

I was called to Colonel Parrish's office after a general inspection. The battalion had rated a ninety-two percent because of our training. I was pleased as punch when he informed me the ratings were a direct result of taking me away from the drill field. He had requested that I be reassigned to B Company. I was to take over a platoon from another DI being relieved for incompetence.

I was on cloud nine as I walked to the barracks to see just how bad this platoon was. My euphoria didn't last long, though. I almost shit when I discovered that, in their second week of training, they could barely march. I asked the CO for two days of drill time to straighten them out. I got one.

During outside drills, these jackasses

Parris Island, SC, 1965

moved in formation, trying to avoid the sand fleas. *Damn! What a bunch of maggots.* The only thing to do was put them in the sandpit and make them crawl around until they were covered with sweat, then run them at full steam back to the barracks and have them pack up their gear. Outside, gear and all, I herded them around the company area until gear was strung out all over the area. I switched them around between squads, then took them back to the barracks.

"If you don't straighten your asses out in one day, you'll all be set back two weeks in training," I threatened.

I and my DI stayed on their asses all day and all night. By the end of that week, they didn't know if they were coming or going. They had never been pushed or shoved by their previous DI, and thought I was damn near going to kill them. I was.

At the beginning of my little tirade, my company officers looked the other way. After a couple of days, I was told to ease up, before I had the recruits trying to get off the island on their own, instead of waiting for orders to Vietnam.

* * *

"You are the worst part of human shit I have ever seen. If you think I am going to make Marines out of you, you're fucking crazy. Good men are dying in Vietnam, and you fucking scum want a free ride in this country. You'll have to prove to me that you are NOT the lowest kind of shit in the world. If I have to, I'll run every fucking one of you into the swamp and drown you before I will let you go into my Marine Corps. I'll ride your asses every minute of the day. If you don't have the guts to take it, you better come see me, because if I catch you fucking off, I will kick the shit out of you."

I gave them one hour to come talk to me alone. If they could prove to me that the Marines were not good for them, I just might let them go. And they came, one at a time, for the whole hour, crying and sobbing about why they wanted out.

I always had more reasons for them to stay than they had for leaving. I told them if they were so chickenshit that they were going try to leave the island, they better do it tonight while the tide was low. The rest of the time the water was too swift, and they would drown.

I had a desk-sized metal file cabinet sitting in the comer of my office. I had removed the screws from it. One of my scare tactics was to slam my fist into it and watch it scare the shit out of them when the cabinet flew apart. It usually showed them they were smart to be a lot more afraid of me than of escaping the Marine Corps.

At lights out, I went outside and waited under the steps. Down the steps came two recruits with their laundry bags. I grabbed them, threw them down, screamed at them, choked them and told them I'd throw them to the alligators. I called the military police and took them back inside the barracks where the other recruits could hear and see the MPs. The police did a good job on them. The two greenhorns thought for sure they were going to prison.

By noon the next day, you would have thought I had the best platoon on the base. They were too afraid to move, unless I told them to. I had to correct a lot of what they had already been taught, but they were ready to do anything I said.

The new DIs, who had never seen a platoon go bad, could not believe how fast mine turned around. Privately, I was the only one who knew this was the first platoon I had ever had to straighten out. I had seen other DIs try their hardest to get a platoon back in training after discipline problems, so I had some thoughts on what to do. Fear of the unknown was best.

* * *

The drill field was tough on Shirlie and the kids. I only saw them once or twice a week. I left the house before dawn and got home after midnight. Sometimes, Shirlie would come down to the drill field and watch me work. Most of the time, I only had time to wave.

Parris Island, SC

My hard work and long hours paid off, though. I made it again to the regiment and went up against the best DIs from the two other battalions. Again, I didn't get picked; my colonel screwed me over. Afterward, I was told by one of the officers on the board that I was the best of the three DIs, but Colonel Parrish had almost demanded that they vote me out. It cost me another chance to make gunny and be the best DI on base.

* * *

The war in Vietnam was going crazy. The commanding general of the 3rd Marine Division had been shot down in a helicopter and killed. Our general at Parris Island was going to take over the 3rd Division.

I finally received a call from regiment; I was selected to make gunny. The regiment commander wanted to see me.

He said, "I heard you know how to bronze boots and hats. Would you bronze one for the general before he leaves?"

"I will, if you will ask the general if I can go with him to Vietnam."

By the Friday, before the general left, I still hadn't heard whether or not he was going to take me with him. A going-away dinner was being given for him, and all staff and officers were invited.

December 1967

At the end of the general's speech, he asked, "Is Staff Sergeant Brandon here?"

I stood up and said, "Yes, sir."

"Start packing your seabag." Then he walked out.

I had my orders for combat duty, after three long years on the island.

* * *

We only had a week to check out, and Shirlie was sick with the flu. The battalion sergeant major came to the house and told me Parrish wanted to see me before I left. I wasn't about to kiss this colonel's ass one more time before I left.

"I'm already checked out, and we are leaving. Tell the colonel I will write him from Vietnam," I told the sergeant major.

The sergeant major said, "Brandon, don't make me give you an order."

"Shit, he screwed me out of gunny and DI of the year. I'm on the list for gunny now, so what the hell can he do to me now, cancel my orders?"

"Okay, Brandon. You made me do this. The order is be at battalion headquarters at 0900 tomorrow morning. Maybe he wants to do something *for* you," he smirked.

Damn, the next morning Shirlie was sicker than a dog. I told her I would see the colonel by myself, then we could leave.

Parrish took me to base headquarters with him to see the general. I expected him to take away my orders any minute. Instead, I was given a General's Mass, an award for outstanding performance. All the commanding officers were there. After the ceremony, the general asked everyone to leave except me. He told me to sit down. He wanted to talk to me man-to-man.

"You are only one of several hundred of the best Marines in the Marine Corps. You stand above almost all the base's DIs. You have an outstanding record, have spent almost three years here and are leaving without one mark on that record. What was your secret?"

I was dumbfounded that the general, a man of such rank, was asking me my secret.

"Sir, I put my hands on the recruits several times and may have hurt one or two of them, but not enough that it kept them from being Marines in the long run. I never asked them to do something I wouldn't or couldn't do; but most of all, I never forgot that I was once a private."

Colonel Parrish was still waiting outside when I came out. "Did the general say anything about me?" he asked.

"No, sir. He just wanted to know about *me*."

As I put my hand out to say good-bye, he asked me to go back to the battalion with him one more time. He had called in several officers and made an announcement: "I have made several bad judgments about Brandon and caused a lot of hardship. If ever there was a Marine who was misjudged or screwed over it was Brandon, and I am sorry."

"Thank you, sir," I said. I shook the man's hand and left.

* * *

During my last days on the base, I thought a lot about my three years at Parris Island. I didn't know how the hell I got out of there with my stripes.

I remembered the platoon that did well until they got to the rifle range. After that, I had trouble with them all the time. They screwed up constantly, and I could never find out why. It turned out to be the fault of a junior DI who charged them a dollar each time they missed a shot. The junior DI kept the money for himself.

I decided to visit old Staff Sergeant Day, this junior DI's supervisor, and see how their platoon was doing. Same old story; they did fine until after the rifle range, then they started screwing up.

"Call in your platoon squad leaders," I told him, "and ask them how much money a recruit has to have to pay for missing a shot on the targets." Turned out he was still charging everyone a dollar a miss and keeping the money.

Well, we beat the shit out of this kid and made him tell the company commander why he'd gotten the shit beat out of him. He was busted to corporal and relieved from the field. And getting ready to ship overseas didn't keep my ass from getting chewed out, too.

* * *

We trapped an alligator one day behind the firing range and tied it up in one of the target sheds. It was darker than hell in those sheds. We sent recruits inside to sweep the place out, then stood outside the door, watching to see what they would do when they got close to the alligator. All the 'gator ever did was open its mouth and hiss, but the poor recruits usually shit all over themselves trying to get out of the shed.

Qualifying Day, Parris Island, 1968:
Morine, Drop 24; Olivar, Drop 8
"Blew the Red Streamer!" Ha Ha!

* * *

One of my recruits had a bad foot and was always falling out of formation. He wanted out of the Marines bad and made no bones about letting me know it. He came back from sick bay one day, saying the doctor claimed he was unfit for military duty and was to be discharged. He had this big shit-eating grin on his face when he handed me the paper. I called him a quitter, told him he was yellow, and that I was going to spray a yellow streak up his back. I found a yellow can of paint, making sure he saw me with it and had him turn his back to me. I switched the paint for a can of bug spray, sprayed it up his back and kicked him out of the platoon.

The next day, at clothing sales, a junior DI told the others I had sprayed the guy yellow. The company series officer overheard the story. He came over and relieved me of my platoon for hazing the recruits.

"Sir," I told him, "we were just bullshitting the man. I know better than to do something like that."

Still, I was told to report back to be investigated. On the way, I stopped at the first phone I could get to and called the sergeant in charge of discharging recruits. I told him to warn the yellow-bellied recruit that, if he claimed anything of the sort had happened, I'd make sure he would have to stay on the island during the several weeks in which I was being investigated.

When the series officer questioned the recruit, he of course denied it ever happened. He said that I had only *told* him I *should* do it. The lieutenant was pissed because he thought that I had somehow scared the recruit into lying for me. He didn't know or believe that I had never actually sprayed the man with yellow paint. Lieutenant Ott spent a lot of sleepless nights thinking of ways to catch me screwing off. Shortly thereafter, he thought he saw his chance.

For some time, as a joke, I had always worn a small feather in my DI hat; most everyone on the island knew about it. I still wore that small feather in my DI hat for laughs. "Chief" I was called, in part because of the feather, and partly because I was part Indian. My platoon had just won final drill, and I stood in front of them. Lieutenant Ott saw the feather in my hat and snatched my hat off the top of my head.

"What the hell is that feather doing in your hat?"

"It's my good luck feather, given to me by the chief of the Sioux tribe to protect me, sir," I lied. *Better Ott in trouble, than me,* I thought.

The colonel, coming to hand me the drill award, asked, "Lieutenant Ott,

Parris Island, SC:
An Honor Man from one of my platoons

why are you carrying Sergeant Brandon's hat?"

"Well, sir, he has a feather in his hat."

"Yes, I know that. Everyone does. Brandon, how long have you owned that feather?"

"A very long time, sir."

The sergeant major almost bit a hole in his lip to keep from laughing. Lieutenant Ott gave back my hat, feather and all.

* * *

The Marine Corps' birthday was always the best of times. Most of the time we got good and drunk, but that year the next day was Veteran's Day. Veteran's Day was always celebrated with a parade, and most of the time, we had to make the floats for the parades ourselves.

My last Marine Corps' ball, stateside, fell in the same month I was to leave. We planned a staff NCO parade. I was chosen to be the adjutant and call all the commands. The final command, PASS IN REVIEW, sounds like PISS IN YOUR SHOE. We always joked around about it and did again that night at the ball. Someone dared me to say "piss in your shoe" at the parade the next day.

Parade day was rainy and windy.

Hell, I can pull this off, I told myself. With my back to the bleachers, I thought no one would hear me. Damn, I did good. I didn't miss a move. I turned around to report, "Sir, the parade is formed."

Said the commander of the troops, "PASS IN REVIEW!"

I did my about-face, marched to my spot and roared, "PISS IN YOUR SHOE." The troops passed in review, looking very good.

Out came the colonel, and said, "A very good parade, Sergeant Brandon, but your last command sounded like 'piss in your shoe.'"

I just smiled and said, "Thank you, sir."

The asshole knew exactly what I had said.

Me and Jay Robert back in boot camp:
"Smile when you say that!"

Chapter 22
Vietnam

I had been driving from Parris Island for almost two days straight. We were somewhere in Texas, on one of those highways that is as straight as a pin for hundreds of miles. It was three or four o'clock in the morning, and Shirlie and the kids were sleeping.

I had been watching a pair of taillights up ahead, and my eyes played games with me. The lights shot off into the sky, or looked like they did. I slammed on the brakes. Over the backseat tumbled the kids and the dog. There we were, all piled in the front seat.

I pulled over and slept for a while but started out again as soon as it got light.

We were just ahead of a storm most of the way through Mississippi and barely missed a tornado. We saw it in the distance several times. Shirlie's flu was getting a little better, but she could hardly talk. We stopped at a little town in Arizona and stayed overnight in a motel room. There was only one bed, but we didn't care. All five of us piled in to sleep, and the dog chased cockroaches under the bed all night.

We made it as far as Redding, California by the fourth day and headed into Oregon early the next day, making it to Shirlie's parents' place. It had been almost five years since we had seen them. My parents had moved to Salem, so I left Shirlie and the kids while I went to visit them.

Mom was not happy to hear I was on my way to Vietnam.

* * *

The next day Shirlie and I looked everywhere to find a place to rent before I left. We ended up in McMinnville, a town only twenty or so miles from Salem in one direction and Grand Ronde, my home town, in the other. All we could find was one old but well-maintained house for sale. Shirlie and I went the next morning to see the owner, a dance teacher, who still taught lessons in the basement of the house.

I was in uniform, and as soon as she saw me, she said. "Oh, I love Marines! I was in Hawaii when the Japanese bombed during World War II. The Marines

January 1968:
Jay Robert in Quang Tri, Vietnam

August 2002: Jay Robert at home in
Pennsylvania with his new (old) ride.

took good care of me and helped me get back to the States."

We arranged to rent the house until a GI loan could be secured. The real estate agent helped Shirlie apply for my loan, as I was leaving in four days. The owner was good enough to take our rent money as the down payment.

I couldn't believe it. A real home. We had lived in some real shacks since we were married almost twelve years earlier. Our household things arrived on a Monday, and I was to leave on a Wednesday. Shirlie hurt her back lifting things and was barely able to walk. She wouldn't be able to take me to the airport to see me off.

Wednesday came, and I kissed Shirlie goodbye. She was lying on the couch with tears in her eyes. "Please Gene, be careful. You know how gung-ho you get sometimes," she said.

I didn't get to say good-bye to the kids: they were already enrolled in the local school. Anyway, they were used to me leaving all the time.

At the airport, Dad said, "Take care of yourself. You have a family who needs you around."

"Dad, I'm a sergeant now. I won't have to be in the front lines. I'm on the list for gunnery sergeant, so I should have an easy job of it." Then I laughed.

It was December 1967.

* * *

It took my plane only an hour to get to San Francisco. A bus took us to Travis Air Force Base. I checked in with the Marine Corps' desk and got a ride to the barracks.

Well, one good thing, the air force sergeant's club is right next door.

The club was packed. There were men from every branch of the military: Navy, Army, Marines and plenty of Air Force.

A few Marines at a table waved me over. "Are you coming or going?" a staff sergeant asked me.

"I'm just going."

"I'm going back for my second time. I've been getting ready by staying on a running drunk for the last month," he said.

"How long will we be here before we fly out?" I asked.

"Hell, as long as you want to be, if you miss your flight. They just put you on the next one. Just check in at flight control by 0800 hours tomorrow morning."

Shit, I'm going tomorrow. The sooner I left, the sooner I'd get back.

* * *

The same staff sergeant was on the desk the next morning, but my name was not on the list to go.

"How long before I get on a flight?" I asked.

"In a day or so," he said.

"How about getting my ass out of here sooner than that?"

"Hell, you'll just be going to wait in Okinawa. Things are backed up all over with troops coming and going."

I said, "Get me to Okinawa, and let me worry from there." I had my reasons for getting my tour started. I had seventeen years in by that time and was due to ship over in four months. I wanted to be overseas when I did, so it would be tax-free.

"Go, get your gear," he said. "Someone always misses their flight. I will put you on standby." I had no more than got my gear inside and sat down when my name was called.

"You leave at 1400 hours on Continental Air Lines, the bird with the golden tail." I have no idea why I remember the part about the "bird with the golden tail." I guess certain memories just kick in sometimes.

The staff sergeant was also in line to leave. He had a good-looking woman on his arm. He was still drunk.

"Hey buddy," he called to me. "Come meet my girl. She's here to see me off."

Damn, she was built like a brick shithouse.

"I think I'll go AWOL and stay here the rest of my life," he said. I couldn't figure out why he signed up for another tour, if he dreaded it so much.

* * *

The plane had just come in from El Toro Marine Air Base and was full of young Marines on their way to Vietnam.

We landed in Hawaii to refuel. The differences between 1953 and 1969 were amazing. In 1953, I had been on a troopship that took fourteen days to get there, and I was seasick most of the way. The airport was like walking into a wonderland of palm trees and fish ponds. I wished I could stay a few days.

We landed in Okinawa in the middle of the night, on the same day we left. Crossing the International Date Line had cost us a day.

I sat in the front of a 6x6 truck with the driver and headed for Camp Hanson, wherever that was. The driver told me that the base was a madhouse, and there were more damn troops waiting to go to Vietnam than they had flights for. He said, "There is extra training because we are changing to a new rifle. The outgoing troops have never fired it."

I checked in and had my orders stamped. The clerk said, "Go find a bunk in the staff barracks. There is a gook in the supply room all night to issue bedding."

Goddamn, the barrack area was a pigpen. It smelled of stale booze and men sat around drinking and playing cards. It was four o'clock in the morning. *Don't these assholes sleep?* I woke up at 0900, and they were still playing cards and drinking. I asked when chow closed down and was told "never." The mess hall was open twenty-four hours a day, or I could go to the staff club for chow.

God, what a mess. There were troops everywhere, and no one was in charge. I sat with a gunny and asked him how things were going. He was just back from Vietnam and waiting for a flight stateside.

"I don't know, and I don't give a fuck. All I want is to get out of here," he said.

I went back to clean up the area near my bunk. A staff sergeant lying on his bunk muttered, "You're wasting your time. No one here gives a shit."

"I can't believe this is a staff barrack."

"We have staff here from every command in the Marine Corps. Those fucking air wingers are the worst. Two years in the Marine Corps, and they're staff sergeants with a chest full of ribbons, and they don't know shit…and don't care."

I wanted to see if the sergeant major might be able to straighten things out.

Instead, he asked if I wanted to go to Camp Swabb and help train troops in the field.

"I'm on orders to Vietnam."

"You're not getting out of here for a few weeks, so if you want to get away from all the transients in the barracks, you can go up to Swabb."

* * *

Camp Swabb was a lot cleaner and did not have as many staff, so we trained almost all day. I was always looking for something to do.

"I'm on the list for gunny and would sure like to be in Vietnam before I ship over," I mentioned to the first sergeant.

"They send out a special plane once a week. I'll try to get you on."

In the barracks, more staff sergeants had arrived on their way to Vietnam. They were scheduled to be there one week before leaving. None had ever seen the M-16 rifle.

I can't believe the Marine Corps could get so screwed up in such a short while. Maybe I spent too much time on Parris Island and forgot that things are not all cut-and-dried.

My name was put on the list with the new group of staff sergeants going to Vietnam. I was going to get over there somehow before the end of the year.

We finally received orders to leave the next morning. We would be going on a mail-run C-130 Hercules transport plane, and a lot of staff officers would go with us. Most of us had not yet been to Vietnam, but some of the officers bragged about having been over several times. I learned later that those assholes went to Vietnam at the end of each month and returned stateside after the first of the following month, in order to draw combat pay for both months.

* * *

We landed in Da Nang. Most of the staff went to 2nd Battalion, 4th Marines, way up north someplace, on the float. We stayed in Da Nang until we could get transportation. In supply, we were issued brand new M-16 rifles, still in the bag.

Shit, these guys will give you anything you want!

There were so many airplanes coming in and out that it was worse than the San Diego Airport. Half the time the jet noise was so loud you couldn't hear a damn thing.

Right after chow, I heard my first warning siren. Everyone was running for cover. I thought the sound was jets passing overhead. Then I realized the truth. *Shit! It's incoming rocket rounds, and they are hitting all over the place. Damn!* We dove for cover. I was scared shitless. *What happens now? Are the gooks coming? Where are the lines? Shit, what the hell did I get into?*

* * *

I was still shaking in my boots when an officer asked who was in charge. It didn't seem anyone had been put in charge, so I told him I was the senior sergeant.

"Get all the troops on the trucks and get to the other side of the base. Stand guard for those companies that are short-handed."

It was almost dark by the time we got where we were needed. I asked to fire our rifles to make sure they were okay. It was the first time I ever had a new rifle right out of the bag. Most of my others were nearly worn out.

Just after dark the shit hit the fan. Rocket rounds came in every ten minutes. It was all we could do to lie there and hope the missiles didn't land on top of us. We tried to dig holes, but the ground was like rock. We just lay there and took our chances.

God, did I step in shit this time.

* * *

I was called to a command bunker.

"Get your troops onto a truck. There is a battalion being overrun on the other side of the airfield, and they need replacements."

Oh God, I thought.

It was so dark you couldn't see your hand in front of your face. The damn trucks sure opened it up driving down the road, and where the hell we were headed, I had no idea. I didn't have a clue about what was happening or what kind of troops I had with me.

At our destination (I still didn't know where we were), the officer in charge said, We need troops on three sides of the base."

I estimated there were about forty of us. By the time we got in place, things had quieted down a little, but rockets continued to come in all night. I was told to watch for a heavy hit at first light.

Damn, I was cold. My legs were cramped and I couldn't move. I thought, sure as shit, all hell would break open, but nothing happened.

Near dawn, when it was light enough to see where I was, I almost shit. We were only ten yards from the front lines, with absolutely no protection of any kind. Shit, the gooks could have come in right on top of us and wiped us out on our first day in Vietnam. I knew my men weren't line troops, but they *were* Marines. The first rule is: always cover your ass. *How fucking dumb.* I was pissed.

* * *

I returned to the warehouse to talk with the security officer in charge. The first man I saw was a skinny second lieutenant.

"Hey, Brandon, how are you," he asked. The blank look on my face prompted him to go on. "Sergeant Willie. I was at Parris Island on the drill field."

Hell, I had completely forgotten him. The Marine Corps had made a whole shitpot of lieutenants in 1966. Every sergeant and staff sergeant who could meet the requirements made officer. I thought: *Hell, one day they'll all be officers.* I didn't have a high school or college diploma, so I would stay a sergeant.

"How long have you been here?"

"Shit, just overnight," I said. "I'm still not sure what the heck is happening. How about you?"

"About two months. I'm a communication officer with the Seventh."

Communications? Damn, are these guys screwed up or what?

In not so many words, I told Willie how pissed I was at where we had spent the night and how slack things around there were. He agreed. It seemed the enemy never came that far north, but now a lot of men were getting killed in North Vietnam's latest push.

"We are short-handed and don't have enough troops to guard the lines," he told me.

What pissed me off even more was the thought of troops held up in Okinawa and how I'd kissed ass just to get over to Vietnam.

* * *

I took the troops on orders and loaded them on the trucks to head back to Da Nang. I was determined to get set someplace before nightfall. That, or leave and join up with my own outfit. I'd had the shit scared out of me the night before.

I met another first sergeant from Parris Island. He was on his way back to the States.

"Do you know what the heck is going on?" I asked him. "This is my second day trying to find transportation up north to my battalion. It seems like they're keeping us here for guard duty as long as they can. That's fine, If I could just get into command center, so I know what's happening. I have a bunch of troops under me and no place to go."

He came with me to talk to the officer in charge of the transit area. We asked if we were to stay or be assigned to a company. We had to at least know what was going on.

"Load up your troops. There's a ship coming in from up north that will take all the troops headed for the Fourth Marines."

We boarded riverboats that looked like old landing crafts off a troopship. The crafts ferried us to a ship out in the harbor. There were already a few hundred troops on board, and with forty more of us, we were packed like rats. There was no place to lie down and too many troops for the ship's mess hall to feed. We ate C rations. *I don't know what the hell to think. I have never seen the Marine Corps so screwed up.* I didn't realize it then, but war screws up everything.

We stayed on the ship all that day. After dark, the troops headed for the 2nd Battalion. Fourth Marines reported to the helicopter pad. The landing pad was only big enough for one helicopter; one bird had room for seven men. At that rate it took us all night to get unloaded.

I made it onto the helicopter about midnight. It was darker than hell, and we had to feel our way up the ship to the pad.

Shit, I hope they don't drop us off out in the middle of a combat zone. We had no ammo and couldn't do shit. I only had two magazines: forty or so rounds.

All I could see below us was water. I felt the bird descending, but there was nothing below us to land on. I didn't even know who was in the helicopter with me. We set down on another ship, an aircraft carrier. Someone flashed a red flashlight at us. *Well, at least we aren't out in the bush.* We were led to the hanger deck below and told that we could crash there for the night and check in first thing in the morning.

I started looking around the ship, hoping to find someone I knew. I spotted some Marines working on a helicopter and went over to talk. I asked, "Where are we?"

"Just off the coast of Dong Ha, the Third Marine headquarters."

"Do you know what the Fourth Marine operations are doing?" All they knew was that 4th Marine was on the float and supporting the operations. I was told to find the gunny in the shop to find out whatever I could about my battalion.

Gunny McCullium just so happened to have gone through boot camp at the same time I had.

The last time I saw you, up at Camp Pendleton, a snake bit you on the hand," I reminded him. We rehashed old times for a while, then he asked if this was my first tour in Vietnam.

"Yeah, I just left Parris Island. I was on the drill field for almost three years."

"Hell, this is my third tour over here. I'm a maintenance chief with helicopters. We work our asses off, but we're safe most of the time. Not like you grunts. You guys are in the shit all the time. If I were you, I'd get the hell out. The shit has been hitting the fan up here. We've been in a hell of a fight now for over three months. Lost a lot of troops and we're not getting any replacements."

I still didn't understand what was happening and said, "There are troops all over Okinawa just sitting on their asses."

* * *

I took off to look for a bunk. I'd been kicked around for over a week and still hadn't seen one.

"Hell, go into the chief's quarters and crawl into one of the empty bunks. Just tell them you're a gunny."

Boy, it was nice and warm in the chief's quarters. I got into the first bunk I came to and didn't even take my clothes off. And then it hit me: *Oh God, I have a whole year of this shit ahead of me.* All of a sudden, a chest full of ribbons didn't sound like such a good idea. I hoped things would get better than my first week.

* * *

I slept like a log. With all the racket around me, I still didn't hear a sound all night.

In the morning I got up, washed my face and went up to the hangar deck. Some helicopters were being moved to a ramp which lifted them to the flight deck. After looking around, I noticed some troops that looked like they were heading out. Damn, I felt like a stranger. This was a whole new Marine Corps for me, and I knew I had better get smart fast. *Maybe I should have stayed on Okinawa for a while and done some training there,* was my first smart thought.

I had no gear, only what came with my new rifle. I had a few uniforms, but no field gear. I asked the supply man of Foxtrot Company where to check in. He took me to his office area. "These guys will show you around."

"Are you assigned to our company?" a corporal asked me.

"I'm not sure. Are you short of staff?

"We only have two staff sergeants, a first sergeant and four lieutenants."

"Do you have a gunny?" I asked.

"Nope, we don't have one. I think the first sergeant is doing double duty. We don't have an XO either." We decided that he would try to get me into his company. I learned the companies were spread all over: some in the field, some in Dong Ha, and the offices were on the ships.

"How many ships are we on?"

"Four. Some of our troops are over on the *USS Cleveland.*"

The *Cleveland* also had a helicopter pad on it. Supplies and troops stayed on the ships. The helicopters flew back and forth every day.

* * *

"Goddamn! How the hell do you keep up with all the troops? Must drive you guys nuts trying to find someone."

"That's the first sergeant's job. Get everyone he can to the field. We're short-handed as hell out there. The only troops allowed in the rear are those who have been wounded at least once."

"You're kidding!" I couldn't believe what I was hearing. "That's the only way they are relieved of duty; they have to be wounded? That's a division order?"

"Yep. If you're wounded, you can't be on the front lines; two times wounded, and they ship you out of the country."

"Are there many troops wounded, now?" I asked.

"In the battalion there are several a day, and a lot of the troops are hurt from other injuries. Seven guys in our company were bitten by rats and had to come in for rabies shots. The shots take seven days, and most of the guys get sick for a week afterward."

* * *

I was assigned to Foxtrot Company. "Because you are on the list and selected for gunnery sergeant, you are now the company gunny." At last! I was a gunny! I was introduced to my first sergeant, Top Duchateau. He was glad to have help come along.

I tagged along with Duchateau for awhile, then he and I jumped a helicopter and boarded the *Cleveland*. Top needed his field gear because we were headed into the field the next day. It only took us a few minutes by helicopter to go from ship to ship.

"Jeez, these helicopters get around fast."

"Yes," he said. "Sometimes that's good, and sometimes it's bad. When the shit hits the fan, they set you down in a hot spot too fast, and we lose too many troops. I like coming in on a ship. It's a little slower, but you can feel your way in."

Top had been in the Marines too goddamn long. He had been a first sergeant in Iwo Jima in 1945. He felt he was getting too old to be humping with the young kids just coming out.

"God, three fucking wars is enough for one man." Then he laughed like hell. "Maybe we should stay on the ship an extra day or two and drink this bottle of *gru-vas-aia.*" Top enlightened me as to his idea of the smoothest drink in the world: you poured a little in a glass and let the heat of your hand warm it. Just slosh it around in the glass and let it roll over the tongue. "It will find its way to your gut on its own," he assured me.

Top "Duke" Duchateau, my first Sergeant. One mean Frenchman, and one hell of a Sergeant.

I agreed that I could use a drink to put me to sleep. I had only slept one night since arriving in Vietnam. I was told to get used to that.

Top took this bottle from his foot locker and opened a small box holding four half-moon-shaped glasses.

"Now, goddamn it, Brandon, pay attention. You don't drink it like whiskey." Holding the glass between his two middle fingers, he poured a small amount into it. Then he took small drink, kissed the end of his fingers and said something in French. "Next to kissing a pussy, this is the best it gets."

He poured me a small drink and I made sure I did it right. Damn, it *was* smooth and burned all the way down. We had several more drinks. I drank a little too fast, and Top said, "Goddamn, Brandon! We don't have a supply truck with that stuff. This might be our last drink for weeks."

* * *

First Sergeant Duchateau said, "Be ready to board a helicopter by 0900. We are going into the company."

We loaded up right on time. We were over land a few minutes later. I saw camp off about a mile. Then Top pointed and gave me a thumbs up; it looked like that was where we were headed. I damn near fell out of my seat as the helicopter banked hard. It scared the shit out of me.

I looked over at Top and saw the worried look on his face. I leaned over and yelled, "What's wrong?"

"They're getting hit with rockets and we're in the firing zone."

Down we went again. Camp Carrol looked different on the ground than it did from the air. It was a lot bigger. We landed and everyone ran for trenches and bunkers. Before we made it that far, the helicopters were up and gone. Man, I was scared shitless.

Top looked at me and said, "Take your pack off. It looks like we're here for a while. Mr. Charles is dumping rockets on us."

"Mr. Charles?" I asked.

"The damn NVA. We've been under rocket attack now for over four weeks. It never stops."

We were only seven miles from our company, but we had to wait for the trucks and engineers to make it through. The roads had to be checked each day for land mines.

My company was just down the road, near a river. Their job had been keeping the roads in the area open. A jeep and four trucks finally arrived for us. Top and I rode with another gunny in the jeep.

It would probably be a lot safer in the back of one of those trucks, I thought, *but here goes. Top's been around a lot longer than I have.*

* * *

"This is home, Brandon."

One big tent, three sandbag bunkers and not many troops. "Are they out on an operation?" I asked.

"This is it. We only have eighty men in the field."

Damn, did I look like the new guy! My new uniforms, clean-shaven face and hair cut stood out like a sore thumb. Everyone had at least a week's growth of whiskers, mustaches and dirty jungle uniforms. Their eyes were sunk back in their faces from lack of sleep.

"Lieutenant Gavlick, this is Gunny Brandon—or soon to be," Top said. "He's just waiting for his number to come up."

The lieutenant had a southern or Texas accent, I couldn't tell from where. He had beans or tomato sauce in the mustache hanging down over his lip.

"Glad to have you," he said.

Later, I met some of the staff: Lieutenant Wainwright. Staff Sergeant Lang, Lieutenant Cecil and Sergeant Rock.

"What the fuck is your name, Rock?" Gavlick asked and started laughing. Everyone else did, too. I didn't know the joke yet. "We're kind of on standby now, sending out small patrols, making sure Mr. Charles doesn't fuck with us. Lang will show you around and what our area of operation is."

Lang said, "Our staff sergeant is acting gunny; he is scared of everything. Now that you're here, he'll go back and be a platoon sergeant."

The troops were pissed and tired. They'd been on the float for two months and had never been back on the ships. They were strung out all over the northern area. Lang only had nineteen men in his platoon.

He pointed to the side of a hill, "And my nineteen men have to cover that whole fucking hill. If we don't get our ass kicked here, we'll be damn lucky."

I told Lang about all the troops still back in Okinawa.

"I don't know. We do the best with what we got," Lang said.

"Well, I'll do my job—just give me a few days to find out what the hell it is."

* * *

The first thing I found out was how badly the troops took care of themselves. No one knew much about our operation and didn't seem to give a shit. They lived one day at a time. I found Marines with sores on their bodies, boots worn out and no socks. The platoon area was a mess. There were full C ration cans scattered all over the place. The platoon commander was an ex-corporal, and a corporal acted as the platoon sergeant. I wasn't sure if it was a morale problem, or if the men just didn't give a shit, I was damn sure going to find out.

They had also perfected the art of "looking busy": going through the motions of appearing to be doing something useful.

One PFC's magazines were dirty. "What are the dark, chalky spots on your face and hands?" I asked him. I thought something from the dirty metal of the magazine had rubbed off on his skin. He just kept looking at me. I again asked, "What are those black spots?"

"I don't know, Gunny. Most of the troops have them."

"Get your gear. Let's go ask the corpsman what the hell that shit is all over you."

The corpsman helped me check the man's marks. They struck me as big scabs from healed sores, but were black instead of dark red. I poured peroxide on one or two of them. After the peroxide foamed for a while, I wiped at the spots. Shit, that's exactly what they were. The damn sores were so dirty that you couldn't tell what they were.

"When was the last time you had a shower or tried to wash up?" I asked.

"I don't know."

"Why don't you go down to the creek and wash up?"

"I don't know."

"Damn, Doc! How come you haven't said something about this to someone? This is bullshit. The troops are too fucking lazy to keep themselves clean. I know this shit of living in the field is hard. But we have a damn creek right in our area."

I asked for a staff meeting where I raised hell about the troops. I made it clear that we had access to clean clothes, soap and towels, and we officers were here, in part, to make sure the men fucking well used them! "Goddamn it, make the troops clean up. If they feel and look like shit, then that's the way they are going to act."

All the long hair and beards were cut. It didn't matter how bad the haircuts turned out, and they all looked like shit to begin with. Then the men were sent to the creek, clothes and all, to clean up.

I sent only half the platoon at a time—even though there was plenty of room under the bridge for everyone—and built a fire so the men wouldn't bitch about the cold water. The troops had been spread out all over the area and hadn't seen each other in weeks. We watched them raise hell: playing horse in the water, trying to drown each other.

* * *

When I first came across the man with the black scabs, I found his rifle magazine filthy and the springs rusted. I was determined to do something about it. I asked more questions about their gear. There were a number of troops who didn't know shit about the new hand grenades.

"Get your troops some cleaning gear and get those fucking weapons cleaned. I'm going to hold some schooling on the new grenades," I said. "Bring your gas masks."

I thought I'd have them throw a few grenades off the point, maybe set off a claymore or two: anything to get the troops' heads out of their asses. I took the men to a point with only one way back to camp…past me.

I started my lessons by pulling the pin from a teargas grenade and dropping it smack-dab in the middle of them. Only three or four had gas masks that worked. The rest fell all over each other, hacking their lungs out while the air cleared. It worked, most of them laughed.

"Well, I can see you're not fucking Boy Scouts: you're not prepared. I know you guys have been in the shit, and I'm sure we'll be there again. But I would rather be in shit and be ready. You assholes know you're not ready.

"You wouldn't be calling those damned gooks 'Mr. Charles,' if you didn't respect them. I'm your gunny, and it's my job to look out for you. I'm the poor son of a bitch between you and the officers. I'll keep them off your ass, if you keep them off my mine. They are not going to screw with you,

Local villagers working in the fields

if you don't give them reasons to. We're here because the Marine Corps put us here. So get off your asses and do what we are here for.

"I have a wife and three kids back in the States, and to protect them, I would damn sure rather fight the enemy over here than in my back yard. Our enemy is close to his home, and he's going to fight a little harder than we are because of it.

"When is the last time you have been together for a class, or just a bull session?"

They looked at each other. Three or four answered, "Never."

* * *

The new float commander was a full colonel and really had his shit together. I knew Colonel Meyers from Camp LeJeune, North Carolina. His brother was a colonel in division headquarters, so I thought that he would help us get the supplies we needed.

I told the men I was working on getting them some in-country R and R; that maybe we could send five guys a week back for showers and sleep.

"But, if you assholes don't come back, I'll come find you," I added in my best threatening voice.

To myself I said: *I hope the lieutenant buys it.* I was sure the new colonel would.

Colonel Meyers and our battalion commander, Colonel Weise, came with their staff to inspect our lines. Colonel Weise introduced the staff and officers.

Colonel Meyers put in a good word for me, saying, "I know Sergeant Brandon; he took good care of me in Camp LeJeune. I know he's going to do a good job here. He's a twenty-four-hour-a-day Marine." Then he asked, "Can we get up over the hill to look across the rock pile?"

"I'll go," I said. "I know a short cut." Like shit I did. I only knew one way, but I wanted to see if I could get new gear for the troops.

"Hell, we should be safe with a gunny walking point."

This was only my second trip up the hill, and I hoped like hell I wouldn't screw up. However, Lang marked his trails very well. The trail was steep as hell, and I took my time: Mr. Charles wasn't dumb enough to screw with us in the middle of the day.

The colonel talked to the troops for a while, then I loaned him my field glasses to look over the rock pile.

He said, "There sure has been some fighting going on over there. I think that's where most of the troops up north are coming through. Now, what's on your mind, Gunny?" Damn, he called my cards right off the bat.

"We just need some supplies, sir. Mostly new jungle gear. The trouble with being out on the float is that we're under everyone else's command, and they seem to forget about us."

I also asked if we could send two of the troops to the rear, to sick bay. I wanted those sores cleaned up and hoped the men would bring back whatever they used, so we could clean up the rest of the men.

"I want them back in two days," he said.

Hot damn!

* * *

I took the troops out on the point to fire rockets, and every one of them showed up with his gas mask. It kind of made me smile. We fired across a river, scaring a herd of water buffalo out of the brush. One troop fired right into the middle of the herd. Goddamn, it blew the shit out of three or four of them. They ran at us, but we were safe enough, being across the creek and up the bank.

It wasn't safe to go down to the creek, but we had to get those animals out of the water or they would foul it. In a few days it would start smelling real bad. I ordered the asshole who fired the rocket to come and see me at first light and to bring three buddies.

At dawn, into the stream we went, pulling the buffalo downstream. Just as we were moving them away from our camp area, the shit hit the fan. A sniper opened up on us. *Damn, here we are, out in the middle of a creek bed, in the open, with no place to hide.* "FUCK THE BUFFALO. GET THE HELL OUT OF HERE," I screamed. I ran like hell and lost my helmet. When I stopped to pick it up, a round hit a rock near my leg. *Oh shit!* I was hit. Grabbing my helmet, I kept running for cover. We opened fire towards the direction of the rounds.

When the rest of the company heard our shots, they called in two tanks to open fire from the point. The tanks blew the shit out of the hillside. If that sniper didn't *"DD ED"* (the gook's term for "get out"), he would surely be dog meat.

That night at chow we were hit again, this time with rocket rounds. Up until that point we had been, or at least felt, somewhat safe. Now we were all alert and stayed on our toes.

* * *

We started getting new supplies, thanks to the new boss. The supply trucks also brought several cases of fresh fruit, mostly oranges.

Four troops from each platoon were sent out on listening points to see if they could pick up movement. One of the patrols opened fire; it sounded like all hell was breaking loose.

The radio call said the troops had been attacked. We sent out our re-act platoon, and I went with them. At the patrol there was no fighting, no incoming, nothing.

"What the hell happened?" I asked.

"We were attacked by apes. They were after our oranges." The apes had beaten them, bruising and scratching them all. Two men were bleeding.

"Goddamn you assholes, fighting over your oranges."

Shit, no one could keep from laughing.

"I'm not shitting you, Gunny. There were at least four of them. They came out of the trees."

Damn, I had a hard time keeping a straight face. The poor kid *was* scared shitless, though; so I looked around and found tracks.

I loaded up a .50-caliber machine-gun mounted on the top of a 6x6 truck. With six men beside me, I headed down the road to find the apes. I still wasn't convinced about the ape story.

Sure as shit. I saw two apelike monkeys about three hundred yards up the side of the hill. I opened up with the machine-gun. Goddamn! Trees and brush went flying. I didn't hit the apes, but I sure scared the shit out of them.

"Damn, that's the way to run a firefight," one of the troops said. The others agreed, most of them never having fired a .50-caliber machine-gun. I let them take turns trying to cut down a tree.

That night the smell of fresh fruit brought the apes in again. No one was hurt, and we cleaned the area and buried the trash. That stopped them from coming back.

* * *

"You sure have made a difference in the morale of the men. Sending the troops to the rear, so they can clean up and rest, has sure made them look better," the CO said. This preceded his news that I was being sent with my troops near the front lines, to the Cua Viet River. The battalion at the river had been hit hard and needed relief.

"Alert your troops and be ready to move on twenty-four-hour notice."

Nothing like good news/bad news.

* * *

I had a number of places to go in order to inform all the platoons I planned to take with me. Crawling up the side of a cliff, I reached up to take hold of a rock and nearly grabbed a three-foot-long lizard. My hand was only inches from its head. It scared me so badly that I grabbed it by the neck and tore it from the cliff. Then I thought, *Shit, I must be crazy. He was big enough to eat me.*

I didn't get much sympathy from Lang, afterwards. He said, "You asshole! I have been fucking that lizard. "

Resuming my climb, I heard a mine explode just over the top of the cliff. You never knew out there whether they were ours or the NVC's. I hunkered down to check the situation, taking caution, only to find a group of men setting off mines to clear brush. In the process the explosion had killed a snake: a monster about twelve feet long. With the weather warming up, the monsters were coming out of their sleep.

You never knew what you'd find out in this strange jungle wasteland.

* * *

My leg still bothered me from the sniper's rock spray.

The corpsman looked at it and said, "You have a leg *and* an ass full of rock." As he picked away at the rock shards, I saw helicopters landing near the battalion.

"What's up?" I asked.

"The battalion we are trading places with at Cua Viet River is coming in," the CO said. "Show them our lines. We'll move out first thing in the morning."

* * *

Well, there I was. On the front lines. Come nightfall, we moved down the road to join up at 1st Platoon's area. None of the four of us: their gunny, two lieutenants or myself ever heard the rocket rounds coming in.

One hit behind us and another just in front of us.

Oh God! My ears have busted! I was lying on the ground, unable to move. The mortar flash had blinded me. *God, where am I?* I tried to crawl away, but I wasn't sure where I was going. I was still unable to see anything. I heard screaming and knew this hit had been bad. Damn, I was scared. I couldn't move.

Someone cried out, "A corpsman's been hit, and his head was blown off. Get everyone off the road. They have us lined up."

From what I could gather four men had been hit and one killed.

I got up and ran into a bank. Damn, I still couldn't see worth a shit. *Oh God, don't let me be blind,* I prayed.

Someone grabbed me and pulled me into a bunker.

"Where are you hit?

"I don't know. I can't see!" But just then my vision started clearing. *Thank God, it must have been the flash.*

The first thing I could make out was 1st Platoon's gunny in front of me. He had taken a full blast in the gut and his innards were spilling out. I had been pulled into the CO bunker.

"How bad are you hit?" someone asked.

"I just lost my sight from the flash—I think."

"You have blood all over your hand."

I touched my wrist. *Oh shit that hurt.* My wrist was bleeding. I moved my fingers. *Oh, the pain!* I had been hit in the wrist. The officer moved my wrist.

"I think it's broken," he said. He had the corpsman wrap and tape the wrist.

I went outside, crawled in behind the bunker, lay there a while and then started to cry. I wasn't hurt; I was scared. God, was I scared. I kept thinking over and over that I could have been in front of the other gunny.

That could have been me. Sleep wasn't going to come that night. My wrist was killing me. I remembered what I'd been told in Da Nang about the wounded being sent to the rear. I was still scared, but I was alive.

* * *

"Gunny, find yourself a radio operator and get the advance party to the new area. Take all their gear and two mortar rounds each. As soon as the helicopters come in, get on the first one. Set in as soon as you land and be ready for anything."

We flew wide open over a river, as low as the bird could make it. I had never flown that fast in a helicopter. It felt as if we were going to shake apart. I saw bombed-out villages and places that had had the shit shot out of them. *Oh my God,* I thought, looking at the scene. We came in fast and hit the landing zone hard. I was out and running. We were pointed to a small road, and away I went, with the troops behind me. There were bodies everywhere. And, God, the stink!

A Marine came up behind me and said. That's where Charlie comes from." He was pointing to the edge of the village.

Someone else yelled, "Here they come!" We dove for cover.

I looked around just when the rocket rounds began hitting all around us. The dust was flying; I heard metal and chunks of dirt hitting near me. Digging in with my elbows, I rolled to get behind anything near. *Where the hell ore those gooks coming from?*

The rockets stopped. All was clear, and we began moving out again. I must have landed in some water—or else pissed my pants. I was soaked. Damn I was scared.

I saw my CO heading my way. "You send the troops forward as they come in. I'll set them up," he said.

Then I spotted Top coming in with a bunch of new troops. I hadn't seen him for two or three weeks. All of a sudden I felt like an old-timer.

"Hey, Gunny. You doing okay? I saw in the combat report that you were hit."

"Not bad, Top. I think I have a broken wrist, but we haven't stopped long enough to see if it's hurt bad."

He turned to the scared-shitless troops to introduce me as their gunny. "He'll let you know what platoon you're in." Then he asked me, "Where are we bunking, Gunny?"

I looked around and found an old chicken or pigpen with a cement wall on one side. "Maybe we could clean out a spot there."

* * *

I gave orders to start dragging and throwing the bodies into a nearby bomb hole. Those poor kids were scared as hell. God. some of the bodies had been blown to bits.

"Damn it," I said, "just grab a body and start dragging. There's no fucking easy way to do it."

I almost threw up myself when some of the bodies came apart as they were dragged. Two or three of the troops puked, too.

One young kid stopped dead in his tracks, like he had seen a snake. Right at his feet lay a smoking hand grenade.

"GET AWAY FROM IT, GET AWAY!" The poor kid was so scared and dumbfounded that he tried to pull the body with him. "Leave the goddamn body! Just get the hell away," I yelled. *You better move faster than that or you won't live long around here,* I thought. I waited a few minutes for the explosion, but nothing happened. Damn, I wondered, *has the fuse burned out or what?*

Well, I couldn't leave the damn thing there. Scooping up the grenade and the dirt it sat on with my shovel, I threw it toward the water-filled bomb crater. It exploded as soon as it hit the water. I had never seen one smoke like that. It had to be one of the new M-33s.

"Gunny, there are two bodies coming to the top," a corporal said, still watching the water hole.

Oh God. It was two of ours. They had been down there for some time and were bloated. The explosion had shaken them loose from the bottom. I ordered two of the troops, who were about to pass out at the sight, to get their asses over the edge of the hole and pull the bodies out. They were loaded onto a flat mule and sent to the battalion aid station. One of the bodies was a Navy corpsman. They were burned so badly that, at first, I thought they were both black men. Only one was.

* * *

Great. Some of the troops were missing. I was thinking we would never get the bodies cleaned up, and now there was that to worry about.

Baby piglets ran around the deserted village. *Those little greasers will probably be mixed with somebody's C rations before the day is over,* I thought as I watched them. Some of the troops were real animals. But food was the last thing on my mind. I wanted nothing more than to get the troops set in, so I could get my hole ready. I knew we would get hit during the night.

I finally got back to my hole and saw that Top had his hand wrapped.

"What happened, Top?"

"I was horny and tried to screw one of those little pigs. I got bit."

"No shit," I said, still the sucker.

"No, goddamn it! I spilled my coffee and burned the shit out of myself. Make me some more while I finish cleaning out our new home."

I'd been right about it being a pigpen. Top had gotten most of the shit out before he burned himself. We didn't know why the villagers had built the cement wall around the pigpen, but we were glad they had. "It sure will make a nice bunker once we get it done. Let's cook chow before we check the lines. If anyone gets through the lines tonight, I want to have some idea which way to shoot," Top said.

* * *

The troops knew, we knew everyone knew that the shit was going to be bad that night. We dug in good and had plenty of ammo and mines ready.

"Don't let any of those little assholes get through to me, okay?" I said.

The old-timers were a little more sure of themselves than I was. The new troops were still digging in. I'm sure they thought "the deeper the safer." That, or they were just flat going to dig the hell out of there.

"You guys keep digging, and you're going to dig up gooks," I warned them. "You know China is down there someplace. Just make sure you can stand up to shoot over the top."

It was black that night. "Did you tell the new troops not to get out of their holes once it got dark?" Top asked.

"Yes, I warned them that you shoot anything you see moving after dark."

"Well, I will. Ain't no fucking gook going to find my ass."

* * *

Top drank more coffee than anyone I had ever known. I said, "You should have brought a thermos jug with you when you came over, so you could keep coffee all night." I didn't know how he could ever sleep with as much caffeine as he drank. "How are you and I going to stand watch tonight?" I asked.

"I would rather sleep early and wake up early in the morning," he said. I had planned to listen to radio sounds during the night, so that sounded okay to me.

We listened to the rockets in the distance. *Oh shit, I hope they're not coming this way.*

Then they started to hit, over our heads at first and getting shorter each time. Somewhere we had been spotted and the NVCs were trying to hit us. We braced ourselves for shit to happen.

All hell broke loose as the front lines lit up, and the gooks were over the front. I could see people running all over the place and tried to keep my sights on one at a time. Damn, they were so close to us.

Oh shit! My legs! Top thought I'd been hit, the way I was squirming around in that hole.

I had cramps in both my legs and was still trying to hold my rifle straight. Bullets zinged over my head, but by God, I had to straighten out my legs!

"Goddamn it, Brandon! You're pushing me out of the hole. Goddamn it, crawl out!" Top said. I could hear the panic in his voice.

I rolled out of the hole and pushed my legs out straight: it hurt. I heard all kinds of screaming but couldn't make out if it was us or them. At least I hadn't heard a call for a corpsman yet.

One of our troops yelled, "I'm over here you cocksuckers, come find me and I'll blow your fucking heads off." He was clearly so scared—or so excited—that he was going nuts.

It seemed like it went on for hours, but after a while, it quieted down. I didn't think my cramps were ever going to let up.

All platoons checked in. No one had been wounded.

I told the Top, "Someone got a surprise; it looks like Mr. Charles met his match tonight."

Top chuckled, "I set off one of our claymore mines when you rolled out of the hole." Hell, I hadn't even heard it go off. He continued, "Someone sure put the flares in the sky, and I saw a bunch of shit fly by. If I did hit any of those gooks, they will be to the left front of us—so watch that area. I'm going to ask for another flare. Maybe we can see if there are any bodies up there."

The flare went up, but we didn't see a thing.

Well, let's take turns trying to sleep," Top said.

I was too scared to sleep. That damn Top must have been tougher than I was. He went right to sleep. My eyes burned, but damned if I could go to sleep. I kept thinking about the live rounds out there. I stayed awake all night. Top woke up twice but went right back to sleep.

* * *

At first light, I saw some of our troops pop up, take a quick look, and duck back down. A few came out of their holes, guns ready. I, too, got my rifle and walked out. There were two dead NVCs about twenty feet in front of the hole Top and I had spent the night in. I ventured out further to the lines; bodies were everywhere.

"Like shooting fish in a barrel," a corporal said. He had shot ten or more right in front of his hole.

Battalion sent down some flat mules to load the bodies onto. In the process, a bullet hit one of the mules. *Where the hell did that come from?*

Shit, another shot hit the ground as we dove for cover.

A gook had hidden in a ditch about twenty feet away from us and was popping off shots at us. I watched as a kid, Corporal Morgan, jumped up and ran for the ditch. As soon as he was on top of the guy, he opened up with a shotgun and blew his head off.

I thought, *The crazy asshole doesn't even have his shoes on. He ran over there with bare feet to blow Charlie's head off? Damn! This is insane!*

We stopped what we were doing and made sure there weren't any others hiding in the area. The enemy soldier had dug a small hole and covered himself, waiting for us to come out in the open. I had been the one giving the orders; he'd been trying to hit me.

The bodies were piled up, stripped of all their gear and pockets emptied. The staff from S-2 came to see what we had.

The captain asked, "What was the shooting about?"

"A gook had us pinned down for a while, but we got him," I told him.

"Can he talk?"

"Not too well, sir. One of the troops blew his head off." He didn't like my answer.

The NVCs had traveled light. All they carried for chow was a small bag of rice and a handful of shells. Among them there were only a few hand grenades and block chargers that looked like dynamite with a blasting cap inside. Most of them didn't even have shoes. Those little bastards were tougher than shit.

The count was twenty-six Charlies. I don't know how many the other companies killed. But we didn't lose one man. Not even any wounded.

I wonder what they were told to get them to charge a line like ours, knowing what kind of shit we would hit them with. And for that guy to lie there all night, wounded, just hoping for a chance of killing one of us. He must have known he would never get out alive. I'd been told they believed that, if they died in combat, they would come back a better person in the next world. He must have.

* * *

We spent the next several days building up our lines, readying for whatever came our way. We received a few more replacements, but were losing eight good men. Their tour was up, and they were heading home.

The CO asked, "Do you have any whiskey?" He wanted to toast the eight men who were leaving.

My radio man was also a damn good supply man. He came up with a half gallon of Jim Beam.

"Make a toast, Gunny."

"Our canteen cup is only one-quarter full of good whiskey, your days can only get better. Men of Foxtrot Company: You're done with your time in hell!"

One corporal cried as I'd never seen anyone cry before. He was a hell of a man. I had seen the bodies piled around his fox hole and knew he was crying for all his buddies who were not there with him for that moment.

I had tears in my eyes watching them leave. They were like part of my family. *Damn, why do I let myself get so close?* I berated myself.

It took me almost all day to get over the eight men leaving. I wondered who would take their places. Would the new men would be as good as the ones leaving for home?

As I talked to the new replacements, I noticed one who looked as old as me. "Where do you come from?" I asked.

"Chicago. I *was* a reserve, but missed too many meetings, so they put me on active duty, and here I am."

He claimed to have been the best machine-gunner in his section and that was what he wanted to do most.

"Well, I'll put you in the machine-gun section, and you can work your way up. Get rid of those faded uniforms. You can keep your mustache, but trim it off your mouth." I was still keeping on everyone's ass to stay as clean as possible. I'd seen it help morale.

One of the new replacements said that one of the guys he'd come over with had had me as a DI.

"Did he tell you I was a real nice guy?"

"No, he said he was real glad he wasn't coming to Foxtrot. He said you kicked the shit out of him at boot camp, and anyone else who screwed up."

"Oh hell, that's a big lie," I lied. "I only shook him a little."

* * *

On an operation with E Company, I saw the kid from boot camp. He ducked his head hoping I wouldn't see him.

"Hey Morris," I shouted to him, "how come you didn't come and see me?"

He jumped up and said, "Sir, the private was scared."

"Now, don't be telling stories about me being an ass kicker. I never did that, did I?"

Still standing at attention, he said, "Sir, no sir."

That got a few chuckles out of some of the troops. I shook hands with him and said, "Be careful. These gooks are tough."

* * *

We made small patrols at first, moving up to company-sized operations. Once in a while, when Top had time, he would accompany us on a company operation. I didn't see a lot of him during the day. But, back at base camp, we always dug our foxhole together at night.

Top always had a good fire going and a can of hot coffee. I usually came to the hole after dark and tried settling in. At the same time, I would let the troops know it was me moving around. I didn't want my ass shot off.

One night, I jumped in feet first. Top was kicked-back, drinking coffee. I landed square on top of him and spilled his coffee.

"Goddamn you, Brandon. That was my last cup. You better come up with one to replace it, or you're not sharing a hole with me."

"Where the hell will I get a cup this time of night?" I asked.

"That's your fucking problem. Now get the hell out of here and find me one."

I was saved (to use the term loosely) by incoming rockets. He let me stay, but bitched me out all night. I got some coffee going at first light. I took some of the whiskey Norris had come up with to toast with and put a shot in Top's first cup. He never said much, but I understood that you don't spill that little Frenchman's coffee: not unless you wanted to be on his shit list…fast.

* * *

My job, as gunny, was to make sure we had plenty of ammo and grenades as we moved north through E Company and along the river. I would accompany the XO and part of the machine-gun section.

I took a corpsman, radio operator and the company clerk. If there were going to be casualties, I would need to set up a landing zone to get them out fast.

I had a good crew to work with. All three were seasoned troops. The clerk, Corporal Bitsy, had been in-country for nine months. He was also an Indian and came from New Mexico.

We moved out at first light. We had only moved a few hundred yards before we were hit. Everyone was on the radio. I jumped up to move through the rice paddy and check the troops. Every time I moved, I got shot at. I yelled for Norris and the rest of my team to stay close. He started to crawl behind a rock. I jumped and landed beside him just as a round hit the rock he was lying behind.

"Get the hell away from me. Gunny. You crazy asshole, you draw incoming," Norris said to me.

Vietnam, 1968. War is Hell. If you've never been there, words cannot explain it.

Chapter 23
The Beginning of the End

That's just about where the story started: How it was that I ended up in Vietnam; why I was in a rice paddy; and the reason I was getting the wounded Marine aboard the helicopter.

In 1968 I was still wondering how the hell I'd gotten there, and I had a funny feeling things were about to get worse.

I'd just talked to the Marine smoking the cigarette. I remembered looking back at him after the incoming blew off his legs. But mostly I remembered fighting with the door gunner of the helicopter, trying to persuade him to leave me behind with my troops, just before I flew out into never-never land.

"GUNNY GOT HIT BY A ROCKET! It blew him a hundred feet in the air! I just saw him hit the ground," I remember someone shouted. He had mistaken the cause of my free fall from the helicopter.

Rising up out of the rice paddy, I was covered with mud. I tried to walk but fell to my side. I sat up and tried to clean the mud from my face. The corpsman was sitting beside me, just looking at me.

"Gunny, you crazy son of a bitch. How the hell did you live through that?" he said incredulously.

"I wasn't hit, Doc," I said. "I fell out of the chopper. They took off when they saw the rocket rounds starting to hit. I just stepped back and fell off."

"Goddamn, Gunny! How high were you?"

It had happened so fast that I didn't even know the height I'd fallen from. I only knew I was all right and thanked God for that.

"Just got the wind knocked out of me." But I knew I'd remember that incident for the rest of my life.

* * *

We were up and moving, and it looked like we were pulling back. I checked in with the CO for the first time that day. Sure enough, we were pulling back to the battalion area.

"Goddamn it, Gunny. What happened to you?" the CO asked.

"Sir, you wouldn't believe me if I told you."

Well, try me!" he said. I told him about my ass-backward swan dive into a rice paddy. I was right, he didn't believe me.

The next morning I was called up to the aid station to identify any of the dead bodies that might be from F Company. According to our platoon sergeants, we were missing four men. The battalion doctor and the chaplain were waiting for me.

"Gunny, the bodies look bad. They were in the river most of the night, and they all have head wounds," Doc warned.

The chaplain asked me if I would be okay.

"Yes."

Doc pulled back the shelter half. *Oh God!* I had to turn away and almost threw up. Then I looked back. The heads were swollen, but I could make out three that I knew. One was a corporal who had just borrowed my pistol to walk point the day before.

I made my report back to the CO. "Have you talked to the first platoon sergeant? Find out what happened to one of our missing."

Things got confused when I asked about the missing man. I was told a kid had been sent to help carry machine-guns back, and he got hit in the neck.

"That guy isn't missing," I said. "I Medevac'd him, and he wasn't hit. This is bullshit."

A corporal said, "He had a clear path to the landing zone. He must have feigned a wound so he could get out."

At the aid station, I called the base where we had sent the missing kid. No one had seen him. It looked like he'd deserted. I reported him to the military police, hoping they would find where the hell the son of a bitch had gone.

* * *

We went on operations everyday, patrolling both sides of the river. Our job was to keep the river clear of mines and snipers. Every operation took us a little more inland. We covered more ground daily and spread ourselves thinner each time.

Moving into one village, we took a few sniper rounds and called for air support. The first helicopter to arrive got shot out of the air, and the second came in for cover. It went down. Shit was happening everywhere. We were caught in a cross fire, hit from three sides. Two Charlies jumped and ran. I opened up, hitting one.

Calls came in from all the platoons. They needed help. They had wounded and were trying to get them to the landing zone. Some platoons were down to five or six men.

The 3rd Platoon sergeant had been hit. Shit, no one was with them. Every one of their NCO's had been hit. Second Platoon had one man hit bad and weren't able to move him. Everyone needed help.

Taking a stretcher from a helicopter, I grabbed Norris and took off to help. We finally made it to where we could see the kid who couldn't be moved, but he was clear across an opening.

"We'll take turns covering each other," I said, and took off first. Damn, I almost bit it in the cross fire. Then I covered for Norris. He came across and he, too, barely made it without getting hit.

God, the kid was hurt bad. He had been hit in the crotch, and his guts hung down between his legs. His whole body was yellow. I pushed his guts up as far as I could and packed bandages around the wounded area. Then I tied his legs together. With me at one end of the stretcher and Norris at the other, I said, "Now or never!" I'll never forget the look in Norris' eyes.

* * *

We jumped up, running like we'd never run before. As we jumped over a dike, a rocket-propelled grenade hit the trees above our heads.

Norris said, "Goddamn, Gunny! That just missed you." We were both scared and shaking.

I thought it was the adrenaline rush that was making me dizzy and tried to sit up. Then I felt the blood on my face and my hands. Blood was shooting out my nose from the impact of the explosion. I had been hit by shards of flying metal.

* * *

The landing zone was full of bodies waiting to be taken out. One corporal had been propped into a sitting position; he had been shot through the side of his face.

We had one platoon sergeant left. One was wounded and the other had been killed. Another company was moving up to help us, setting in to give us cover while we regrouped. We only had twenty men in the troop left.

The sergeant from 1st Platoon came crawling back. He said, "I need help. Almost all of my platoon has been hit."

We went back in the lines to check reports from other platoon sergeants. Only 3rd Platoon still had an NCO. Staff Sergeant Lang had been shot twice, but was alive. He was sent out.

God, the shit had been kicked out of us that time. Sixteen were killed or missing and twenty wounded. Things looked pretty bleak.

* * *

I made my report to my CO. He suggested I make the report to the battalion commander.

"Sir, can someone else go?" I asked. I wanted to stay and help.

He jumped all over my ass. "Goddamn it, Gunny. You make the report!" Off I went to the command bunker.

The colonel and his staff were inside. I was crying, and all I could say was, "Sir, it was bad." My thumb was black-and-blue and three times its normal size, and I was caked with blood. The colonel told the sergeant major to take me to another bunker and calm me down.

The sergeant major gave me coffee laced with booze. After a few minutes, I went back to make my report. The colonel asked why my lieutenant wasn't with me to report.

"He was too shook up."

"Can you take care of things down there in his place?" he asked me.

* * *

Back with the troop, our CO had a hell of a time dealing with the losses. He began to lose it. I had to yell at him for doing things the troops should have done.

Our battalion returned to the village the next morning without our company. We fought for two days trying to get in and lost several more men. After the fourth day, we were ordered back to the village for cover. There were still a few snipers, and we still got hit with rockets.

We went after our dead and retrieved all sixteen of them, loading them onto the helicopters.

April 1968: Aboard ship, near Vietnam

As we pulled out of the village, two more Marines were wounded. When they had been Medevac'd, we walked back to our lines.

Someone had captured an NVA soldier and killed him. Afterward his head had been cut off. It was laying alongside the creek. *Goddamn, what are we coming to? We better get off the lines for a few days and regroup.*

* * *

Just when I thought things couldn't get any worse, we received word that we would be assigned as the company in reserve for a while. Maybe we could get squared away.

New clothes and special package packs were supplied. They were the first SP packs I had seen and came with whatever the sender wanted to place in them. We had cigars, chewing tobacco and candy. And necklaces of every kind, like the damn hippies wore back in the States. Someone's idea of a joke. It gave us a good laugh. We all wore "love" beads.

* * *

"Get the troops together in formation. The battalion CO and chaplain are coming to hold services for the men who have been killed."

When the company commander came out, I had the troops in formation, waiting for the battalion CO. He saw the troops with necklaces and beads around their necks, including me. "What the fuck's going on, Gunny? Get those damned things off."

"Too late," I said, The colonel is right behind you." Lucky for us, the beads even got a laugh from the colonel.

* * *

We had five days rest before returning for a battalion sweep. We were ordered to find the gooks' base camp. Because they regrouped quickly, we knew their base camp must be nearby. We came across small groups of their troops and wiped them out fast.

One of our companies crossed into the demilitarized zone on point. They caught a company of North Vietnamese regulars in what they thought had been a secure area. We kicked the shit out of the NVCs, then pulled back several miles and set in for the night. We found several of their wounded. The CO tried to get as much information out two of them as he could.

We were to be re-supplied by the amtracks, but they got stuck on the other side of a mine field. Only two hundred yards away from us, and they couldn't cross to supply us. Water and chow that close, and we couldn't have it.

I crawled out, trying to determine what kind of mines were in the field. Hell, they were tank mines and easy to spot. I grabbed Norris and crossed to the amtracks. We returned with a case on each shoulder, then went back again for cans of water.

When we made it back with the water, a gunny from another company

10 a.m., April 6, 1968: In a bunker

asked where we had gotten our chow.

"Across the mine field at the amtracks."

"You crazy asshole, you wanna go back and bring me about six cases?"

I did, but I made him go with me.

It was nearly dark when we got back.

"I'm not going back again. If you want water, you're on your own." He didn't go back.

* * *

Damn, by the time Norris and I got back to our company, it was completely dark. We dug our hole in the dark, digging right into an anthill. To make things worse, we took constant rockets hits and had to stay in the damn hole all night. What a night! We were covered with bites the next morning.

In the morning, we moved back toward the river and found two more prisoners. One had been wounded, and my men were forced to carry him. Back near the rear of the company, I heard someone scream and went back to see what happened. One of the prisoners was dead. "What happened here?" I asked. No one would say a word. I knew by looking around who had killed him, but it had already been done.

"Don't you assholes understand?" I said. "These guys are no different than we are. They do the same shit we do, because their country tells them it has to be done. When they're wounded or taken prisoner, it's all over for them. You better respect them for that. Damn it, that's our job."

The man I suspected said, "But he tried to get away."

"That's bullshit and you know it. The poor fucker was almost dead. He wasn't going anyplace."

* * *

We met up with new troops—some were replacements for our company— and a team from naval gunfire. They were forward observers for the battleship *New Jersey* and had a Marine gunny in charge.

My CO informed me that we were going to hit two villages along the river. "But we have to move fast because we have a battalion of South Vietnamese troops coming up the other side of the river as a blocking force."

We left on a forced march, moving through large, open areas. This type of terrain scared the shit out of me. I just knew we couldn't get across before we would get hit. And they tried: three or four rocket rounds hit way up in front of us. Everyone hit the ground as two more rounds landed behind us.

I started yelling, "GET UP! START RUNNING! THEY ARE WALKING THE ROUNDS IN ON US!"

Sure as shit. The very spot we had just left got hit by two rounds and then several more. Two of my men were hit, but we couldn't stop in the middle of all that shit; we picked them up and ran. One of the men had been hit in the guts and was bleeding badly. The helicopters made it in to pick up the wounded, but the NVCs weren't finished with us yet.

We were only a short distance from a village when we were hit with small-arms fire. The gunny from naval gunfire called for fire support. I was behind a dike when the gunfire from the ship started coming in. The first two rounds hit, and the whole ground shook like an earthquake. *What the hell are they shooting?*

The next two rounds came in right over my head.

Oh God, I couldn't breathe. *What the hell is going on?*

Norris jumped up and started to run. He was yelling, "I can't breathe, I can't breathe!"

And over the radio, "Pull back...pull back." Norris and I both had nose bleeds and my ears were ringing.

"That was the *New Jersey's* sixteen-inch guns firing; the rounds came in a little short." They must have been only a few feet over the ground when they went over our heads.

* * *

The village had been emptied, but for a few civilians, by the *New Jersey's* barrage. Pigs and chickens were going crazy. They must have been in shock, too.

I was standing, telling the troops where to set in, when a gook came up and saluted me. He'd been told to point out a leader, and when I grabbed him and threw him to the ground, the sniper's fire just missed us both. I lay there next to him, choking him until my hand cramped up. I thought I'd killed him; he just lay there. The sniper had taken off after the troop opened up on him. We didn't know if we hit him, but we must have come close.

* * *

We dug our holes for the night and called in the amtracks to haul the civilians out of the village. I passed by the place where I'd choked the gook; he was gone. *Someone must have moved him,* I thought.

Not so. A few Marines had witnessed him get up and walk to the amtracks. Damn! I couldn't believe he was still alive. I had to see for myself. At the amtrack, the gook screamed when he saw me. He was sure I was going to choke him again. Not that he didn't have it coming.

The driver of the amtrack looked at me and said, "Damn, Gunny. You sure have these gooks in line."

I'd have to remember that: Choking!

* * *

We had just set in for the night when we heard the first rounds came in. One of the platoons had seen movement in front of their lines. We called in for flares. Screams came from the direction of the machine-gun section. A canister from one of the flares had fallen and hit one of the troops, cutting off his leg.

I crawled over to where he was laying. The leg below the knee was gone. Damn. Another wounded.

We were deep in the trees. How the hell we would get him out of there, I didn't know. There was only a small clearing, and I wasn't sure if the

April 1968: Me and Cpl. Murry, a buddy from Portland

helicopters could chance setting down in a spot that small. And it was darker than hell to boot. This poor kid was hurting bad, and the bleeding just wouldn't stop. I heard the Medevac coming. We only had a small light for them to spot us with. All of a sudden, the Medevac bird turned on his belly lights, lighting up the whole damn area. We ran like hell to load the kid. The bird was only off the ground a few seconds before the shit started.

Gook spotters were good. Real good. Within minutes they'd called in a mission. We were lucky to be in the trees, after all. The rockets went off in the tree tops. *Just keep your head down, Brandon!* I thought. *God, this is hell.*

* * *

One platoon got hit. It was so dark we couldn't tell how many of the enemy were inside the lines. Eighty-One Mortars was called to light the area with flares.

Damn, there were four gooks running like hell, right at me, about fifty yards away. Five of us shot back. I hit one dead in the chest about four times, knocking him off his feet. We tangled for about an hour before things quieted down, then we stayed on fifty percent alert. One man awake per hole.

I was in a hole by myself, and Norris and his radio were ten feet away from me in his hole. He had taken a hit in the cheek earlier and was in pain. Because he couldn't sleep, he told me to try to grab a wink or two. If he got tired, he would wake me.

We still didn't know how many gooks were inside our lines, or if some were still alive and just lying out there in the dark. It was far too dangerous to go check, and so we waited for first light. My K-Bar was stuck in the side of my foxhole where I could grab it fast if I needed to. With my pistol in hand, I tried to sleep.

At the bottom of my hole, I rested my head on my knees. Something crawled in on top of me. *Goddamn it!* It started squealing. *Shit, a pig!* It clawed my back all to hell trying to get out. Everyone was awakened by the commotion me and my friend were causing.

"What the hell's going on? Are we being hit again?"

"Someone has a pig in the hole, getting a little pork," one man yelled.

"Hey, who the hell is fucking that pig?" someone else yelled. Everyone was laughing, but for the life of me, I could not get that pig out of the hole and off my back.

The CO was up and yelling, calling for me to get the troops to quiet down.

"I will as soon as I get this pig out of my hole." That was certainly the wrong thing to say.

"Hey, it's Gunny! He's screwing the pig!"

"Hey, Gunny, is that good stuff? Is it tight? Kiss her for me, will you Gunny?"

After that, it took half the night to quiet them down. I just sat there. I knew I'd take some shit in the morning.

* * *

Morning was just like being back on the farm. The rooster was still alive and crowed before it even got light. As soon as I could see, I looked for the four gooks that charged me the night before. The one I'd shot in the chest was so close I could touch him. There were the four bullet holes in his chest; half his back was gone where the bullets had come out. Those were the only bodies, the rest must have made it back out through the lines. I had been sure we'd hit a few more.

* * *

We had been away from base camp for seven days; then it looked like we would pull back. We needed to get back near the river to clean up: boy, did we smell bad.

We made it to base camp and got two days' rest. It was hard sitting around, trying not to think about the mess we'd been in or the things we saw. We tried to keep our minds busy as best we could.

One day a sergeant with the new Marine Corps' press people came to our area. With him was a Marine who had a full mustache and long hair. As they came closer, I saw the sergeant had a pistol trained on the other Marine. It was the Marine who had deserted. He'd been missing for over a month now.

"Where the hell did you find that asshole?" I demanded.

"In Saigon, dressed as an army captain in the Special Forces. The MPs turned him over when they heard I was coming up here."

I just couldn't stand looking at the deserter. My blood was boiling I was so angry.

I said, "You no good son of a bitch. I oughta take you out and turn your ass over to the NVA and let them see what you're made of."

"Gunny, I can explain," he started, "I made a mistake. My religion doesn't allow me to kill. I thought I could, but when it came time, I just couldn't do it."

"Why did you take off like a coward, cover yourself with bandages and pretend that you were wounded?"

"I was scared."

"What the hell do you think the rest of us are? A bunch of fucking heroes? We are all scared. There's a big difference in being yellow and being scared. You're going to stay with us until we get out of here. Then you're going to answer to the old man for taking off in the face of the enemy."

"I will not take up a weapon against my fellow man," he insisted.

"I don't give a shit if you do, or if you don't. But you *will* go with us when we go on operations. You *will* go."

I told the lance corporal who was to guard him, "Work the shit out of him and don't let him rest for anything."

* * *

Two days had gone by, and we were due to head out on patrol again. I wasn't sure what I was going to do with the asshole deserter. If I sent him to the rear, I knew he would take off again.

During chow, the lance corporal asked, "Did the guy I was watching come get a shovel from you?"

"I haven't seen him." I had a bad feeling.

"I sent him over about ten minutes ago."

"Damn it! I told you not to let him out of your sight."

I radioed the boat docks and talked to the shore party in charge of all departing boats.

"Is there a Marine down there trying to get on a boat?"

"Yes, sir. He said he had to get some teeth fixed."

"Hold him there. Stick a gun to his head until we get there. He's a deserter trying to get away." I sent two men to get him.

The CO and I were talking when they brought him back. The deserter walked up to me and said, "Gunny, take this fucking Marine Corps and shove it up your ass. I'm not digging any more holes for anyone."

I was so mad that I pistol whipped him across the face. He went down, but I kept right on kicking the shit out of him. The CO yelled at me to stop. The man was bleeding from the mouth.

"Take the yellow son of a bitch to sick bay."

In the CO's bunker I was told I couldn't do shit like that. Not even if the yellow bastard was tough on the troops' morale.

* * *

"I have news, Gunny. I'm being relieved as your CO, and a new captain will be taking over."

"Are you going home, sir?" I asked the CO.

"I don't know yet. Don't make a big deal to the troops. I just want to walk out of here. Don't tell anyone until I'm gone."

I felt sorry for him. I thought he felt he had failed us in some way.

* * *

On my way to see the battalion doctor about the deserter, the sergeant major stopped me.

"Your new company commander is a rookie, and this is his first time in combat. He'll need a lot of help." Then he asked what I was doing in sick bay.

"I hit that deserter in the mouth. I might have broken something." We both went in.

The doctor said, "I think the kid has a fractured jaw, and his mouth is swollen shut. What do we do with him?"

The sergeant major didn't hesitate. He said, "Send him back to duty. If he's sent to the rear, we will never see him again. Gunny, take him back, but keep your hands off him."

The next morning the deserter asked for a rifle.

"I will do my job." He could barely talk. "I don't believe in what you are making me do, but I can't take the shit you're giving me."

"You made the choice to be a Marine. You just turned yellow when the shit hit the fan. I have a job to do, and it's a damn sight harder than the one you have to do."

We were all scared. He didn't understand that, if our time came, there wasn't a damn thing any of us could do about it.

* * *

My new CO was a good listener most of the time and knew it was up to me or the XO to keep the troops in line. Not an easy thing.

Most of our operations occurred in secured areas, and we only had a few close calls. We were sent in to clean up a village where duds and mines were going off. We collected them, placed them in a bomb hole and set charges underneath them. Norris and I stood a few yards from the hole while they set the charge.

The explosion gave me a mild concussion; I started bleeding from the nose.

I was sick all that day and threw up blood. We were hit again that night with rocket rounds, and my nose bled again.

I went out just before dawn to check the machine-gunner covering the river. He saw movement on the water. Two gooks were floating a Sampan down the river.

"Sink them!" I shouted. The gunner kept missing his target. I sat alongside him to settle him down, and the whole world went spinning in front of my eyes. I started throwing up: all blood. My guts felt like they were coming out my ass. I pulled down my trousers; my shorts were full of blood.

Norris was scared at the sight and asked what was wrong with me.

"Maybe I got too close to the explosion and busted something open inside." I sure as hell didn't know!

* * *

I was lying in my bunker when the new CO entered.

"When you gonna re-enlist, Gunny?"

I was so sick I didn't even know what day it was. I said, "Maybe this weekend, if we get off this operation. What's the date, anyway?"

"The twenty-seventh of April."

Good God! I started laughing.

"Hell, I'm a civilian. My time was up on the twenty-fifth!"

"You have to go back in," he said. "The major will chew my ass out if he finds out your enlistment is up."

He promised to send me out on the first helicopter the next morning. My guts were burning bad. Every time I tried to take a crap nothing but blood came out.

Norris said, "I'm going to call in a Medevac and get you out of here, now!"

"I'll kick your ass first."

* * *

Too sick to sleep, I went on a listening post with four of the troops. It was quiet during the night, until just before light. Then four NVAs came toward us across a rice paddy. We let them get within forty feet before we opened up on them. They never knew what hit them.

That was almost my last tango with combat.

* * *

I was so sick by the time the helicopters came that I barely got myself through the door. I was flown to a hospital ship: clean sheets and hot water; I felt better already.

I eventually ended up in Da Nang. I heard Top Duchateau was down there somewhere. Since I wasn't going back to the field, I decided to look him up. I found him at the Seabees Chief's Club. I had my first cold beer in months. Top downed only a few; he had to get orders on his new incoming troops.

After he left me, I met an old DI buddy who was in amtracks on the other side of Da Nang. He took me to stay with him. Damn, those guys had tents with built-up sides and canvas bunks. All the comforts of home.

* * *

The next day I ended up at Marble Mountain, where I met several old buddies. They *really* lived good: hot showers, their own mess hall and a club that was open twenty-four hours a day.

We were enjoying a drink when a siren went off. Everyone took off for their bunkers and safe cover. They left me in there with all the booze. Hell, I decided to stay put and drink. I'd take my chances with all this booze. I wasn't going in any bunker. Boy, did I have a hangover the next morning.

* * *

At the first opportunity, I caught a helicopter heading north and got back on the ship. I was four days over my enlistment, and the old CO was right: the major was not happy with me.

"Where the hell have you been. Gunny?"

"I got on the wrong bird and ended up down in Da Nang. It took me awhile to find my way back."

"How many years are you going to sign up for?" he asked.

"I only need three years to get my twenty in."

"Okay!" he said. "But you're going back to Okinawa." I raised my hand and swore to serve the United States of America for another three years. Division orders said I had to leave Vietnam. I'd been wounded three times.

"I want to stay here."

"Can't do it, Gunny. Ask to sign a waiver when you get to Okinawa. They might let you come back after a year."

"Shit, sir. Can't I do that here? You know how short we are on staff and officers."

No way. I wasn't going to win that argument.

* * *

I went back one more time to say good-bye to the troops. I was talking to a lieutenant when I saw a gook hunkering down on top of a building about three hundred yards away.

"How often have you been hit with rockets?" I asked him.

"At least three times a day."

"Are they getting close?"

"Yes, closer each time."

I walked back and asked a sniper attached our unit if I could use his rifle. The gook was still on the building watching us, and I was watching him through the scope. When he sat up, I fired one time. He jumped and slid off the building. *That should put an end to the rockets homing in on these guys for a while,* I thought smugly.

The CO came over to see about the shooting.

"What the hell are you doing back here, Brandon? You are supposed to be on your way home," he said, more than a little pissed.

"I only came back long enough to say my goodbyes. They are sending me back to Okinawa."

He cussed me for shooting when there were troops in the direction I'd just popped off. Then he called the patrol in so I could say so-long. I told him about the new lieutenant coming in. I had given the new guy all my gear. I wouldn't be needing it: I wasn't coming back.

I talked to the guys for a while, then thanked them and left to catch my helicopter back to the ship. I've never had an easy time with good-byes.

* * *

While waiting on the hangar deck for a flight to Da Nang, I heard the PA system announce incoming wounded. I went up on the flight deck to see who it was. Four helicopters came in full of wounded. It was *my* company. I talked to one of the wounded men who said the whole battalion was under attack.

"Almost everyone in our platoon was wounded or killed," he said.

I grabbed some gear. I didn't care who it belonged to. I got on one of the helicopters and went back. I had to see what was going on.

* * *

Damn, wounded men were everywhere. My company had been caught in a village, Dai Do, just up the river from the battalion area. I could hear them calling for help over the radio. Other companies were getting the shit shot out of them, too.

The wounded came in on boards and amtracks. I grabbed a seat on an amtrack and headed up river. The driver stopped to let me run out and see what the hell was going on. I asked where Fox Company was. Bullets were hitting all over the place; I could hear rounds hitting the amtracks.

They were loading more of the wounded on the amtrack I had come in on. I went to help. There was an explosion and a bright flash went off beside the vehicle.

April 1968: Injured and semi-conscious, waiting for helicopter Medevac.

Chapter 24
The Twilight Zone

I never was able to connect the events after that. I didn't know what had happened. Things seemed to jump around on me. The next thing I remembered was carrying my half-full seabag. I wondered where the rest of my equipment was.

Then I was in full uniform, trying to fit several bottles of booze into my bag. My seabag was full, yet the last time I'd remembered it, it had only been half-full. I was with all kinds of troops from the Army and Air Force, and my ears were ringing.

Next, I was talking to a policeman who made everyone open their bags for inspection. When I opened mine, he said, "Get out of here, Gunny. Go home."

* * *

Now I'm in a barrack! This was all crazy to me. No one, including me, had shirts on. We were drinking and some were shaving. A Marine gunny started chewing me out.

"What the hell are you doing drinking in the barracks?"

"You better get the hell away from me. Where I just came from was hell enough, and I don't need anyone giving me shit."

"Who the hell are you?"

"Someone you don't want to know," I answered.

* * *

"What the hell is going on? Where the hell am I?"

I was sitting at a shoeshine stand, having my boots shined. Two black girls walked up to me and started calling me names. One of them spit at me. I jumped out of my chair and tried to hit one of them.

I kept going blank. I would end up in new places, and I didn't know how I had gotten there. Hell, now I'm standing in my shorts and a lady is pressing my trousers.

* * *

There I was, with no idea how I'd gotten on that plane. Looking out the door, I saw my brother Gary, Shirlie and the kids.

I had just left Vietnam a day or two ago. I thought I must have been dreaming.

Shirlie, the kids and I stayed to visit at my parents' house only for a little while. I wanted to be with Shirlie. As soon as I got to our house, I shaved off my mustache. The kids had run away from me at the airport when they saw it.

I knew I was home, but I kept blanking out. I would be in the house one minute and then in the car or at the ocean or sitting in a bar drinking a minute later.

* * *

I received letters from my company. Some of the office troops wrote occasionally. They told me how badly our company had had the shit kicked out of them. Thirty-three of our men had been killed, and almost everyone else was wounded. The battalion commander had been wounded and the sergeant major killed. The lance corporal who had been nicknamed "Gunny's Shadow" had been shot in the head six times. Three of the guys who had died were from Oregon.

I phoned the Marine office in Salem and asked if they had the names of the Oregon Marines killed in Vietnam. They did. One of them, from Eddieville, had been in my company and his funeral was the next morning. I had to go.

The casket was closed, but I could almost visualize him. I heard his family talking behind the curtains. "I wonder who that guy is? Look at all his stripes. He must have known our son. He's crying."

I asked to speak with his family. They met me outside and I introduced myself. Yes, they had heard their son talk of me.

"He was a good Marine," I assured them.

"Did you know my son called you the Big Kahuna? That means 'big crazy man.'"

"No, I did not."

His father leaned over and touched my cheek with his rough, work-hardened hand. "My son thought you were the toughest Marine ever. No one messed with him when you were around. Not even the officers."

* * *

I didn't go straight home. I got in my car and headed back to Salem, to the reserve center. I wanted orders to go back to Vietnam. I was told I had to sign a waiver because I'd been wounded too many times.

"Okay. Just get me out of here."

* * *

What the hell is wrong with me? I go days at a time and can't remember a thing. Then at times I know what's going to happen before it happens.

* * *

I receive orders after thirty-six days. Back to Vietnam and the 3rd Marine Division, 2nd Battalion, 4th Marines. I'd had been drinking a lot and put some weight back on. My uniform was tight. Well that old shit would stop. I had to keep my thoughts sharp!

I didn't understand what was happening to me. I wouldn't talk to anyone about it, mostly because it scared me to have anyone else think I might be insane. I'd just sit by myself. I didn't think about Shirlie and the kids. I was just blank.

What in the hell is wrong with me?

* * *

Things were a little better in Okinawa, but I had an empty feeling. I felt all alone. Once I got to Vietnam, I caught a ride to Marble Mountain. It was no trouble catching a helicopter north.

That was early afternoon, and I thought I could be back on the ships before dark. I couldn't believe the battalion was still on the ship.

"Can I go back to Foxtrot Company?"

"Wait until you get out in the bush and talk to the battalion commander or the sergeant major."

I bummed a ride on a mike boat to go to another ship and draw supplies.

I still hadn't seen any troops that I knew. Damn, I had only been away from Vietnam about forty days. Where the hell was everyone?

* * *

"Hey, Gunny! Goddamn, I'm glad to see you!" It was my old radio operator, Norris.

"Damn, Norris, where the hell is everyone? You are the first F Company trooper I've seen since I got back."

"There aren't many left that you knew. Almost everyone is new."

"Are you going to be company gunny?" he asked me.

I didn't know. I knew I needed all new gear, and Norris was in charge of ship supplies.

"Well, fix me up."

He issued me a .45-caliber pistol, a shotgun, a K-bar and a survival knife. He also gave me an M-1 carbine that had the barrel and stock cut off. It had ten magazines, half of them banana clips.

"Goddamn, Norris. You want me to look like John Wayne?" I asked when I saw the getup he'd put together for me. "At least put some black polish on it or spray paint it black!"

I landed in Dong Ha, but no flights were headed to battalion. I had to catch a truck convoy the next morning.

* * *

I was stuck in the landing zone in Dong Ha. Damn. It was hot here, and the dust got into everything. The few pounds I put on while I was home didn't help at all.

I hated sleeping above ground and went looking for a hole to sleep in. The company hadn't been hit in over two weeks, things were safe, and old Charlie was on the run. That is what I was told. Hell, with all the noise the generators made and all the truck traffic, how the hell could they hear incoming anyway?

I was thinking about chow when I heard an explosion down at the ammo dump. Then another. Shit, the whole dump was blowing up from the incoming rounds, and we were only a few hundred yards away. *I better get my ass in a hole.* There was tons of shit going on down there. It was too late to try and get back down the hill now: too much flying through the air. The explosions went on for over four hours and lit up the sky brighter than the Fourth of July.

* * *

Damn, my head hurts. I hope I'm healed enough inside so I don't start bleeding again.

Dark was coming, and I just had to get away from that hillside. I took a chance and ran down the hill, grabbed my gear, and looked for a bunker or a fox hole to dive into. It looked like it would go on all night. My nose started bleeding. I didn't have any water to try to stop it. Damn! I couldn't believe I was so screwed up. If I lived through this mess, I would be lucky. I made up my mind to get the hell out of there first thing the next morning. Maybe, once I got in the bush, I would be okay again.

There were enough sandbags on those trucks to stop a huge mine. But, boy, LZ Stud looked bad. Holes all over the place. They took a lot of incoming there. The few tents I saw had holes all over them. *I'm sure as hell not sleeping in one of those!*

Damn. I hadn't been off the truck five minutes when I heard incoming. Shit, close incoming at that!

Lying in a hole with a sergeant, I asked, "How often do they hit?"

"Anytime they want. They may not hit us until we start lining up for chow, so let's go in the tent." He said that he had cold beer there.

We were just finishing a cold one when a bullet came zinging through the tent. We hit the dirt.

"What the hell is going on? I thought you said they wouldn't hit us until chow!" I said.

Hell, he didn't know what was happening, either.

Someone opened up on our tent, a whole magazine full. I looked up and saw a Marine standing beside the tent. He had blood all over his face and was obviously the shooter. He aimed his rifle at the sergeant and pulled the trigger.

Click. The chamber was empty.

Two Marines jumped him and held him down. His head had a hole the size of a baseball. Shit. He had gone crazy when he got hit. We got him to Medevac, but it was certain that he wouldn't make it with a hole that size in his head.

* * *

I landed the next morning at my battalion command post. They were on a mountain overlooking Khe Sanh. That was the first time I had seen Khe Sanh, but I knew that's where the shit had been happening for months. Hundreds of Marines had been killed or wounded there. I wondered what the hell we were doing up there. The countryside had had the shit shot out of it. There were bomb holes everywhere, and most of the trees were blown to hell.

I didn't know anyone. I asked to see the sergeant major and was pointed to a group of Marines eating chow.

"I'm Gunny Brandon, reporting in."

"Brandon, are we glad to see you. I'm Sergeant Major Walker and this is Chaplain Whitne. We've heard good reports about you, and we were glad to hear that you were coming back."

I sat down and joined them for coffee and chow.

E Company didn't have a gunny or a first sergeant. In fact, they only had three officers. That's where they were sending me.

"It looks like you are going to have more than one job up there." That was my kind of assignment, but I wouldn't be able to join them till morning.

* * *

"Where is F Company located now?" I asked Walker.

"They are the reserve company right now and have security around here," he said. I'd been Captain Butler's gunny before.

"When he heard you were coming, Butler wanted you back. But we need you in E Company."

I took my bottle of Johnny Walker scotch and a canteen cup of coffee and walked around to find Butler.

"Hey, Shipper, want a good drink of coffee?" I said.

"Good to see you. Gunny. I heard you were coming back, you crazy idiot."

* * *

Damn, that was one steep hill, I thought, climbing the trail to join up with E Company. I was out of shape. It had to be over ninety degrees. *What the hell am I doing going up this trail by myself? Well, too late now. I have to get my ass up there.* It took me over an hour to make it up the hill. I hadn't gotten my combat nerves back yet and was a little scared. Shit, I was a whole lot scared.

A Marine, sitting on the edge, looked down over the edge at me. "Hey man, you come up here by yourself?" he asked.

"Yeah! Nobody wanted to break from chow to come with me."

"Are you with this company?"

"I am now. Gunny Brandon. I'm your new gunny."

"Are you a new guy?"

"I'm new here. But am I brand new to combat? Am I a boot gunny? Don't worry buddy," I assured him. "I have some field time. Me and Mr. Charles have been introduced several times in the last year.

We walked through the company area. Things didn't look good here. Only about a dozen men were up and around.

"Where is everyone?" I asked. "Sleeping. We stay awake at night. That's when things get busy up here."

A young lieutenant was watching me approach. I walked over and introduced myself. "I was sent up here to take over as gunny."

The lieutenant, Lieutenant Wells, was company commander. He was going over the maps for the night's operation. The colonel had already told him at the morning's battalion briefing that I was coming. He even knew that I had seen a lot of combat, gotten wounded and was sent back to the States.

"You requested to come back to our battalion?"

"I was company gunny in F Company before. I got hit too many times, so they sent me home." It had just dawned on me what my problem had been all along. "I found it hard to leave my job undone," I said.

* * *

The staff was made up of three lieutenants, three staff sergeants and two sergeants. There were sixty men in the troop. They were definitely short on personnel.

I only saw three white officers and four colored staff sergeants. I thought they all looked pretty young. I guess I should have been flattered when the young lieutenant thought I was "new." Hell, I felt a hundred years old compared to these kids.

I said, "How many of you have been here more than ninety days?"

No one responded.

"Has anyone here been wounded?" One sergeant raised his hand. "I know you from Parris Island, don't I?"

"Yes, sir. I was in First Battalion with you."

I wanted to go myself to meet the men in the platoon. I promised to make it around before dark. In 1st Platoon, I recognized a kid I put through boot camp.

"How are you doing. Majors?" I asked. He'd made lance corporal. "I'm glad you don't want to call me sir anymore." We both laughed.

I continued on to 3rd Platoon's area. It was the farthest platoon from the company commander and was a shit hole. There was trash everywhere. I saw a pile of shit only a few feet from a bunker. I looked at the platoon sergeant, and he looked away from me.

"I can overlook a little trash. But I don't overlook this," I told him. I ordered his platoon out. I wanted to see them.

"I want to tell you first off what you already know. This place isn't fit for pigs, let alone a bunch of Marines. I'm sure that's what you are, a bunch of Marines who don't give a shit. I have been here before. This is not my first tour in combat. I signed up to come back because I care about the Marine Corps. I don't give a shit about what you think of me, right now. But how can you be so fucking low that you would shit inside your own living area?" They were living like animals. But even animals didn't shit in their own beds. "This place better shape up, or you are going to wish you never heard of me. I don't screw with the troops, and no one else will, as long as I'm gunny. But you better damn sure do your job. Start acting like you give a shit and get this place cleaned up."

As we walked away from the area, I warned the platoon sergeant to earn his stripes and quit buddying up with the men. "When the shit hits the fan, they need to know who is in charge—or they'll get you killed."

* * *

I'd no more than got back to headquarters when I saw a fight break out in the same area I had just come from. I walked back. The platoon sergeant I just chewed ass on was fighting with one of his troops.

"I said clean up the shit, not kick some more of it out," I yelled.

* * *

The next day things looked somewhat better. As I talked with the troops, I could tell the morale was not the best. But at least I had made them nervous. I assumed Majors had told stories about his boot-camp days with me, because the troops stayed busy when I came around.

A Marine from the engineering company attached to ours came over to talk. He'd also been with F Company, and recalled the incident about the deserter.

I said, "Did you say anything about that to the troops since I got here?"

"Yeah, to a few other Marines." Now I knew why the troops were scared of me.

* * *

The engineer's Marine had come to ask help with some mines that had been double-booby trapped. I called

June 28, 1968 (one day before my 33rd birthday), about 9:00 a.m. My last letter home before receiving the wounds that would send me home.

the platoon sergeants together and asked if anyone knew anything about the mines. I also told them to spread the word that I wasn't going to go around beating the shit out of them.

Some of the mines had been set in place by the company we had relieved. We had also set some mines since I'd gotten there. We would be spending the next few days making the mines safe so we would know what the hell we had in front of us.

My company commander said, "We need more barbed wire and trip flares set up along our line. I want to start in the morning, just as soon as the patrols have gone."

Damn, it was June 27. In two days I would be thirty-three years old and have seventeen years in the Marines. Unless I saw something a lot different, I was going to get out once and for all after my twenty years.

Around midnight, we heard movement inside the lines. It came from a cliff about forty feet high. Damn. Charlie wasn't dumb enough to try and hit us from that side, was he? We didn't even have troops over there.

The only thing between me and the movement was the cliff. *I better crawl over there and see for myself.* Well, it wasn't an animal; it was walking on two legs. I threw a grenade and spotted three, or four bodies move when it went exploded. Damn, old Charlie was trying to come up the cliff. I would just have to wait until first light to see whether or not I'd gotten them with the grenade.

* * *

I had just finished eating chow when I heard the helicopter coming in to pick up daily reports and outgoing mail. I had written a letter to Shirlie that I wanted to send. It never took long for the helicopters to come and go: they only set down long enough to throw out bags of mall and catch ours before they were gone. I guess that's air mail.

Talk about a rag-ass patrol: supply man, corpsman, two clerks, a radio operator, two attached Marines and me, the gunny. The patrol coming with me to check the cliff started out slow, the point man had to move slowly through the jungle. It was almost impossible to get through. The point man stopped in his tracks and didn't move.

I went forward to see how bad things were. Pulling back some brush, I bent over to crawl. Suddenly, something popped and caught my eye. Then I saw a bright flash and an explosion. Everything turned red, and I felt myself flying through the air. I landed on my butt, then my back, but I didn't seem to care. Someone was shooting. I could hear someone screaming in front of me. I tried to move, to roll over or sit up. *Damn. I can't move.* My chest felt like something heavy was sitting on it. I kept seeing everything in red, and my skin was burning.

"My legs! My legs!" I heard someone scream. Thank God—it wasn't me.

I kept trying to raise my arms and open my eyes. Then I heard a voice next to me. "Oh shit, it's the gunny. Get a corpsman! Gunny, can you hear me? Say something. Gunny."

I'm talking. Can't you hear me? Shit, and I began to laugh. *Oh God that hurts. What the hell am I laughing at?*

"Gunny is hit bad. Get on the radio and ask for the chaplain."

"No way is he going to make it," I heard another say.

What the hell are you saying? Can't you hear me? I'm screaming as loud as I can. Still, no one heard me.

"Gunny, talk to us."

I am, damn it! Can't you hear? Oh God. I'm going to throw up. I'm sick. Oh God, put me down, my guts are burning.

"What the hell are you doing? Pour water on his guts and push him into the bag," I heard.

Goddamn it! Don't put me in a bag!

"What happened to his thumb?"

"He pulled it off."

"Gunny, don't pull your arm back," they shouted at me. "Leave your hand under your arm. You have a bone sticking out."

Oh God! Oh God! Don't move me, damn it! Can't you hear me?

"Hold on. Gunny. We are sending you on Medevac, it's coming," they promised as they dragged me over the rocks.

God, I'm throwing up. I'm hot. GET ME OUT OF THIS BAG! What the hell did they put me in this bag for? I was gagging and choking and couldn't breathe. *Help me. I can't breathe. Something is in my throat.* I still couldn't believe no one could hear me. Oh God. They dropped me. *Help me. I'm choking.*

This guy in the bag is moving," someone finally said.

Damn. I'm back on the helicopter again. Where the hell am I? Can't anyone hear me?

* * *

"Tell us your name, Marine."

"My name is Brandon," I said.

"Where you from, Brandon?"

"Shit, you can hear me? I'm from Second Battalion, Fourth Marines."

"What's your rank?"

"Gunny."

"Gunny, what company you in?"

"F Company. No! No! E Company."

"Where's your home, Gunny?"

"Grand Ronde, Oregon. I mean McMinnville, Oregon."

"Are you married?"

"Yes."

"What's your address?"

"I don't remember. We just moved there. Where am I?"

"You're on the hospital ship, *USS Sanctuary*."

I was on an operating table and the medical team was trying everything they could to keep me awake.

"Where do your parents live?"

"Salem, Oregon. But don't tell them about me. My mother is sick."

"What's your wife's address?"

"I don't know. Am I lying in the sun? My eyes hurt. Can I go to sleep?"

"No! Gunny stay awake. We need to talk to you. How long have you been in the Marines?"

"Seventeen years."

"Gunny, this is going to hurt. Keep talking to us."

My eyes hurt, and yet I could see myself. Was I looking in a mirror?

"What did you say, Gunny?"

"Shirlie. Tell her I love her. Please let me sleep. I can't help it. I have to sleep. I have to sleep."

Aftermath, July 1968: US Navy & Veteran Hospital Repair Shop

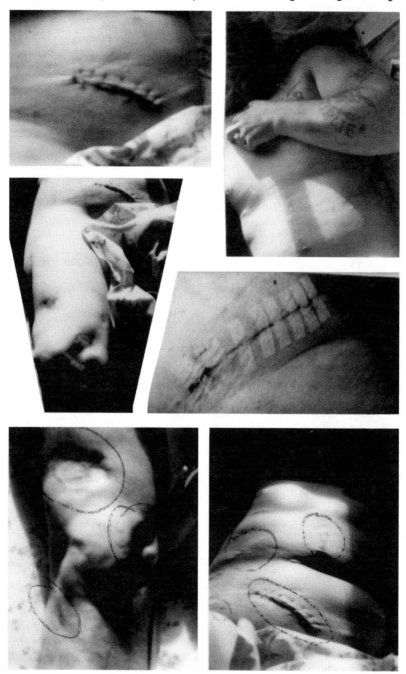

Chapter 25
Epilogue, or: "Gunny's Last Chapter, His Life Without the Marines"

July 8, 1968…Somewhere in Vietnam…

"Oh my God, my body is burning, where am I? I can't see…where am I?"

"Gunny, you're on the *USS Sanctuary*," someone said. "You've been out since the end of June. Boy, you sure got the shit blown out of you!"

"What's the date now?" I asked. The guy I was talking to said he was a Lance Corporal and that he had been wounded in the hip. He told me it was July 8th. Damn…I'd been out for over ten days.

"You mean I haven't even woken up to eat? How have I been eating?"

"Shit, Gunny, you got tubes coming out of you all over."

"How do I get a hold of someone? I have to take a leak."

"Just go, Gunny, there's a bag hooked up to you."

"Welcome back, Gunny, how do you feel?" someone asked.

"Who are you?"

"I'm the Duty Corpsman," he replied. "The doctors will be coming to see you soon. I told them you were awake, but you need to have all your bandages and tubes changed. There is a special Corpsman here who will come to do that."

"Gunny, I'm Doctor Skinner," said a new voice. "I was on duty when you came in and I did all your surgeries. I want to go over your injuries so you know what's going on. We had to remove your spleen, you have several broken bones, and the tip of one finger and half of the left thumb was taken off. Several wounds were sewn over; by that I mean flesh was cut away and sewn together. No skin grafts have been done yet. You have several wounds to your eyes, mostly powder burns. What we're most worried about is your right leg. There are some bad wounds and a lot of infection…and we don't think we can save it."

"Oh God, how much will I lose?"

"Most all from the knee down, even if we can save it, you may never walk on it again. We'll start changing your dressing now and we'll have to do this four times a day. You have head, chest, stomach and lung wounds so we can't give you much for pain. Open your mouth and bite down on this: it's two tongue suppressors wrapped with gauze. Try not to move while we change the dressings."

"OH GOD, OH GOD, PLEASE GOD, HELP ME…GODDAMN PLEASE STOP!! OH GOD, MY SKIN IS BURNING…GOD, PLEASE STOP…PLEASE, DEAR GOD, STOP…OH SHIT, IT HURTS…WHAT THE HELL ARE YOU DOING?!"

"Lay still, Gunny, we have to pull all the bandages off and clean the wounds."

"OH GOD DAMN, I CAN'T STAND THE PAIN!"

"That's all of them, Gunny. Three more times today and I'm done. I'll be

BACK...HA, HA, HO, HO... Listen for my song, HA, HA, HO, HO!" he sang.

"Oh shit, that hurt!" I said.

"Damn, Gunny, you sure scream loud. You must be an ex-DI."

"God, what the hell was he doing?" I asked.

"Gunny, he takes all the bandages off, then dips some gauze in some orange-looking shit and wipes out all of your wounds. I think the asshole enjoys his work: he's the same one who cleans up all the wounds in this ward."

"How bad do I look?" I asked the Marine who'd been talking to me.

"Gunny, you look all black and blue, maybe some burns on your legs and face. All your wounds are open except for the ones on your head. It looks like your fingers are sewed up. You sure are lucky to have made it here."

"Oh, Gunny," a Corpsman said, "the doctor told me to tell you he will take some of the tubes out after the next bandage change, but to try to control yourself. Don't fight the Corpsman that's cleaning up your wounds."

"How the hell do I do that? I never had so much pain in my life. I've been wounded before and they never hurt as much as that did."

"Well, all I can tell you is you'd better try. Did the doctor tell you what was wrong with you?" the Corpsman asked.

"Yes, he was telling me just as the Corpsman started taking off the bandages, then I lost control from the pain."

"Well, you don't have to worry about holding your penis, you can just piss through a tube, and your tattoo was blown off...No more Shirlie on your arm." Then I could hear him walk away.

"Who was that?" I asked the Marine I'd been talking to.

"He's a big fat ass Corpsman who thinks he's hot shit. He collects the bullets and metal they take out of the wounded."

"What the hell does he want that shit for?" I asked.

"I don't know, he is just a shit head," said the Marine.

* * *

I can hear the wheels of a gurney or a cart coming. "Oh shit!"

"HA, HA, HO, HO, I'm coming your way...HA, HA, HO, HO," the Corpsman sang. "Hey, Gunny, you ready for me once again?"

The pain is almost more than I can take. This time I bit the tongue suppressor in half, and two more times that day he came back.

"Shit, Gunny, I can't stand to hear you scream!" the Marine said. "I wish I could get out of here when they do that to you."

"The next time that asshole comes to change my bandages, I'm not going to make a sound. I hope I'll pass out first." (I begged God to please help me...I can't take this pain much more).

But the next two times the pain made me scream...*I'm not going to scream again...I will fight the pain...I'm not going to cry.*

* * *

"HA, HA, HO, HO, I'M COMING TO TAKE YOU AWAY...HA, HA, HO, HO." *Here comes that asshole again.* "Gunny, you're going to x-ray; you have to get out of bed and get on the gurney."

"Someone is making me sit up, OH GOD THE PAIN!!!"

"Help us, Gunny, push yourself over on the gurney."

"Oh shit, the x-ray table is cold…Oh shit, oh shit, the pain. God, at last I'm back in my bed. Boy, those assholes don't give a shit how bad it hurts."

"Here comes the asshole to change your bandage."

"How come he isn't singing?" I asked.

"There's a nurse with him."

"Gunny, this nurse will be helping me change your bandages today."

Oh God, don't let me scream. I can feel my bandages coming off; I never felt them come off before…shit it hurts, but not that bad. *I can take it, I can take it!* I keep telling myself.

The Corpsman said, "Gunny, your leg looks like some of the swelling has gone down."

Damn, they're done and I never screamed.

"Gunny, you did the Marine Corps well, not a sound," the Marine said. "You'll have to piss on your own now: they're taking the tube out of your pecker." This Marine had become my eyes; he even wrote letters for me.

"How the hell am I going to hold on to my pecker? Both of my arms are in a cast."

"Don't ask me, Gunny, I can't get out of bed. That asshole Corpsman will stick the pisser on it, then let you piss all over yourself when it slips out." He was right. "Damn, Gunny, you'd better stop! It's going to run over."

"Shit, I can't feel it. Oh shit, now I can. Shit, my ass is all wet." I thought the Corpsman said I would have to piss through a tube from now on; lucky I got a short pecker. They missed the end of it.

"Hello Gunny, this is Doctor Skinner. Good news: we're sending you to Japan to the Army 106th Hospital for a few more operations and then on to the States. You'll be leaving on the 1400 flight, stay overnight in Da-Nang, then fly out in the morning. You should be in Japan by noon tomorrow. Good luck and take care."

"Thank you, Sir, I will do my best."

The fat ass Corpsman, as my Bunkie Marine calls him, gave me a small cloth bag and told me that was all I had, the rest of my stuff would be shipped and would catch up to me if I was lucky. He helped push me up to the flight deck and loaded me on a helicopter. I said, "Thanks for the care."

"Fuck you, jarhead," he replied.

* * *

We must be close to Da-Nang. We were landing and had only been in the air a few minutes.

"Boy, it's hot here," I said.

"You'll be inside where it's a lot cooler," they told me.

"Can you eat solid foods, Gunny?" someone asked.

"I've only been drinking juice and eating Jello."

"Well, we'll keep you on that while you stay overnight."

OK, I think I'm feeling better now just knowing that I'm heading home. I'm not sure how long it'll take. One thing, I can sure sleep a lot and it doesn't hurt as much now when they change my bandages. I wonder how long before they do skin grafts?

"Wake up, Gunny. We're going to be loading you in a few minutes to go to Japan; the Air Force will be taking you there."

Boy, I don't know who's flying this plane but it sure is rough, and God it's hot: my guts feel like they're coming apart. I sure wish they'd take these bandages off my eyes. It must be 11 days now since I was able to see, and I know I'm just hoping, but sometimes I think I can see some light through my bandages. There must be other people on the plane, but I haven't heard a sound since we left. Sure wish someone would talk to me and tell me where we are. We must have been in the air for several hours now and it feels like we're coming down now. Oh God, that was rough, we must be landing.

"Where are we? Is anyone here?" I asked.

"Hey Marine, we are landed." I couldn't hear what they were saying; something about an Air Force base. I could feel them taking me out of the plane.

"What am I in, a Jeep?" I asked.

"You're in an Air Force ambulance. You'll be staying here until morning, then they'll take you to the Army 106 Hospital in Yokohama. That's where they'll do the surgery before they send you to the States."

I hope they keep me a while before they send me out by plane again. That was a rough ride.

* * *

I still couldn't remember what Air Force Base I was at, but the doctor said he was Air Force. This was a first for me, the doctor and someone else were taking off my bandages. *Damn, they're taking them off my eyes…Oh, I can see light; boy, is it bright.* My eyes started to water up just like I was crying, but it didn't hurt.

"Well, that's a good sign," said the doctor. "Your tear ducts are working good, but we're going to cover them up because your eyes are swelling very bad."

"What do you want to eat?" someone asked me. I had only been able to eat Jello because all my teeth were loose. The doctor thought that when the swelling went down they would be okay.

"I don't know how you ended up here," someone said to me. "You're the only Marine in the bunch and the only one wounded. Most Marines go to the Navy Hospital in Yokosuka." *Hell, I hope I stay here, the treatment is great.* "We don't have the means to do the surgery that you need and your orders read for you to go to the Army 106 Hospital."

"Hello, Marine," I heard this woman's voice say. "I'm a Red Cross worker. Is there anything I can do for you?"

"I'd like to send my wife a letter and let her know where I am," I said. "I think I had a Red Cross worker write a letter for me just before I left Vietnam, but I'm not sure. I just want to tell her I'm doing OK and not to worry and that if all goes well, I may be back in the States in a month or two."

* * *

It sure was a short night, or it seemed that way, and now they were loading me on a helicopter. Our destination must have been close because they told me it would be only a half hour ride. The ride was smooth so it must have been a big bird.

"Mr. Brandon," someone said, "I will be the doctor taking care of you."

"Thank you for calling me 'mister,'" I replied, "but I'm a Marine Gunnery Sergeant, Sir, and most of the time they just call me Gunny."

"Well, that's okay with me. We are crowded for bed space at the present time, so you will have to be here in the ward hallway until we can make room on the ward for you."

"Marine, I'm the duty medic and I will be taking care of you," someone said. From his voice, I guessed he was black. He changed my bandages and must have been washing off dry blood, because he was pushing very hard and I could feel all my bandages pulling loose…boy, he sure was doing a shitty job.

* * *

I could see a little under my eye bandages: nothing with my right eye, but I could make out some kind of movement with my left. I could see a Japanese woman near my bed. She must have been a maid, because she was wiping down my bed.

"Ohayo gozaimasu," I said. If I remember right, that means "Good morning."

She said the same thing back to me.

I tried another phrase. "O genki desu ka?"

She laughed and said, "Hai, genki desu Paddy." (I think that means "Paddy, I am fine.") Then she started talking real fast to me in Japanese and I laughed. I only knew a few words but she spoke good English and asked me where I learned to speak Japanese. I told her that I had been stationed way up north near Mt. Fuji, back in the early fifties. She came by my bed several times during the day to talk to me.

* * *

I started getting pains in my stomach and felt like my asshole was going to blow up. I pushed the button for help.

The same medic that changed my bandages came in and said, "What the fuck do you want? You're getting to be a pain in my fucking ass."

I said, "This is the first time I've asked for anyone."

"Well, what the hell do you want?" he said.

"I don't think I've gone to the bathroom in several days," I told him, "and my ass feels like it's going to bust."

He shoved a cold bed pan under my butt and left.

"Oh my God, I'm busting open," I started to scream. "Oh God, help me."

The same medic came back. "What the hell is wrong with you now?"

"Goddamn, my ass is busting open," I said.

He pulled my legs open, said something, and called for help. The doctor who was taking care of me arrived quickly. My ass was bleeding; there was a turd so big it wouldn't come out. I don't know what they did, but it felt like all my guts came out.

"How long since you had a bowel movement?" the doctor asked me.

"This is the first time since I was wounded June 28th. I'm not sure when it was before then, and today is the 11th of July." My ass was still hurting, but God, what a relief. The doctor told them to get me out of the hallway and move me into a small ward and put me under 24 hour care. They also took that asshole medic off my care.

* * *

They took both bandages off my eyes now and I was able to start making out some items, but could only see parts of things. I could close my eyes and then open them and could see well for about a second, and then they would cloud over when the light hit them.

The Japanese maid came by and I asked her if they had a hospital store where she could get me a pair of dark glasses. I knew that I had two fives and some ones in military payment scrip and asked her to take five and see if that was enough.

She brought me back a big pair of those wrap around glasses that you wear over regular glasses, but they worked. They kept my eyes from watering and I started to see better, but never told anyone because they never asked. I had yet to see an eye doctor, so I just played dumb. This was my third day and nothing was said as to when I was going to have surgery or skin grafts over my wounds.

* * *

I was waiting for the doctors to make their rounds, and when they got to my bed they told me I was being sent back to the Air Force base. I would be leaving for the United States in the morning by Air Force jet, medical evacuation. I just laid there because I was in shock. In a matter of minutes I was on my way to a helicopter, back to the Air Force Base.

It was good to be back at the Air Force Hospital; nice clean sheets and the best of care. Shit, I could stay here, I don't care.

Boy, that was one long night. I was glad to see morning come and had my first solid food: scrambled eggs, toast and milk. It was kind of hard trying to swallow, but I got most of it down.

* * *

Boy, what a big plane. It looked like all they had were bunks, but I still wasn't able to see very well. We sure took off fast, or maybe I was just used to the old prop planes that were kind of slow. The crew was all Air Force. A little fat guy said he would be my caregiver and told me we would make a one-hour fuel stop in Alaska, then continue to Travis Air Force Base in San Francisco. I told him I went through there when I went to Vietnam.

I must have gotten my bowels and kidneys working because I had to pee about every hour or more, but the guy never said anything. He would just grab my dink and poke it into a paper tube or something, and when I was done he would give it a little shake, never saying anything. He took good care of me.

We were told that it was 11 am in the States and we would be landing in a few minutes. I must have slept most of the way because I only remember waking to pee and when we landed in Alaska. I also remember drinking lots of milk and orange juice.

* * *

Boy, air conditioned buses made into ambulances. I think there were maybe only four or five people on my bus. As soon as I saw the hospital, I remembered it from back in 1957 when we played football at Travis and one of our team got hurt and we had to pick him up at this hospital that sat up on a hill. They unloaded us and took us to a private room with our own toilets. Up to now I had to sit on a bed pan, so I asked if someone would help me to sit on the toilet. Both my arms and one leg were broken, but I made it. *Oh man, just let it go, then bring on the food.*

"What do you want to eat, Gunny?" they asked. "Just name it and we will do our best to fix it."

"Steak, french fries, milk and toast," I said.

"We can do that," they said, "and you can make a phone call anywhere you want for ten minutes, all paid for by the Air Force Sergeants Association. That will give us time to fix your meal."

I called Shirlie, but she wasn't home. So I tried her at her mother's house and she was there. When I told her where I was, she wanted to know how I was going to pay for the phone call. I told her it was free, but she wasn't sure if it was and didn't want to talk too long. I told her I would be landing at McChord Air Force Base in Washington about noon tomorrow. It was the 17th of July.

When my food arrived, I tried to eat but my throat and teeth were still tender and it hurt to swallow, but I tried my best.

I was trying to get over the big meal I just finished working on when in walked about ten Air Force medics, some men, some women. They were from a reserve unit near Los Angeles and were on two weeks training. They wanted to know if they could take care of my wounds as part of their training.

As they did so, some of them got sick because my wounds were still open and you could see bones and torn tissue. The right side of my body was burned black. I was numb now, so I wasn't able to feel much pain. They were sure pampering me, and I loved it. I knew it would end soon because I was leaving in the morning for the state of Washington.

Most of the friends I'd made in my short stay at Travis were there to see me off when I was loaded on the plane. I guess these guys didn't see many guys like me…shot full of holes. I was thanking a bunch of young guys who were weekend military people, who'd never even had a thought what it must be like to fight a war. I know one thing: my feelings for the Air Force sure changed. I'd always felt they got a free ride while we Marines did all the dirty work. Well, maybe we do, but the Air Force sure did their part when it came to taking care of me.

* * *

I wish I could see out of the plane because it would be good to see all the green trees that I never thought I would ever see again. It feels like we're landing, so I might be able to see some trees when we get off the plane. I sure can't see very far, so if things aren't close, I can't make them out.

"Transportation from Bremerton Hospital will be here to pick you up soon," said the guy who'd been taking care of me, "so you shouldn't be here long."

"Hi, Gene!" someone said.

I looked to where I'd heard my name. It was my younger brother, Bill, here to meet me. *I didn't know he was stationed here.*

"Everyone knew you were landing here today," Bill said. "I'm glad to see you. How are you doing?"

"I'm okay, just tired and sore."

Bill stayed with me until they loaded me on the ambulance and said he would get over to see me since it wasn't too far to the hospital. I asked him how far it was and he said he thought about an hour.

The ambulance driver, unsure what road to take, was bitching at the road signs. *Great,* I thought. *A dumb fucking swabby carrying a wounded Marine, lost somewhere in the State of Washington.* I was glad to see the gate as we pulled through; at least he'd made it that far.

* * *

I lay in the ambulance for a long time while and was wondering if that asshole had forgotten me when someone finally took me out and then left me lying on the floor. I lay there until someone from the ward I was going to came and got me. *Oh shit, the damned Navy again…hurry up and wait.*

A female sailor who said she was in charge of new arrivals took me to my ward. She looked dark skinned to me, maybe Indian or something. I was going to a ward called Ward B Dirty Surgery. Two people were trying to lift me on a gurney…*shit, sure as hell, they're going to drop me on the floor. Shit, why didn't they leave me with the Air Force? At least* they *had plenty of help.*

As they wheeled me on, I noticed there were rows of bunks on both sides of

WESTERN UNION TELEGRAM

```
RWUB080    BC TNX..
O-
WUB087 SSK106 PR SEC292 GOVT DL PDB
TDSE TLX BREMERTON WASH 19 1115A
PDT
MRS SHIRLEY BRANDON
   142 EAST 7TH ST MCMINNVILLE ORG
191613ZTHIS IS TO INFORM YOU THAT YOUR HUSBAND GYSGT
PERCY EUGENE BRANDON USMC 137 23 56 ARRIVED AT THIS
HOSPITAL 18 JUL 68. HE IS HOSPITALIZED FOR TREATMENT
OF WOUNDS OF ALL EXTREMITIES AND STOMACH WITH PERFORATION
OF THE STOMACH AND SMALL INTESTINE. HIS MEDICAL CONDITION
IS NOT SUCH AS TO REQUIRE YOUR PRESENCE HOWEVER YOU WILL
BE VERY WELCOME IF YOU WISH TO VISIT HIM. HE MAY RECEIVE
MAIL AT THE NAVAL HOSPITAL BREMERTON, WASHINGTON
98314. YOU WILL BE NOTIFIED OF ANY SIGNIFICANT CHANGE
IN HIS CONDITION. C.P. ROOT CAPTAIN MEDICAL CORPS
U S NAVY COMMANDING OFFICER NAVAL HOSPITAL BREMERTON,
WASHINGTON
   NAVAL HOSPITAL
1221P BC///////1221P PDT JUL 19 68
```

July 19, 1968

the room and most of them looked like they were full. I got put in a bunk right next to the nurse's station. Damn, there sure were a lot of nurses around the desk; I was the only new patient coming to this ward.

"Hello, Gunnery Sergeant Brandon. My name is Doctor Goubler. I'm the duty doctor on this ward and I'll be going over your wounds with you. The surgeons who'll be doing the operations will be in to see you later."

All my bandages were taken off and there I lay, bare ass naked, with all those nurses looking at me. Damn, it was cold. "How long is this going to take?" I asked. "I'm freezing."

The female nurse that helped bring me to that ward showed up with a bedside cleanup station and started cleaning my wounds.

"Some of your wounds are starting to heal," said Dr. Goubler. "We may have some trouble with the skin grafts."

"What will that mean for me?" I asked.

"It'll be up to the doctors doing the surgery to tell you that."

After the doctor left, the female nurse explained, "They cut away the flesh so the skin graft will take."

I didn't know what that meant, but it never sounded good. *Well, shit, I'm at their mercy.*

I had just gotten all covered up and was getting warm when some more doctors came in. They took all my covers off and start pulling at my wounds. They were the surgeons who would be fixing me up. One of them was a light-skinned black guy; he said he was the Ophthalmologist and would be working on my eyes. That kind of scared me because, at the time, I didn't know I still had metal in my eyes.

The surgeons told me I wouldn't have surgery until August 23rd because my wounds wouldn't be ready until then. Once they were done examining me, several Marines came to my bunk to talk to me. One of them was a gunny that had been blown up in an ammo dump. He was lucky to be alive: I'd seen an ammo dump blow up in June when I was at Dong-Ha; the explosions went on all night and several Marines were killed. He was kind of short with his answers; maybe he didn't wanted to talk about what happened.

* * *

I hadn't been at the hospital very long when I heard someone say, "Is Gunny Brandon on this Ward?"

I knew that voice…it was Shirlie. *Boy, she sure got here fast.*

"I'm over here!" I said.

She came over and touched me and kissed me. I could see, but not well, as my eyes were blurry from having the doctors looking at them. She had on my favorite color, a red sweater. She must have looked good, because someone whistled at her, but everyone got pretty quiet when they saw that she was *my* wife. Shirlie had come up on the bus; her Mother was taking care of the kids. She had only been there a few minutes when they told her she would have to wait out in the waiting room while they changed my dressings…she said she wanted to stay.

Up to this time I hadn't had a chance to look at my wounds to see how bad they were. The Navy Corps wave who was taking care of me came and took all the bandages off and started cleaning up my wounds. *I must be getting tough because I don't feel much pain from what she's doing to my wounds.*

After the Corps wave put the dressing back on my wounds, Shirlie described them to me. "I can see into your leg: I can see cartilage and part of the bone. Your leg looks the worst; the hole where the bullet went in and came out took a lot of flesh with it. It looks like maybe three or four wounds are open so much that maybe they'll have to have skin grafts to cover them up."

"I wonder where they'll get the skin from to cover my wounds."

"They'd probably take it from somewhere else on your body."

"Oh shit, that means I get cut some place else and shit, the only place I didn't get hit was on my back and butt. I wonder how that can work. I can't lie on my belly, and if they take it off my back, what the hell will I have to do, stand up to sleep?"

"Maybe they'll take it off the sides of your legs."

"Damn," I said, "I'm going to be one sad looking case; I don't think I'll be lying on the beach any more."

Shirlie stayed at a motel in Bremerton and came back each day to see me. She eventually had to get back to Oregon to take care of the kids, but said she would come back the first weekend she could. She told me my brother Gary and my sister wanted to come see me, so maybe she would come up with them. My brother Bill lived only 50 miles away; maybe everyone could stay there. Then they could all come and visit.

* * *

I had a lot of x-rays and blood tests all week before my surgery and I was due to go in first thing Thursday, August 23rd. Damn, it had been almost two months since I was wounded and they were just now putting me back together… or maybe not that long: I was so screwed up I wasn't sure what the hell had happened. I did know that I'd be glad when I could get healed up and the hell away from all that.

When I was in the Air Force Hospital, they would help me out of bed when I had to take a shit. But when I asked the duty Navy Corpsman if he would help me get on the toilet, he said I wasn't allowed out of bed and that I would have to use a bed pan.

"Bullshit," I said. "I've been out of bed for over a week as long as someone was there to help me."

"Tough shit," he said. "Those are the doctor's orders."

The toilets were clear at the other end of the ward and there was no fucking way I was going to sit on a bed pan.

I got out of bed and started to walk, and then…*Oh shit, my leg hurts like hell, but to hell with it now, I've made my move and I'm going to finish my trip to the shit house.* I thought I would never make it. All the Marines on the ward couldn't believe what I was doing—and I wasn't sure I was, either—but it was too late now.

I made it to the shit house, but I was hurting so bad that I knew I could never make it back to the bed.

I heard the duty Corpsman asking, "Where the hell is Gunny at?"

One of the Marines in the bed near the shit house said, "He's in the head."

Boy, was this guy pissed; half my bandages were off and spread all the way from my bunk to the head. "How the hell did you get here?" he asked.

"I walked," I said, "and if you could wipe my ass and bring me a wheelchair, I'd like to get back to my bunk." I was hurting so bad…but I wasn't about to let that prick know it. He took me back to my bunk in a wheelchair.

One of the troops on the ward told the duty Corpsman, "Don't fuck with the Gunny…all Gunnys are half crazy; who else could walk the full length of a ward with forty holes in him and a broken leg?"

The Corpsman must have told the duty nurse what I'd done, because she and the doctor came to my bunk and told me it was necessary that I follow orders.

I told them, "I know what I need to do to get well and get the hell out of here…all you have to do is sew me up and I'll get out."

The next time I had to use the shit house, they put me in a wheelchair and took me there. I never had to sit on the bed pan again. I did, however, pay for my bravado. Even though my leg was killing me, I wouldn't ask for any painkiller.

* * *

The night before I was due for my operation, they didn't give me any food or drink, so it was a long night. At 0800 they came for me and I remembered the song that asshole Corpsman sang to me on the *Sanctuary* off the coast in Vietnam. "Here they come to take me away, HA, HA, HO, HO. They're taking me away, HA, HA, HO, HO," and some other dumb words.

In the operating room, the doctor told me it would take about two hours to do what had to be done. First, they would work on my eyes, and then all the skin grafts would be done, with the skin coming from my left side. He said they shave it off one layer at a time until they get it all covered. Then he told me to start counting backwards from ten….

I only got to eight.

* * *

I woke up back in my bunk and it seemed like it was afternoon. I don't know why I thought that, because my eyes were taped shut. I also couldn't move my arms or legs.

Someone said, "How are you feeling, Gunny?"

"My body's burning up. What's going on?"

"The burning sensation is from the skin grafts. As soon as the bleeding stops, it'll go away. If the pain gets *too* bad, I can give you a shot."

All I could say was, "Oh Shit, Oh Shit, Oh Shit"—and then I passed out.

When I woke up, it still hurt, but the burning was almost gone.

"What time is it?" I asked.

"Seven o'clock," someone said.

"At night?"

"No, it's Friday morning."

Shit, I had slept all night.

* * *

"Boy I'm hungry," I said. "Will I get any chow?" I still couldn't see.

"Your chow is here," said the duty Corpsman, "but I'll have to feed you because both your arms are in casts."

He gave me a drink of milk and then a bite of scrambled eggs and then I never heard him say anything else.

When I asked for another bite, someone said, "The Corpsman went to the other end of the ward." *Damn that asshole.* I was hungry.

I could move my left arm a little, so I felt around until I found the fork. I was able to get it stuck in my hand cast and started to feel around on my tray for some food. I felt the fork stick into something; trying to get it to my mouth with a cast on my hand wasn't easy, but I made it. Cold scrambled eggs; I must have had the whole piece on the fork and stuck it all in my mouth. I don't think I chewed it enough because when I swallowed, it got stuck. I started choking but it wouldn't come up. I jerked my left arm and hit myself on the chest...up came the eggs, but the pain in my chest made me sick and I started to puke.

I heard someone yelling, "Corpsman, Gunny's choking!"

"What the hell are you doing, Gunny?" the Corpsman said.

"Trying to eat, you asshole!"

Boy, puking up with all my wounds almost killed me, and the cast on my left hand and arm was broken all to shit. I didn't get any more to eat and I got my ass chewed out good by the doctor. I never said how my cast got broken, because the Corpsman would have gotten his ass in a sling.

*　*　*

After chow, the doctors made their rounds, and the eye doctor took the bandages off my eyes. The left one hurt like hell when the light hit it, so he covered it back up. He left the other eye uncovered.

With my right eye, I could just make out movement when someone would come near my bed. Now, at least, I could see when my chow came, and I made sure I chewed it up good and made that asshole Corpsman stay there until I was done eating.

As the day went on, I got to seeing even better, but I never said so.

"Can you see anything?" they would ask.

"I can tell if it's light or dark," I would reply. I didn't think they needed to know more than that. When the eye doctor told me I should be able to make out movement in a few days, I just said, "OK."

They only put half a cast back on my left arm, so if the Corpsman left before I was done eating, I could feed myself. But when the corpswave fed me, I could look at her tits and she never knew I was looking at them.

*　*　*

Shirlie, my brother, sister and their friends came to see me the third day after I got out of surgery. I think it was a Saturday afternoon. While we were talking, the duty Corpsman came up and said it was time for my pain pill. I told him I was OK and didn't need one. He said something about me trying to "act tough" in front of my family; I told him I hadn't taken *anything* for pain yet.

"Well," he said, "you *do* have to have a shot of penicillin in case of infection." And he gave me a shot in the ass.

Shit, it burned like hell! All I could say was, "Oh shit, oh shit! I never had a shot burn like that!!"

My brother and sister left for home, but Shirlie stayed so she could come back again Sunday.

When the doctors made their rounds Monday morning, I asked why the shot had hurt so bad; the burning was about to kill me. The doctor asked me who gave me the shot, and I told him. Later, I heard the doctor chewing out the Corpsman's ass.

Later that day, one of the Marines in the ward—despite being in a body cast—grabbed the Corpsman around the neck and beat the shit out of him. I'm not sure what the Corpsman had been doing, but that was the last we saw of him…and the shots never hurt anymore.

* * *

I had over two hundred stitches on my chest alone and as they started to heal, the itching was driving me crazy. When I tried to scratch around the wounds, the stitches started to come untied, so I would pull them out. By the time they were ready to take the stitches out, there were just a few left. The doctor never asked where they went; he just gave me a dirty look.

* * *

I was able to get out of bed some days and sit in a wheelchair. When the corpsmen weren't watching, I would leave the ward and roll around the hospital. We were on the "dirty surgery" ward (so called because some of us still had open wounds) and weren't allowed in the Post Exchange. I would roll down there and get some milk and a donut.

One day, a corpswave saw me down there and told me if I didn't help them keep the Marines on the ward in order she was going to turn me in. Most of the Marines on the ward were assholes to the Corpsman, so I went around to all the troops on the ward and told them I was in charge of the ward now and if they had a bitch with the Corpsman to tell me about it and let me take care of it.

Their biggest bitch was that even the guys who *were* able to get out of bed and move around the ward in a wheel chair were never allowed to do so. I made friends with the corpswave running the EKG office (heart test program) and got her to steal some wheel chairs and bring them to our ward. That took care of most of the bitching, but some of us still got in trouble for leaving the ward.

* * *

The main doctor in charge of the ward had gone back East for two weeks for some special schooling, and the new doctor was scared to make any changes. Some of us were ready to get out of bed and try walking, but he said NO. I would get out of my bed when I could and stand, making my bed before the duty changed, so I was the first one ready for a bath and a change of clothes. Since I was in a private room, they never got to see how I was always the first to get my bath and be ready for chow.

I was getting so strong that I could get in and out of bed on my own and jump in a wheel chair. I would hide out in the office with the corpswave and miss all the shit on the ward until this backfired on me.

This corpswave was an Indian Eskimo from Alaska and we got to be good friends. One night she went out and got drunk and came on the ward to see me. Not only was she drunk, but she wanted my body, I think. The duty Corpsman told her to get out of the ward.

That's the wrong thing to tell a drunken Indian.

That ended my visits to her office, but not her visits to me. She got drunk once more and got in trouble trying to come and see me. She was a great lady, but sure got mean when she drank some of that fire water.

* * *

One day my parents drove up to see me. As soon as my mother saw my hand she said, "Oh, your poor hand. How will you be able to write?"

"I think it'll be OK," I said. "I'll just have to learn to write with my right hand."

I had a few dollars and asked my mother to take it to help pay their way back home.

My dad never had much to say; my mother did most of the talking. She asked me, "Are the Marines going to let you come home for good?"

"I want to stay in," I told her, "but I don't think they'll let me because of my wounds. I'll just have to wait and see. I don't think I'll ever have to go back to war again, though."

* * *

The doctor in charge of our ward had returned from his special schooling and was making his rounds. I still wasn't able to bend my right leg, so I was sitting in a wheel chair when he got to me. I asked him, "Will I be able to get off the dirty surgery ward soon?" I knew I would never get to go outside until I was off this ward.

"As soon as you can get out of that wheel chair and walk," he said, "you can be moved to ward 'A.'"

I got out of my wheel chair, walked to my desk, emptied it and said, "I'm ready now!"

So I got to move that day but, once again, it backfired on me. I was put in charge of all the Marines in the hospital…all the sick, lame and lazy ones that never wanted to follow orders; who just wanted to sleep, sit around and smoke. We were having trouble with them just calling a taxi and leaving the hospital, going to town and then going home…it wasn't an easy job.

However, on the nice days, I *was* able to go outside and lay in the sun, then eat in the hospital mess hall. I got to eat in the Navy chief private dining area. We were taken good care of and that was fine with me, because I wasn't where the troops could bitch at me.

* * *

I was finally given the okay to leave the hospital, but only for four hours, and I had to stay on the base. Shirlie and the kids came up to see me and she brought my uniform with her. I would need that to get out of the hospital. Boy, what a shock: I had lost over forty pounds and my uniform just hung on me; but I wanted out so I put it on anyway.

Shirlie had called a taxi so we could go to the Navy Chief Club. I wanted to be able to walk up to the bar and order me a cold Olympia beer.

The funny part was, when the doctor told me I wouldn't be able to bend my fingers on my left hand—that he would have to set them so they wouldn't just hang up on everything—I told him to just set them so I could fit them around a cold bottle of beer.

He did a great job: they fit just right. Unfortunately, I couldn't drink because the beer was so cold it burned my throat. I tried several times to drink it but it hurt too much, and by then my leg was hurting so bad I just left my beer and we took a taxi back to the hospital. I guess I wasn't as tough as I thought.

Shirlie and the kids went back to the motel and I went to bed. I still had a long way to go before I was back in shape.

They came back for a while on Sunday, but I was still hurting, and my youngest daughter got sick after being stung on the foot by a bee, so they left to go back to Oregon.

* * *

I spent the next few weeks going to the hospital gym and working on trying to get my strength back. A female nurse, a Lt./Commander, was in charge of helping us with a program and we had to pass all the tests before we could get leave out of the hospital.

I'd had enough of this place. We only had to go down once a day, but I went *three* times a day. I had to be able to lift enough weights to prove I was back in shape. At first I could only lift 1-1/2 pounds with my leg…and the test called for twenty pounds. Shit, I was never going to make that much and it hurt like hell.

One day, the Commander was working with me, trying to help me get my fingers to bend. Ever the wise ass, I asked, "If we can get my fingers to work, do you think I could play the piano?"

"Sure!" she replied.

"Boy, that's great!" I said. "I never could play it before!"

That went over like a fart in church. She made me do all my exercises by myself after that. The best part of her working with me was when she held my hand to her chest while she tried to get my fingers to bend, so I got to cop a feel once in a while. I'm sure she knew she was giving me a thrill; maybe she knew I needed that.

* * *

I woke up one night and my ear was killing me.

The duty Corpsman looked in my ear and said it was plugged up. He went to get some kind of ear wash and put it in my ear; it hurt so bad I thought I would die.

I had to wait until an ear, nose and throat doctor could see me. He looked in my ear and said I had a piece of metal stuck in my ear drum. How the hell it got in there, I don't know, but he operated the same day and took it out.

That screwed me out of getting out of the hospital that time.

* * *

I wasn't sure how long ago the doctor had told me it would be before he would let me go home on a 30 day leave, but he did tell me I could go whenever I was ready. I called Shirlie and asked her if she could drive up and bring me home.

She told me that she had done it before, with three kids, a dog and a car full of ammo, when I was on ship back in 1963, so she could do it again. She could come up in the morning with Rita and pick me up; we could be back home the same day.

It sure will be a good feeling to get out of the hospital and away from all these sick people. It won't hurt me to get away from these Marines, either. I think they all hate the hospital, and the young guys just don't care about the Marines—all they want is out.

One thing I didn't plan on was that, because I couldn't bend my leg, I wasn't able to help drive home. I couldn't even get in the front seat. Shirlie had to drive, while I rode in the back seat…and picked on her all the way home. "If you don't keep your fingers out of my ears," she warned me, "I'm going to stop and kick the shit out of you!"

* * *

Our house sure looked good to me, and to be home and away from the hospital was great. I couldn't believe the house. The floors and the walls were all finished. The house looked great and I asked Shirlie how this all happened. She said she did it all, stripped the floors and walls by herself and repainted everything. I think she had started it while I was in Vietnam and I saw part of it when I was home the last time, but I was so screwed up I wasn't sure. She sure had it looking good.

We were supposed to have the whole weekend to ourselves, but my family all thought they should come and visit us, so we had our share of company.

At first, Shirlie got to know some of the people through her parents, and one of them was the lady who ran the swimming pool. Her husband drove a logging truck for her brother, so she let me come to the swimming pool and swim whenever I wanted. I only lived about four blocks from the pool, so I would walk there. I still wasn't able to see very well and the guy who owned the Shell Gas Station on the corner would watch for me and make sure that I could get across the street. The swimming sure helped because I was getting stronger real fast and my leg was starting to bend a little. I knew I was on my way back…if only my eyes would get better.

* * *

After being home only a few days, my hand started hurting bad. I couldn't sleep at night because of the pain, and I was afraid I might have to go all the way back to the hospital. Shirlie wanted to go to the Air Force Base near Corvallis, only 40 miles to the south. I agreed.

The doctor I saw there thought I might have an exposed nerve in my hand. He gave me a shot and some pain pills, and *MAN* was I floating on air. I was higher than a kite when we went to the commissary to get some food, supplies and a six pack of beer. I wasn't sure I could drink anything that cold, but it sure tasted good.

* * *

It was towards the end of the summer, and during the time the local farmers burned their fields. As we started through an area where a big field was burning, I started to have some flashbacks of Vietnam. I started shaking.

I told Shirlie, "Hurry and get out of here," then closed my eyes.

Once we got away from the area that was burning, I was okay.

* * *

I found out I was good to drink beer, and I was looking forward to my brother, Gary and his family coming down for the weekend. We were going to go out to my old home town of Grand Ronde and Willamina and see some of my old school friends.

Until we were sitting in the bar having a beer, I hadn't realized how much weight I had lost after I was wounded. A friend I had known all my life came into the bar. I wasn't sure who he was until he started talking, and I still couldn't see that well.

He asked my brother Gary, "How is your brother doing in Vietnam? I heard he'd been wounded."

Gary said, "Why don't you ask him yourself? He's sitting in the booth."

This guy never even knew who I was because I had lost so much weight and was white as a ghost from being in the hospital.

* * *

Although the swimming helped me get back into shape, I was still drinking every weekend. My brother came down once or twice, and because I still couldn't see well enough to walk to town on my own, I had Shirlie take me to the bars so I could drink. She never liked that, because I was never ready to go home, and she worried about the kids coming home. Money was also very short, as I hadn't been paid and we weren't sure how we would make it.

We had a few words over that. She told me I didn't need to go to the bars every day, but all that did was piss me off: I don't like being told what I can and can't do. I decided to go back to the hospital and get clean so I could get back to duty and not have to ask her to help me again.

* * *

I returned to the hospital at the end of September 1968 and started going to the hospital gym every chance I could. One way or another, I was going to make this stiff leg of mine bend. When I got in the whirlpool, my leg would get numb and then I could bend the heck out of it. Once it started to bend, it took just a few days to get almost half the use back.

The eye doctor took me back in, did some more repairs on my eyes and fit me for glasses. Up to this time, I was seeing well enough to get around, but wasn't able to leave the hospital unless someone was with me.

While I was lying in bed waiting for my glasses, I got a phone call from the Marine Reserve Center in Salem, Oregon. It was their Commanding Officer, Captain Williams.

"Will you be able to get out of the hospital for the Marine Corps' Birthday?" Williams asked me. "If so, we'd like you to be the Guest of Honor."

"Yes, sir, I'm sure I can," I replied. "I'll be there. Thank you, sir."

When the eye doctor brought my new glasses, he put them on me and asked me what I could see. One of the Navy Corpsmen who I was good friends with gave me the finger and said, "Hey Gunny, can you see this?"

I looked at the clock; it was 2:00 p.m., so I said, "The little hand is on the two and the big hand is on the twelve. That's so all you swabbies will know what time of day it is when I shove Crothers' finger up his ass!" Everyone laughed. I couldn't believe that, just a few short months earlier, I didn't know if I would ever be able to see again.

When the doctor made his rounds, I asked him if I could go home for four days, so I could be the Guest of Honor at the Marine Corps Ball.

He said, "Go!"

I got in my uniform and headed for the ferry to Seattle. From there, I could catch the train to Portland, then change to a bus in time to get to McMinnville.

I made the train in good time and, being in full uniform, I was the target for all the old military guys who were on the train. They wanted to know all about what was going on.

I met this one old guy who must have been a dairy farmer who milked lots of cows because he pumped my hand with a grip of steel. He pushed on the piece of metal still embedded in my hand until I thought he was going to kill me before I could get my hand free. You'd think I would be smart enough not to let him get my hand again, but shit no, he got it again. I was sure glad to get away from him.

He asked me what the hell we were doing over there anyway. I didn't have a good answer for him…until I saw a good-looking girl sitting in one of the seats. I said, "I'm keeping the enemy over there so he doesn't make that good looking woman a victim of war!"

I made good friends with the bus driver, who said he would drop me off next to my house when he had me on the bus because he only had to go around the block. That was great because I still couldn't see that well.

It was just getting dark when I got home and told Shirlie the good news.

* * *

Shirlie hurried around, trying to put together an outfit for the ball. With her mother's help, she bought green velvet material and began making her dress, so she was keeping pretty busy.

Meanwhile, I was trying to find some flowers for Shirlie. I went by a house that had a flower shop in the back so I asked the lady if she could make me up a special flower for Shirlie. I wanted to get her a yellow rose.

It took the next three days until we were ready to go. On the bases we went all out to make sure we looked good, so I was doing the same here.

We left the kids with Shirlie's parents, and waited until we got to my parents' place in Salem before we changed into our clothes for the ball. This was the first time my mom and dad had ever seen Shirlie and me in full dress.

I remember the last thing my mother said as we were going out the door: "I wish I could be a little mouse and sit in the room and see you come in and hear what you will say." In the years since my mother died, I have thought of that many times and still wonder why I never thought to ask them to go.

* * *

The ball was held at the American Legion Hall in Salem. I wasn't very steady on my feet yet, so I was still walking with my cane. I had my traveling booze

Parris Island, 1967: Shirlie & me at the previous year's Marine Corps Ball

bag that held three bottles of booze, which I got as a gift at Parris Island, South Carolina. The dinner was first and then the program, so I was feeling good by then and had made my talk to last only about fifteen minutes. I knew *I* never wanted to hear the bullshit, and wanted to get down to doing some drinking.

About halfway through the night they started running out of booze, so I broke out my cache and we began drinking it. I didn't know any of these guys, but they liked to drink and that was OK with me. Soon, two old guys came over to the table. They were pissed at us, and told us that was how they made their money to operate the club. By then, we didn't give a shit about anything, so I threw away my cane and went out dancing my ass off.

The first sergeant of the company came over and gave me some shit, wanting to know why I needed a cane when I came in. I said, "Well, I was sober then, but right now I'm feeling no pain."

I'm not sure what time the ball was over…the last thing I can remember was when we stopped somewhere and I ordered a chili burger. I got about half of it eaten when I made a run through the door and started puking my guts out. Boy, I had a hangover that would kill a horse.

* * *

It was about noon and I had to head back to the hospital. I knew I would be coming out of the hospital soon, so I was going to take a chance and take our car up with me.

Monday morning, the sergeant major from the Marine barracks came up to see me, and asked if I wanted to stay at the hospital and be in charge of all the hospital Marines. They weren't sure if I was going to stay in the Marines because of my wounds. I asked the sergeant major if I could stay on limited duty for a while to see if I could pass my physical so that I could stay in. I wrote several letters to some of the officers I knew to see if they could help me at least stay on limited duty for six months to see if I could make it.

I was pretty lucky, because in just a few days I got several letters back, and every one of them had a lot of good to say about me. My commanding officer from Parris Island, South Carolina, went to the commandant of the Marine Corps and asked for me to be able to stay in active duty. He said "half a Brandon was worth more to an outfit than most whole Marines."

The commanding officer from the Marine barrack was an Air Wing Col, but his XO officer, Jack Westerman, was a colonel I had served with. Jack got me orders to Camp Pendleton, California, for six months of limited duty at the Marine Corps Base. He also wrote a letter for me to the Chief of Staff, Colonel Emils, asking him to take care of me and make sure I got a good job.

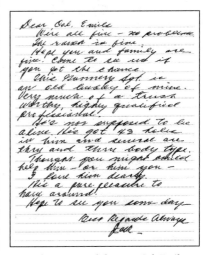

Jack Westerman's letter to Col. Emils

I had to wait a few days for the medical board, because they said I should be discharged because of my wounds with only thirty percent or about $60 a month. I was just now starting to walk without my cane. *How the hell do they expect me to support a wife and three kids on that?* The Sergeant Major told me I could go home and wait for my orders; he would call me if and when they ok'ed me to stay in.

* * *

I'd been home only three days when I got the call: my sea bag had shown up, and my orders were in for Camp Pendleton.

Shirlie made me lunch: it was a long trip back to Bremerton, Washington. I was going to check out of the hospital, get my sea bag, pick up my orders, and get out of there. Since I was only six months limited duty, I was taking a chance I wouldn't get to stay in. More bad news came when they found out I'd been overpaid, so all I was going to get was a little travel money. It wouldn't be enough to take Shirlie and the kids, or even *think* about having a house.

* * *

Done with the hospital, I went to Salem to say my goodbyes to my parents.

My mother was worried about me driving on my own. "Let your dad go with you. We have friends who live just fifteen miles from the base, and he can visit them. Then your sisters"—who lived near Los Angeles—"can pick him up and get him on a bus."

I wasn't sure how the hell I was going to make it, with no pay due, and me in California and Shirlie and the kids in Oregon, but my dad and I took off early in the morning. My mother had packed us enough food to travel for a month. We ran into some winter weather before we got into California, and had to travel several miles in the snow.

My dad wanted to pick up a bottle of whiskey…he said it would let him rest and sleep better. That was one of two or three before we got to my sisters' place where we would stay overnight.

I thought my dad should stay with my sisters, and I could make it on my own, but he wanted to visit these people they knew, so off we went. My dad liked his whiskey, so it took us another bottle to go the last 160 miles.

* * *

I wasn't sure where I would be going when I got to the base, so I stopped by the base swimming pool. I was hoping some of the old civilians I knew when I was stationed there several years ago would still be there. I asked a lifeguard if Sam and Paul still worked in pool maintenance and he said, "Yes."

"Who's in charge of the pools?"

"Staff Sergeant Charlie Vorce."

I almost shit…Vorce and I ran the pools back in 1960 and 1961. Vorce came out of the office to see who was here and I said, "Hey, Charlie Tuna, are you ever going to leave these pools?" Damn, it was good to see him; he was one of my old drinking buddies.

Well, it wasn't long before we had a case of beer and another jug of booze. My dad and I were both loaded by the time we got over to their friends' place, and that wasn't good because they were not drinkers. We had something to eat and went to bed.

* * *

I got up early, ate breakfast, and said I would see them later: I had to get to the base and check in. I went to the swimming pool and changed into my uniform, then went to headquarters and checked in.

I had a letter from Col. Jack Westerman to Col. Emils, so I asked to see him. He knew I was coming and he said he wanted me to work for him in the G-Three Section with Training, but I didn't need to be to work until Monday and today was only Wednesday. I was to take the rest of the time to get checked in and settled.

That only took about half a day, so I went to talk to Charlie to see if they still had some special service job that a Marine could work part time...my ass was broke.

Charlie was good friends with one of the guys who ran the outdoor stores on base, so I got some part time work stocking shelves and working in the Christmas tree lots at nights. Each night we would end up with several branches that had broken off some of the trees. The guy I worked for told me to just throw them in the dumpster. I asked if he cared if I made them into Christmas wreaths and sold them. He said I could do with them as I wanted. Well, you just knew quite a few trees would lose their bottom branches, because I was making several bucks extra selling wreaths, and boy, did that come in handy. All my money was going home to Shirlie and the kids.

* * *

My job in the G-Three Office was an easy one, but I was having trouble dealing with it because the scars from my wounds were still tender, and wearing my uniform kept them bleeding.

My job was to interview the Marines coming back from Vietnam. We were making up a training book on things they learned in Vietnam. The troops never wanted to talk about what they did, and most of the staff NCOs and officers were full of shit. They spent more time telling me how good they were, and how they should have gotten a Navy Cross, and how the Marine Corps had made a mistake by not having them up on the front line, because their skills were wasted in the rear. The Marines who were actually doing the fighting never made it to my office.

One day the Colonel came into my office. "What would you like to be doing?" he asked.

"I want to be back with the troops."

"Because of your disabilities, that's not going to happen," said the Colonel. "But perhaps you could go to Base Special Services and be in charge of the troops there. They need a gunny who knows how that part of the headquarters runs, and since you've run the pools, you should be able to keep up with the troops."

Shit, this is great...I can be my own boss. All I had to do was check in with the major in charge of the company.

The major hated his job and was on the Col.'s shit list. He told me to get the Col. off his ass, and he didn't care how I did it.

The major's personnel consisted of almost three hundred of the base's worst screw-offs, staff included. There was a staff sergeant or gunny in charge of almost all the areas: golf course, rodeo grounds, swimming pools, Lake O'Neal Boat Shop, bowling alleys and the rest of them. None of them wore uniforms;

if they did, it was half civilian—and that was the Col's big bitch. He never knew who was a Marine and who was a civilian because we had both of them doing the jobs.

The first place I went was Lake O'Neal. I knew the staff sergeant there and that he was a first class screw-off. We had been drinking together and he looked like shit. He said he had five Marines and one civilian working for him. I went to check them out; as far as I could tell, he had four Marines and two civilians.

The black kid, who the Ssgt said was a Marine l/cpl., had an afro, long fingernails, Marine dress shoes and God knows what the rest of his uniform was. I walked up to him and asked, "Do you know who I am?"

"Yes, sir, you're the new company gunny."

"Then you know that I don't make the rules; I'm only a gunny, and my job is to make sure the rules are followed."

From what I could see, he damned sure was working under his own rules. The Marine Corps *I* was being paid by would never allow *me* to run around like that. He also told me he didn't live in the barracks, that he lived with his wife and two kids in town.

"You've got two hours to get looking like a Marine," I told him, "or your wife and kids will be strangers to you before you get any time off."

The major and I talked, and decided we needed to have a clothing inspection on the bunk. I thought we'd have to throw most of them in the brig, because 90 percent of them never had a full sea bag. I thought maybe we should just call for a uniform check to see what they could come up with. We put out the word that we would have a uniform inspection and the major would tell them what section would wear what uniform, so they had better have at least one uniform of each ready.

That worked well. Everyone had at least one uniform of each item they were issued, but knowing Marines I knew I wouldn't be lucky enough to get them all straight.

I had one Cpl. back from Vietnam who never wanted to put up with anyone's bullshit, and some of the other troops were kind of holding back to see how much he was going to get away with. He wasn't going to do shit, he was a short timer and damn sure not going to buy any uniforms or stand any inspections. His attitude was, "When that fucking gunny shows up, I'm gonna show him my Purple Heart and let him know I paid my dues."

So I showed up in my uniform with only one ribbon and my Purple Heart with three gold stars and told him, "If you ever want a gold star on your Purple Heart, I'd better see a uniform hanging in your locker before the major gets here."

This major knew he had some of the worst bunch of Marines on base, and that was the best he was going to get. We were known as the sick, lame and lazy company...and we truly were. Most everyone had been hurt in Vietnam, and many of them weren't wounds from the enemy, but other injuries bad enough to keep them out of full duty.

After the major left, I told them, "You are to have at least one uniform of each issue ready. If your job calls for civilian clothing, then wear it, but if the Col. wants to see you, you better have a uniform to wear. As long as *they* are off *my* ass, I'll be off yours."

That seemed to work fine; too fine, in fact, because I had more time to play…and Vorce and I played a lot. We were both wheelers and dealers, and were always cooking up some kind of scheme so we'd have money for drinks. Vorce was in the shit house with his wife, and I wasn't at the top of her list of people she wanted hanging around her old man. By noon every day, Vorce and I were ready to just lay back and have a few drinks. As always, we were broke earlier each week.

I had to make the changeover at the boat ramp at Lake O'Neal. Some fast-talking salesman for Mercury Boat Motors had got to someone in a predicament. They were changing over from Evinrude boat motors, and all the old boat motors were to be turned into base disposal to be sold as surplus. We wound up with twenty motors, and boxes of all kinds of parts.

I turned in the motors to the civilian running the drop off point; he signed me off and told me to throw the rest of the stuff in the trash. I told Vorce one of the boat dealers in Oceanside might have some use for the parts.

The Evinrude shop looked at the parts I had in the trunk of my car and asked me what I wanted for the lot of it. "Make me an offer," I said.

"I got a case of Cutty Sark Scotch and some other booze left over from a party," he said. "How about that and fifty bucks?"

I hauled the booze up to my room, hunted up Vorce, and we got bombed out of our minds. Vorce left to go home, but was back in two hours. His wife was on his ass and he said, "Hell with it, I'm staying at the base." He showed up with a frying pan, refried beans, flour tortillas and whatever else he could get away with.

We stayed loaded all weekend, drinking and eating bean burritos fried in a pan of grease. My room smelled like something I had never smelled before… and don't want to ever smell again.

By late Sunday we'd both had enough. Vorce said he had to go make up with his wife, and I had to clean my room. His old lady was sure going to kill me…we didn't have many days we missed drinking that booze, and I was glad when it was gone.

I had to get my head out of my ass and start taking care of myself. My time in front of the medical board was drawing near, and I would have to prove to them that I could pass all the tests. I tried to stop drinking and get myself in some kind of shape.

* * *

After all the drinking Charlie and I had been doing, I had to work my *ass* off to get in shape. I started running and cut back on the booze and was doing great. My only trouble was with rope-climbing: with only two working fingers on one hand, I had a hard time holding on to the rope.

I was able to pass all the fitness parts and just had to go in front of the medical board in four days. The Thursday before I was to go, I got a pain in my stomach near my navel, so I went to the hospital. The doctor—who had a cigarette in his mouth, and I think he'd been working on his car, because his fingernails were dirty—told me I had a small piece of metal trying to come out. He put on some rubber gloves, gave me two or three shots in the belly, and started to dig at the piece of metal.

I felt my chest tighten up and then I had trouble breathing. Someone said,

"He's going into shock!" I don't know what happened after that, but they kept me on the ward for two days and let me out on Sunday.

* * *

Tuesday, I went in front of the medical board. The Marine Captain who was to help me had been drinking the night before, and he fell asleep just as the board members came in. When I saw he'd fallen asleep, I said, "God damn it, sir, this is my career, wake up," and hit him in the side with my elbow…almost knocking him out of his chair.

The head medical doctor—a Navy Full Captain—saw me, and it pissed him off. I think he made up his mind right then that I wasn't going to get an OK from him to stay in. They read my medical report and he said, "I think you need to be retired on temporary medical and sent home. You will be required to report back to a military hospital every six months and we will make a ruling that you have to improve to come back on full duty."

I told the Marine Captain he'd cost me my career in the Marine Corps, because jarring him awake was what had pissed off the Navy Captain.

"I'm sorry I fell asleep," he said.

* * *

I had two days to get checked out and get my retirement orders. I only went to say goodbye to my buddy Vorce. We both had tears in our eyes…"The Marines won't be the same with you gone, Big P!" he said.

Vorce went to my room and helped load up my car. It was about 11:00 a.m. and I just wanted to leave. My eyes were watering up, and I knew it was wrong, but I thought that maybe after six months I could come back, and Shirlie and the kids could come with me, and we could get squared away again.

* * *

I made it past Los Angeles and was on my way to Bakersfield by early afternoon and just kept driving. I couldn't understand why I wasn't tired…I stopped only for gas and snacks.

I drove all night, and it was early the next morning when I crossed into Oregon. I stopped at a rest stop, made a phone call to Shirlie and told her I was coming home for good…maybe never going back…because the Marines were sending me home.

The feeling that I wasn't going back suddenly hit me, and I started to cry. Stopping only once for gas, I drove the rest of the way home and pulled into the driveway about 4:00 p.m. Thursday evening.

Shirlie and the kids still weren't sure I was going to be home for any length of time. My brother came down that weekend and we drank every day. He asked me, "What are you going to do?"

"For a week or two, just before I came home, I went to school to be a car salesman," I told him, then added, "Let me put a Dodge in your garage," and laughed.

* * *

After I got home from the hospital, I met the owner of the Dodge Garage and Sales Lot. He'd been a Marine during WWII, a Marine Raider who'd won the Navy Cross (the second highest combat award) and a Battle Field Commission.

"If you want a job," he told me, "come see me."

So, on Monday morning I walked to his business, which was only three blocks from our house. He said I could work as a car salesman and he would train me if that's what I wanted to do. It was a lot of standing around, talking to a lot of people.

I made my first sale on Saturday; I'd only been working there about a week. An older couple driving an old Ford station wagon (it looked like they were living out of it) wanted a Dodge van with nothing but two seats. One of the other salesmen laughed and told me to practice on them.

When the lot closed for the day and I got off work, my brother said they were going to the boat dory's races at the coast. There was a lot of beer and lots of people. Rita, my youngest daughter, got lost in the crowd and it took a little while to find her. It shook me up; I started to feel my chest get tight and I couldn't breathe. I told Shirlie and the kids to get in the car: we were going home. The pain got so bad I couldn't drive, so I got in the back seat and laid down, with Shirlie and the kids in the front. When we got back to McMinnville I was in so much pain we went straight to the hospital. Everyone thought I was having a heart attack!

I was tended to by Dr. Treneman, who told me my symptoms suggested a heart attack, but my heart sounded good. He had several tests run; nothing showed up.

Bert, the owner of the car dealership, came to see me and said a lot of guys had problems when they came home from the war. He said maybe that was part of my trouble.

Bert also asked me about the van I'd shown to the older couple, because they'd come in asking for me. He said they'd paid cash for the van, and I'd get a good commission for the sale. I told him I didn't think I wanted to sell cars because I hated standing around. He told me to stop by when I got out of the hospital and maybe he could help me find a job I liked.

After I left the hospital, I went to see him, but the salesman I was training under stopped me at the door and told me that it would be best not to come on the lot because of my health. He was in a hurry to get me out of there, so I left and went home.

The lady who lived next door to us was the bookkeeper at the dealership. When she came home for lunch she wanted to know how I was doing. She told me the older couple had come in to see me, and had told her *I* was the reason they'd bought the van. She said that the salesman I was working with had claimed it was *his* deal and that *he* was to get the commission. When Bert heard about this, he fired the guy.

I saw the salesman later in a bar and he tried kissing my ass. He said he had only been trying to help me get my share.

* * *

I was having a drink when one of the guys who picked up laundry came in, so I had a drink with him. He told me he'd been in the Marines during WWII. "We had some wild times after WWII," he said. "Korea and Vietnam guys never had it as good when they came home."

I told him I'd quit the car sales...it was too much standing around and thinking.

"One of our drivers is going to quit," he told me. "Maybe you could get his job." We talked about what they did, and it sounded like something I could do.

When he started calling me Sarge, I asked him not to say much about my being in the Marines. I still had bad feelings about not being able to stay in. "Just call me Gene," I told him.

* * *

The next morning, I went to see the owner of the laundry. He told me he had been in the Navy in WWII, and he gave me the job. I was to ride with the guy who was quitting, so I could learn the route.

This was a great job—driving around town, meeting all the working people in the shops, garages and stores. I picked up dirty laundry in the mornings and took back the clean in the afternoon.

On his last day, the guy I was riding with ran over a little white poodle. When I saw all the blood and knew the dog was dying, I felt that tight feeling coming back into my chest. The lady who owned the dog came out and assured us it wasn't our fault. I thought the dog might still survive, so I asked if I could take it to a vet. When we got there, however, it was dead.

I eventually overcame the feeling in my chest…but little did I know how much trouble this would be for me over the next few years.

* * *

The laundry job helped me fit into the town. Everyone called me Gene, and I liked that just fine. I always had a lot of fun with the guys at the shops and garages, and enjoyed sharing dirty jokes with the two other drivers.

After work, we always stopped for a few drinks. Most of the people working at the laundry were women, and a few of them came to the bar to drink. On Friday nights we usually stayed until the bar closed.

More and more people got to know that I'd been in the Marines. One guy, whom I knew because his wife was one of my kids' school teachers, asked me if I wanted to have a drink at the Elks Club. I'd never been there, since you had to be (or be with) a member. I remembered the place as a kid, when we would come to McMinnville once a month from Grand Ronde, and my Mother would tell us to sit on the steps and wait while she went shopping. There was a little popcorn wagon there, and she would buy us each a bag. The part I remembered most was being chewed out by some guy who told us, "You goddamned Indians get off the steps and stay off."

He took me to the Elks Club on a Friday night, and there were a lot of guys there, so he took me around to meet the ones he knew. One of the guys worked for the phone company, had been in the Navy during WWII, and had a son in Vietnam. I told him I had been in Vietnam as a company Gunnery Sergeant. He said, "Don't they call you guys 'Gunny'?" He was a great talker, and was well known because he took me to meet everyone.

What a big mistake that was: everyone wanted to know about Vietnam. There was a story in the local paper about an Army guy whose dad owned the local drug store…he'd been given a Bronze Star. One of the guys I met was a reporter for the paper; he asked if he could do a story about me.

The next day, I told my boss the local paper wanted to do a story on me and asked for some time off. I put on my uniform and they took some pictures and the reporter asked me a lot of questions about the war.

A week or more went by and I never heard anything until the Saturday morning paper came out. There I was on the front page; only the start of many bad days ahead for me. Everyone wanted me to speak at the men's and women's clubs and join for free membership. I was the local hero…and I knew I wasn't.

* * *

The next day when I returned to the laundry, Shirlie was waiting outside for me. She looked worried. I got out of my truck and asked what was wrong.

"Your mother's dead," Shirlie replied. "She fell down some stairs at your sister's house."

"Where is she now?"

"I think she's still in the house. Your brother Gary's on his way there right now."

I took off as soon as I could and drove to where my sister lived…about 45 miles away.

When I got there, Gary and my dad were standing by their car. Some people from the fire department were there, too. I asked where Mom was and my Dad said she was still in the house. I asked Gary if he had been in the house and he said he'd been waiting for me. So we went in.

The house was a mess…it looked like it hadn't been cleaned in months. My sister had moved out and just left it the way it was.

My mother was covered with a blanket, but one of her arms was uncovered. She'd been laying there for several hours. I asked the ambulance driver why they hadn't taken her out, and he said they were waiting for someone to help move her.

"We will help," I said, and pulled the blanket back. She was lying in a pool of dried blood. My brother started to throw up, and ran out the door. It took four of us to lift her onto the gurney.

I asked how she died, but no one knew, so I asked when we *would* know. The guy who was doing the talking was evidently the cororer; he said, "not until we do a check at the morgue—unless someone signs papers saying not to do that—in case there may have been some other reason she died."

"My mother had fainting spells," I told him, "and she's hurt herself many times because she never has control of them once they come on."

I still hadn't asked my dad what had happened, and didn't see why I should…nothing was going to bring my mother back to life.

We went back to my parents' home in Salem. I asked my dad what he wanted to do about the funeral, and if he would be OK at the house. He asked if he could come stay at my place for a while.

I had a bar in the basement of our house; my father asked if he could go down and have a drink. After we'd both had several drinks, he said he wanted to get some sleep. I told him he could sleep in my son's room. He took a half bottle of whiskey and went upstairs to bed. My mother's brothers and sisters lived in Canada and other places, so it would be a few days before the funeral.

* * *

During the funeral, everyone stayed at my house, and most of them stayed for a week. Shirlie was now cooking for twelve people, and trying to find

everyone a place to sleep. It sure took
its toll on her.

When it came time for my dad
to go back to his place, he asked if he
could live with me. I said, "Sure."

My father and I would have some
hard times, as we never did have much
in common. I was military-minded
and wanted everything my way…he
drank a lot and just laid around, read
a lot and slept. That sure put a strain
on our lifestyle, and with my brother
and his family coming down every
weekend, there was a lot of drinking
and going to the bars.

*1969: A family photo taken
after our mother's funeral.*

* * *

Shirlie and I were having our
troubles. We got a big Social Security settlement of several thousand dollars,
and I was being an asshole on how we were going to manage our money. I was
getting regular check ups at the Veteran's Hospital, and made it a point to stop
at all the bars on my way home.

One time I ran into a former Marine and we got loaded. I brought him
home and told him he could stay with us. That made Shirlie mad; she wanted
to know how the hell we were going to make a life if I kept bringing someone
home with me, and all I did was drink. So I took him out to the highway so he
could hitch a ride.

The next morning, I was still pissed off. When I saw the kids lying in front
of the TV, I told them to get their mess cleaned up and get dressed. They asked
Shirlie if they had to…and I blew my cool. I grabbed them and was going to
wipe their asses good with a small wooden cane when Shirlie jumped in and said
I didn't need to hit them.

"You're an asshole," she told me, "and you always have been."

My response: "If you think you can raise the kids, go for it."

I got my sea bag, put some clothes in it and took off. I had no idea what I
was doing or where I was going. I still didn't know the area, so I just headed out
of town until I found a back road that lead up into the mountains.

I had walked maybe 15 miles when I came to a side road leading to
McMinnville's water system. The guy in charge of the watershed wanted to
know what I was doing clear up there. After talking with him, he let me use his
phone. I called Shirlie and told her how to find me.

Shirlie and I had a long talk, and it helped. "Why do I have to cook for
everyone who shows up at our place?" she asked. "All they do is eat and drink!"
And she was right.

After that, we made it a point to be gone on the weekends.

* * *

I still missed being around my military friends, and knew nothing about
the armories or veterans groups. One afternoon a man in some kind of uniform

came to the house…it turned out to be a member of the Veterans of Foreign Wars. I knew him from when I was a kid. He asked me to join the VFW, and said they were all old military guys. I was sure looking forward to meeting them.

The first night I went to the VFW, I saw that they were all old WWII guys, and the women kind of ran the show. They served cookies and coffee: not what I was hoping for. I thought maybe there would be a bar at the end of the meeting.

They pulled down a large chart on the wall, and there was my name—"Gene Brandon, membership chairman"—and a place for a hundred other names. They said that with me being a local hero, I would be able to get a lot of guys to sign up, and they gave me a pad for membership.

After the meeting, I headed for two guys I knew. I told them I was the new membership chairman for the VFW and asked them to join up.

One of the guys looked at me and said, "Take that VFW and shove it up your ass. Those guys treated me like shit when I came home." He went on to tell me all the bad things he could.

I got up and left and threw the VFW's member pad in the trash. I stayed clear of joining them until I knew what was going on.

I liked the Elks Club and decided to become a member…they were a fun bunch and boy, did they like to drink.

* * *

I was doing well with my job and getting to know lots of people. All the former Marines in McMinnville knew me from the newspaper article. I asked one of the guys what they did on the Marine Corps' birthday, and as far as he knew they didn't do anything, but some of the old veterans got together for breakfast at the drug store. Since I had a small bar in my basement, I invited as many as I knew to come over to my house. About 12 guys showed up, including one guy who brought his buddy that was in the Army. We kicked him out; he stayed upstairs and played with the kids.

The next morning, I went to the breakfast, and there were the old guys from the VFW. They wanted to know what had happened to me. I told them, "I'm not ready for anything yet," but I did feel I needed to have that friendship of the former military guys. I started hanging out with the guys in the military, and when we were drinking, we would talk about the war.

One night I started feeling that strange pain in my chest again. It got so bad I couldn't breathe, so Shirlie took me to the hospital. The doctor told me to breathe into a paper bag. It never helped, so I asked for some oxygen. He said I didn't need it. I went wild in the hospital room. They panicked, strapped me to a gurney, and sent me to the Veterans Hospital.

When I got there, the doctor told everyone to leave the room. "I'll take care of him; I've seen other Veterans like this before." Once we were alone, he slapped me in the face several times and told me, "Knock that shit off or I'll put you in the nut ward!"

"You son of a bitch!" I yelled back. "When I get out of this I'm gonna kill you!" Two other doctors came in and gave me a shot…then I was OK. They let me go home, and I knew right then that I never wanted to go back there.

* * *

I'd been driving for the laundry for about two years when the boss called me into his office. "I'm giving you a $5 a week raise, and I want you to be the route supervisor. The other drivers don't want the job."

After work, I asked some of the other laundry people to come have a celebratory drink with me. When I told one of the drivers I was getting a $5 a week raise, he asked, "How much are you make now?"

"$125 a week," I said.

"Well," he said, "I make $130 a week."

"Well, that's shit!" I said. "I work two or three hours more than you, and I get less money."

So the next morning I asked the boss why our pay was like that.

"Hell," he said, "you're a double dipper!"

I'd never heard that term before. "What's a 'double dipper'?"

"Well, you guys come out of the military with a pension, and take jobs away from the men who don't have pensions."

"I put my *life* on the line for what I got," I told him. "I never wanted to do that." Then I gave him my two weeks' notice and quit. He tried to get me to stay, and even offered me more money, but I was pissed.

* * *

One of the guys I drank with had been fired from the local newspaper after wrecking a company car. He suggested I apply for his old job, working with a bunch of kids delivering newspapers. I applied, and they hired me.

The paper came out only two days a week, so I had a lot of time for running around. I could make as much money as I wanted—part of our pay was on commission—and we were able to draw on our pay whenever we needed to. Within two months, I was making *twice* the money I'd made driving a laundry truck. I had more time to drink, and as long as I kept new orders coming in for the paper, I was my own boss. The kids liked working for me, and with my expense account I could take good care of them.

One day, the owner of the paper called me in and said they were going to run three days a week, and print a big "6" the full length of the paper. This was the first time they'd had over 6,000 customers and they said they had me to thank for it.

I was becoming more involved in everything that went on at the paper. I took pictures of basketball and football games for the sports reporter, and showed up to help with parades. The little towns we delivered papers in bought me a 1923 Model T car, and I drove it in all the parades.

* * *

Being with my old Marine buddies was always in the back of my mind, but it seemed we only found time to get together on our Marine birthday, November 10th.

I'd heard about a bunch of Marines who were building a memorial in Beaverton. One of them had lost three sons in the Marines and was building this memorial in their honor. Once or twice a month I went up to spend some time with them. We got a lot done...and did a lot of drinking too.

The day was set for the memorial and it turned out to be the biggest event I had been to that was attended by so many Marines. It was the first time I wasn't wearing my uniform and I had never felt so empty or ashamed. *God, I'm not a Marine anymore.* I started feeling all alone and was drinking heavily.

Accompanying the guest speaker was an officer I knew from my time with the 2nd Marine division back in 1964. He had several medals, Purple Hearts and Bronze Stars. He remembered me, and I told him I was only temporarily retired and hoped the Marines would call me back. I also told him I had been put in for a Bronze Star but hadn't gotten it.

"The Marines aren't bringing back any of the guys who've been sent home," he told me. "There are hundreds of them, and with Vietnam slowing, the Marine Corps is overloaded with personnel. I'll take your name, though, and see what I can do."

Everyone else seemed like they were having a good time, but *I* wasn't. By this time, I was so drunk I couldn't stand up without holding onto something.

What happened next seems like a dream to me....

I started seeing the faces of Marines, standing in the dark. I went out and got in my car, their faces still in my mind: I thought I knew them but I wasn't sure from where. I was crying and driving very fast and I lay down on the seat of my car. I felt like I was floating and I don't remember anything after that.

It still felt like a dream when I sat up in my car. I was on the side of a hill, just off the highway. I didn't know how long I'd been there, but my car was still running. I put the car in reverse, backed onto the highway and drove home. I didn't even get out to see what had happened. I don't know how I made it home.

It was Saturday and I was supposed to work that morning, but I told Shirlie to call and tell them I was sick and couldn't come in. I suddenly remembered my dream and went outside to see if my car was OK.

There was grass and dirt stuck under my bumper.

Oh God, it wasn't a dream...I did *run off the road.*

* * *

By now, I knew I wasn't going to get back in the Marines, even though up to this time I had kept my sea bag packed. My uniforms were clean and I had kept my weight down, but none of my uniforms fit. I asked one of the reserve Marines I knew if he would come over and pick up all my uniforms and all my Marine stuff. I only wanted to keep two uniforms...I don't know why but thought that when I died, maybe they could bury me in one of them.

The strange thing is, two or three years later, I loaned my dress blues to a Marine recruiter until he could buy his own; he and his wife split up several weeks later. One night, at a local motel where they were having a party, her new boyfriend followed him into the bathroom...and shot him five times.

He was wearing my dress blues, so they buried him in them.

* * *

I wanted to get rid of everything around that reminded me of being a Marine. Shirlie had kept all the letters I'd sent her in the years we'd been apart. I told her to get rid of them because I didn't want any memories of the Marines. The feeling never lasted very long, though: my old Marine buddies kept coming to see me, and we'd do lots of drinking.

We moved from our home on 7th Street to a much bigger house on 12th

Street. This house had a fireplace, a built in barbecue, and a full bar in the family room. I converted an old fridge into a beer cooler and kept a whole keg in it. My house quickly became *the* place to party.

My job with the newspaper was going great. I was making good money and was involved in everything. I spent most of my evening time with the kids who delivered newspapers for me. I had two or three other people who worked for me, and I started letting them work with the kids. That gave me more time to hang out in the bars.

* * *

Another thing I liked about the newspaper was how it helped support many local events, like Crazy Days, Turkey Rama, and the Yamhill County Fair.

During Crazy Days, everyone dressed up in costumes. I rented a gorilla suit in Portland, got a mini motorbike from a local bike shop, and drove through the bars...in one door and out the other. Then I went into a jewelry store, where one of the girls was dressed as a baby, with a diaper and a halter top. I picked her up, carried her to the bank and left her there, screaming all the way. I then proceeded to the laundry where I used to work and scared one of the girls so badly she almost passed out and wet her pants. The best part was that no one knew who the hell was inside the gorilla costume. That night I had a hell of a time in the bars; I had to drink through a straw to keep from taking off my mask. It was fun, but I'll never do it again: I had a hangover big time.

Turkey Rama was, and still is, a big event in McMinnville. One year, I set up a bike race to which hundreds of people showed up, and we also had a frog jumping event. Using a fish hook and a red piece of felt, I cleared the frogs from most of the local ponds, and gave them to any kid who wanted one. A week after the event, there were still frogs all over town. After the fair, I participated in a boat race from Willamina to Sheridan. I used a small rubber raft I'd only used once before, and paddled it for 4 or 5 miles in the rain. I almost killed myself.

The best part was the parade. Everyone had the same thought: parade, then party...and most of the time, the party lasted two or three days. Shirlie had stopped coming with me, because she always ended up driving my drunk ass home.

One year, while pulling a float in the Sheridan parade, my Marine Jeep ran out of gas. It held up the parade for half an hour, and I was sure on the shit list in Sheridan for a while. I got shit from everyone when I showed up for a parade

Turkey Rama Turkey Trot, 1980-something:
Anything she can do, I can do...maybe...

Or maybe not...
Man, I'm too old for this!

after that. "Hey, Brandon," they'd ask, "you got gas in your Jeep?"

* * *

Every time a holiday neared when Veterans were needed, it seemed I would be called to raise the flag or to fire detail, and every November 10th we would have a Marine party at my place. The next day, of course, was Veterans Day, so I always tried to get the guys together.

One year, I asked the owner of the Westward Ho (a McMinnville restaurant and bar) if we could have a breakfast at his place. He said their dining room could hold about 60 people, so I told him to go for it. I was going to be the big spender and pay for everything.

I ran an ad in the paper: "Free Veteran's Breakfast—room for 60 people." Only four or five guys agreed to attend, and I told the owner I might call it off.

"Hell, Brandon," he said, "don't give anything away for free…people don't think that way. Make them pay and they'll show up."

So I ran another ad: "Due to the huge response for the Veterans' Breakfast, there will be a $2.50 charge per person to cover the cost of breakfast and drinks." Over 160 people showed up. The place was packed, and we ended up partying until the next day, Sunday.

The next year, over 400 people signed up. I asked the Elks Lodge club manager if he could help me, and he said we could have the breakfast there. I asked everyone to wear all or part of their uniforms; there would be prizes for the best and worst fit. Local recruiters would be the judges. We drank the Elks Club dry, and the "breakfast" lasted until the club closed. That event went on for several years…maybe it still is.

These breakfast events stayed with me all year, and may have been the start of my many bad times.

* * *

I was getting more and more involved with the Veterans. I was commander for the Disabled American Veterans for nine years, Commander of the American Legion, held an office with the VFW, went to some kind of meeting almost every week…and drank *way* too much. I often drank at the Elks Club, where the leaders of the community gathered. I got along with them all, and it made me feel good that I could drink with the owners of banks, construction companies, and other local businesses.

One afternoon I was drinking with the owner of a paving company. He was bidding on a big state job, but to get the contract, 10 percent of his employees had to be minorities.

"Hell," I said, "the Indians are a minority and I'm a disabled veteran, so you can get both by hiring me." I was just kidding, but he asked me if I could prove it and I said, "Sure, I can! I got all my membership papers." When he told me what the job paid, I almost shit: it was nearly $13.00 an hour more than I was making at the newspaper. He told me to bring the papers to his office in the morning. I told him I needed to give my boss a week or two notice.

"Fuck him," he said. "I want you to start today."

I felt bad when I told my boss at the paper I was quitting. He was a hell of a guy to work for…but $13.00 an hour more was hard to pass up.

Little did I know about drinking until I went to work in construction. We worked hard and we drank hard. We worked closely with three or four other companies, and they all drank big time: every night after work we would all meet for a few drinks. Many times when we got back to the shop, someone was already there with one or two cases of beer: the first ones in had stopped to get a case or two, and the rest of us would chip in a few bucks. We never lacked for beer. Once in a while, Shirlie made the mistake of coming by the shop to see when I would be coming home. I would send her for more beer.

I was now pulling in $500 to $1,000 a week...*way* too much money, because I was getting crazy with it. I would buy whatever I wanted, whenever I wanted it. At one point, I had nine cars, motorbikes and dune buggies. To keep up with the Joneses, I had to buy, sell or trade anything I could, and I would stay in the bars until closing almost every night. I was a real asshole and never came home sober. We had an above ground swimming pool in the back yard. I would jump in—clothes, boots and all, make a mess, pass out in bed, then do it all over again the next day.

All the while, Shirlie kept asking me to slow down. She was working at the laundry, and the kids were basically on their own while Shirlie tried to keep up with me. After about three years of this, I could finally see the writing on the wall. I decided I'd better change jobs or quit drinking, because I was hurting myself health wise. Weighing in at over 280 pounds, I could drink a case of beer a day and sometimes a fifth of whiskey too.

* * *

A Marine buddy of mine who owned the Sears Store in town was working with a big contractor out of Portland to build a big trailer park near the airport. He wanted me to go to work for him and help build the park. I had hurt my shoulder and was off work, so I told my boss I needed to slow down and was going to change jobs. He was sorry to see me go, and told me I would always have a job with him anytime I needed to work.

The change in jobs was a big mistake. I worked by myself a lot and only had part time help. The drinking was just as bad, only now we drank a lot of whiskey. I knew *nothing* about contract work, sewer lines, underground sprinklers, concrete driveways...and I was killing myself trying to do it all.

When people started to move into the park, we discovered the sewer system couldn't pump out the lines. One day, I was under a trailer trying to clean out a plugged drain (the lady that lived there had flushed some diapers down the toilet). As big as I was, I never had much room under the trailers, so it was rough going. Suddenly, I felt a sharp pain in my stomach, but I kept on working. In a few hours I was getting sick from the pain so I went home to rest, but the pain got so bad I went to the hospital.

After some x-rays, a doctor came in and told me I had gallstones and some kind of metal all over my insides. I told him that had been from my wounds in Vietnam. He wanted to operate on me the next day but I told him I had to go to the Veterans Hospital.

The Veterans Hospital was a mess; they screwed with me for four days. They said they weren't sure what was wrong with me, so they were going to do "exploratory surgery." I asked them what that meant, and they said they would open me up and see if they could find anything. I'd had *that* in Vietnam six years earlier, and it was *hell*...but I had to stop the pain, so I agreed.

They said the surgery would take only an hour or two…it ended up taking over *nine*. When they opened me up, they found that my liver was bleeding from an old piece of shrapnel, so they took it out, sewed up my liver, and took out my gall bladder while they were there. When I came out of it, I was hurting real bad.

The care was the shits. I was in a room with two old WWII veterans. One of them was dying from something in his blood; I don't know what was wrong with the guy next to me, except that he kept trying to get out of bed. On about the third day, he finally made it out, but started to fall towards my bed. When I instinctively tried to catch him, I tore open my stitches and started to bleed, so they had to take me back in and fix me up.

I thought I would never get out of that hell hole, and it took me almost a year to recover. I had lost over fifty pounds, which was, I think, the only bright spot. I was also limited now on what I could eat, because I would get cramps and sick if I ate any greasy food, and that helped me keep my weight off.

* * *

I went back to work part time for the paving contractor, just doing work around the shop and helping repair equipment. Then I started driving the service truck, delivering gas and diesel to the job sites. Sometimes they were short handed, and I'd stay on the job and drive the pavement roller. It didn't take me long to fall back on my old ways of drinking and staying in the bars all hours of the night. I was a big spender, too: when I drank, everyone drank on me. It was nothing for me to drop $200 or more a night drinking.

I also loved to dance. One Friday night, I must have smelled like all the women I danced with, because Shirlie got mad at me.

"You smell like a French whore house!" she said. "What the hell were you doing? You'd better do something about the way you're acting."

I got mad and told her, "I don't answer to anyone. If you don't like what I'm doing, either I can get the hell out or you can." I was really drunk and I started pulling my clothes out of the closet. "I'm getting the hell out of here."

Once again she gave in. "I won't say any more tonight, but could you *please* slow down on your drinking, come home early once in a while so you can be with the kids. The only time they see you is when you're half drunk."

* * *

It seemed like whenever I worked hard, that's when I wanted to drink, but an opportunity arose to get away from the construction work.

The guy running the old National Guard Armory was in the hospital recovering from a heart attack. He told his boss I would be a good guy to take his place until he was back on his feet. It turned out to be a great job: I just had to keep the place clean and take care of renting the place for events.

The building was pretty run down: they'd started building a new Armory near the airport, so they weren't putting any more money into the old one. I quickly ran out of things to do, but I had that old building shining in no time. Some of the old locker rooms had been shut down for several months, so for something to do I cleaned them up, then started an old men's basketball league. I had about 10 teams who played three times a week, and since I was in charge I never charged any fees. It was going great; soon I had something going on almost every night of the week.

The officer in charge came over to see what I was doing, because I'd had more rentals in the three months I was there than they'd had in the previous year. When he saw how clean I had the place looking, and what I'd done to open up some of the old locker rooms, he asked me if I wanted to stay on full time: the guy I was filling in for had health issues that wouldn't allow him to return to work.

He had me work with a town committee that wanted to make the old Armory into a community center. Every day I showed people around the place, telling them all the good things that could come from this building. Soon, the deal was made. I would have to start turning in all the property from the building into a place in Portland, and I would get a military license so I could drive a truck.

Shit, this was great…I was back working with the military, and the more work I did…the more they liked it. My boss was a retired army Colonel, so I could do almost anything I wanted. They'd set a goal to get the new Armory open for some big event in October—and it was already July—so I was to move out to the new Armory and keep the old one going.

15 hour days were short for me, but I loved every minute of it. I would go to the base in Portland once or twice a week and pick up supplies. Everything was brand new and still in boxes. Office equipment, new lockers, tables, chairs…and I was in charge of everything.

By this time I'd made friends with anyone who could help me…plumbers, landscapers, you name it. I had plenty of stuff to trade, and an open budget to get the job done. All the guys in the Guard were fired up to see the new Armory completed, so there was always someone to help me. All I needed was some beer and some chow, and with hundreds of wall lockers and desks there was plenty to do. Once I got the building inspector on my side, nothing was going to stop us. All I had to do was ask for it and I got it. They built a portable stage, with steps I could move by myself, and bought all brand new cleaning equipment. The other Armory manager almost shit when he saw what I had. The storeroom was full of all new gear and I pressed uniforms every day. I'd even ordered my own special uniform with my name on it.

Once I started getting things in order, I opened a bar in the day room with a fridge full of beer, beer sausage, and bar snacks. I had more help than I needed. We were way ahead of opening date, so I was able to take care of all the small things from my years in the Marines. I knew how to put the military protocol together: the military bullshit *I* knew was *way* more than the National Guard ever got into.

We had more food than anyone could eat. All the local businesses gave us anything we asked for, and I had enough cookies to feed 10,000 people, thanks to Archway Cookie Company.

My biggest trade was with a nursery supply company in Beaverton. I will go to hell with my secret on this one, but several hundred trees and plants are part of the Armory landscaping to this day.

* * *

At the Armory's grand opening, someone showed up from every military unit in Oregon. I got away clean with everything…with one exception.

The Commanding General for the State of Oregon was to land in the open field across from the armory. I'd been able to pick up a couple smoke grenades, and I thought it would be great if we marked the landing zone with them. Since this was a big deal, I told the ground control guy to just throw *both* smoke grenades. One was green, and one was red. All the officers almost shit…this was a NO NO…some dumb rule that got my ass chewed out. Since I was a civilian, though, it never hurt much.

Besides, the General was happy as hell when he saw the crowd of people and all the military bullshit. "I never knew the state had so much military surplus equipment," he told me, "and most of it never belonged to me."

My thanks came when everyone gave me a standing ovation. "This couldn't have happened," the General said, "if not for one tough son of a bitch, a good old Marine who got the job done."

* * *

Once the big event was over and we'd settled into a day by day operation, my boss told me I'd earned over 300 hours of overtime, and I could take off all the time I wanted until the overtime was used up. That meant only working two or three hours a day—and sometimes not going in at all—and that gave me more time to play.

The school system was having an insurance shake-up over some trampolines and other high risk equipment which had to be taken out of the school, so I got a lot of the equipment for free. Some I used at the Armory and some I traded to make sure I had plenty of beer and snacks for the bar in the day room.

I heard I was the only Armory who got away with that, but I kept it under control.

* * *

My first November at the Armory, I planned a big Marine Birthday Party and a Veterans Day breakfast the next morning. Up to this time, all my Marine parties had been for Marines only. We would go to the Elks Lodge for breakfast, but the parties were always at my house. They would get a little wild, but Shirlie always kept us in some kind of order so we didn't tear the house down.

So this was going to be a big one: the first year anyone other than Marines would be at our party. Each Marine could bring a guest, so there were about a hundred of us. Everyone would pay $20 each to cover food and booze. I still had plenty of money left over, so I thought some entertainment would be nice. I talked to a guy who was going to get me a comedian or someone who could tell some good jokes, and he asked me if I wanted some strippers: for $400 I could have it all. Something should have told me I was stepping into some shit, but I went for it anyhow.

I woke up in the middle of the Armory, with my face stuck to the floor in a pool of dried blood. Several State Police were standing over me, wanting to know what the hell had been going on. All I could say was, "I think we drank too much."

In no way will God let me in for what happened that night, nor will I ever attempt to even tell. We had a fight or two, a few women almost got mauled, and sixteen men got lost in the mountains. The City, County and State Police all came looking for me…they'd had wives calling all night for missing husbands.

I still had to greet several hundred veterans who were coming to breakfast in about an hour, along with several angry wives wanting to know what the hell happened to their husbands.

About that time, in came all the missing men—mud up to their asses. After the party, someone had said, "Let's go up in the mountains and go four wheeling," and they'd gotten stuck.

* * *

I was on a lot of people's shit list for quite a while. You might think I would have learned something by now, but I got a lot dumber.

In my collection of cars, I had a 1966 Cadillac limo with a full bar and TV. With all my free time I would go bar hopping once a week...and always found something to get into. I found my way into the little farming town of St. Paul, Oregon, a few miles away, and made the mistake of stopping for one drink. The owner of the bar was an old drinking friend and an ex-policeman.

After several drinks, he told me the little bar across the street, called The Rodeo Inn, was for sale, and said I should buy it. The lady who owned it was a real bitch, so no one would drink there, and she was about to lose the place.

She opened late that day and I went over to see her. As always, I had my head up my ass and couldn't see past my beer can. She said I could buy her out for $34,000. Somehow, I talked Shirlie into going to look at the place. "With my buddy owning the other place in town," I told her, "we can work together and make big money."

Somehow, we put the deal together. I gave up my job at the armory and was now a big time bar owner. That was only the start of many, many sleepless nights, weekend drunks and fights.

In nine months, car accidents killed six people in that little town. Another guy was run over, and another was killed when he was beaten over the head with a pool cue.

* * *

I now weighed almost 300 pounds, and never drew a sober breath. I needed to get out of this or I was going to kill myself. My old wounds were killing me from all the weight I'd put on.

Since there was a lot of building going on in Newberg, a town about five miles down the road, my place was packed every day by 5:00 pm. Most of the contractors from Salem stopped at my place for their first cold beer after work. We had good music there, too. One day, a real estate agent who sold businesses for a living asked me if I wanted to list my place, but I wasn't ready.

I also had several poker machines that paid off well and saw a lot of play: several hundred dollars a week, and I got half the profit. I have no idea how much money actually went into the machines. Another machine owner who wanted to buy me out and put their machines in my place asked to look at our books.

The next day he gave me a check for $15,000 as a down payment and another $7,000 to buy the inventory...and I was out of the bar business, with a contract that would pay me several hundred more dollars for the next few years.

During the nine months I owned the bar, I could not account for over $30,000. That's what I drank and pissed away. It never took me long to go through money. The tax people were after me, too. Though I'd only had the bar for nine months, my profit was so much that they wanted several thousand dollars more from me.

* * *

My blood pressure was out of sight; I needed to stop drinking and take care of myself. I spent the next two months in and out of the Veterans Hospital, trying to take care of some old wounds. I had two operations at the Veterans Hospital, and they screwed up both of them. They were supposed to remove two lumps, but they came back in just a few weeks. One of them was near my right testicle and was killing me to walk. I just said the hell with it and took the pain.

* * *

A friend of mine who'd owned a beer warehouse had sold his business, and the building was just sitting empty. When I asked him what he was going to do with it, he said he could rent it or sell it to me so I could build the Veterans Club I always talked about. *That might help me get free of the tax people*, I thought. *I'll just tell them 'I gave my money to the Veterans so they could build their club to care for other Veterans'*…and maybe have a small bar. Shit, was *I* a dreamer!!!

With what little money I had left over from selling the bar, I jumped in feet first. I was up to my ass in debt, working two part time jobs trying to get enough money to finish what I'd started. The funny part was that I was breaking every rule in the book: I had no building permit, and no plans turned into the city…and the city manager lived just across the street from me. I told him what I wanted to do was just have a place for Veterans to hold meetings and maybe drink a few beers; he said he didn't care.

I found some places in Salem that contractors were going to tear down, old buildings with walk-in coolers, bar chairs and tables. Most were well used, but good enough for a bunch of old Veterans to hold meetings. The guy who owned the warehouse still had 399 cases of beer left in the cooler; he sold that to me and I started my building.

I was moving along and had gotten a lot done, but made a mistake by leaving the doors open. The building inspectors stopped by to see what I was doing and jumped all over my ass. They were going to red tag the building because I was working without a permit.

Most of the building had been done, so I told them all I was doing was cleaning it up. Since they were both Veterans, they gave me a break and I offered them all the beer they wanted. One of them showed up every night and drank his share of beer.

The word got around, and a lot of guys started showing up after work. Many were guys I'd worked with in construction. Their wives knew where to find them, and my crowd got bigger every night. Some would help with the building, but mostly we drank. Some nights I never went home…I would stay all night, drinking and fixing the place up.

One day, a bar owner came to see me and told me I was in big trouble. I was cutting into his business, and other bar owners were going after my ass.

I had applied for a license, but had broken so many rules I was having a hard time proving what I was trying to do: "where was all the money coming from?" they wanted to know. I told them I'd paid for almost everything myself, and worked on the side to make money to finish it.

The lady who was working on my license said I was some kind of con man; no one would do what I have done. I almost went crazy. I told her I would get every Veteran in the country, and we would sit in her office until she came down and checked to see what was going on.

They put another man on the case. He came down to see what kind of operation I'd been working on, decided I was doing a good job, and approved my license.

Some of the bar owners in town said I'd paid off the liquor board because no one gets their permit that soon...I'd only had to wait three months.

* * *

This had to be my worst mistake since leaving the Marines. Up to this point, I'd been drinking to be with my buddies—mostly former Marines. Now, I was dealing with the guys from *all* branches of the service...and drinking is what they did. My drinking got way out of hand...again. I could drink two fifths of whiskey and no limit of beer; I just did it. My weight climbed to 311 pounds, and most days of the week I didn't have a clue what I did with my life.

* * *

On Thursday, New Year's Day 1981, my brother-in-law stopped in to visit. I hadn't seen much of him lately. About the first thing he said was, "Boy Gene, you're as fat as I've ever seen you."

I was hung over and in no state of mind to hear anyone's bullshit, but to keep peace in the family, I kept my mouth shut. He did, however, say something that made me listen...

"Whatever happened to that gym and fitness center you said you wanted to build?"

"For one thing," I said, "I spent most of my money building the Veterans Club. The rest, I drank up."

He never liked hearing that: to him, drinking and smoking were a waste of life. "What do you think it would cost to build a gym?" he asked me.

I didn't have a clue. The first thing I needed was a building and then an estimate of the cost of a gym with equipment. What he said next was hard to believe... "I can loan you maybe 10 or 20 thousand dollars, if you think you could do it with that."

The feeling I got was so great I forgot I had a hangover. He told me he would look around for a building and get me some prices, to see if we could pull it off, then left me with my thoughts.

* * *

There was a building that just might work. It had been a roller skating rink for many years, but was now the Moose Lodge. It was closed, and I knew they wanted to get out from under it. I could get the building for $40,000, plus another $15,000 to assume their debts. I knew many of the people the debts were owed to: plumbers, electricians, lumber mills, and so on. They agreed to just sign it over to me with no money down.

The building had been let go: it was in bad shape and had lots of leaks, but I wanted the challenge. The contractor who'd been owed money thought it was going to be a loss, so he said he would help me get started. I was off and running, working day and night, and was going to get it done...but I ran out of money, just when I was ready to open.

My brother came by to see how I was doing. I told him I was ready to open, but lacked the money to buy equipment. He asked if $20,000 would be enough, then borrowed it from the bank and said, "Get it done!"

* * *

During construction, many people stopped by to check on my progress. They wanted to join, and couldn't wait for it to open. The first few months I was open, though, no one came by, and I had to take an extra job to keep the money coming in.

Soon, however, I got a big shot in the arm, when Linfield College students heard about my gym. Within one month, I gained over 200 members, just from the college. It became their hangout, and I was able to offer three or four students part time jobs. The students would talk up my gym, and it kept members coming.

* * *

"Gunny's Gym" was doing great, but I was still drinking and hadn't lost any weight. In fact, I was getting bigger, because I was now lifting weights.

One day I stopped by my old club, which Shirlie was now running. By this time, things were not going too well for us, because we were never together. I was also hanging out at the bar with a young crowd of good looking women, so things were getting a little shaky.

While I was drinking at the bar, this little retired Air Force asshole walked up behind me and said, "Hey Brandon, that gym of yours isn't doing anything for *your* fat ass!"

That was a wake up call. I quit drinking and joined a diet center. The weight started coming off big time: within 6 months, I'd lost 60 pounds and was strong as a bull.

* * *

Besides running my gym, I'd been hired by a steel company in Portland. We turned out to be the best crew this company had, so we were getting all the work, and I was making good money. It also happened that my crew worked out at my gym.

A federal prison was being built in Sheridan, a small town about 15 miles away, and they made a deal to pay me $2000 a month for their employees to use my gym.

My gym was going big time. I had weight-lifting contests every 6 months, and within 6 years we got to be well known. Mine was picked as the best gym in three states, and I got to meet several of the big time body builders, several of whom came to visit.

The world's strongest woman worked out at my gym for a while, while her husband was in the Sheridan prison…for dealing in body-building drugs. She had moved to McMinnville to be near him.

* * *

Everything was going well…except for my marriage. I was doing my own thing and leaving her out of my life. In my mind, I said 'to hell with my club'—but behind my back, there was trouble. Some of the members wanted me and my wife out of the operation, and planned on taking over. The club was having financial problems, and my wife was using all the extra money we had, trying to hold things together.

Now that I'd stopped drinking, I was staying away from the club and spending all the time I could with the gym operation. My mind, freed from alcohol, began to clear…and started drifting back to my memories of the war. I started having bad dreams, and wasn't sure what was going on.

One day in 1989, some Marine books came to the gym. On the front cover of one of them was a drawing of three Marines walking through a rice paddy, and my thoughts were somewhere writing a story about Vietnam. As I looked through the book and came to the story about the cover photo, there was a picture of my commanding officer from Vietnam. He was relating the story of a battle that killed over 90 men and wounded several hundred others.

I started reading the story in September of 1989…and that was the last thing I remembered for the next four years.

* * *

How my life went on during that time, I don't know; I remember only bits and pieces. Most people—including Shirlie—never even knew anything was wrong with me. She only knew that I stayed away from her, and wouldn't talk to her. There were times when I would just take off, without even knowing where I was going. I would get on a plane and just fly somewhere, looking for an old Marine buddy. Meanwhile, my gym and club were falling under. I'd spent nearly all the money the gym had brought me.

* * *

My gym belonged to the McMinnville Chamber of Commerce. Once a month, the Chamber held an evening meeting for business after hours, and every Friday morning we had a group called "Greeters."

During one of the evening meetings, I suddenly came out of my blank mind. I couldn't remember anything, not even how I got there. The last thing I *could* remember was sitting at my desk, reading about my outfit in Vietnam.

One of the members started talking to me. "Gunny," she said, "it's your turn to find a place for us to visit on Friday morning."

I still wasn't sure what had happened. "Who should I ask?"

She pointed out a lady that worked in an office that did massages. "Why don't you ask her?"

I did, but she told me she only rented an office. She was a counselor who could put people to sleep and help them control their memories. I asked her if she'd ever worked on Veterans. She hadn't, but the lady who trained her had.

I went to see her, and got into a program that cost $40 an hour. At my first session, she just talked to me, and I went into a deep sleep. I knew what was going on, but I couldn't wake up, and I wouldn't tell her anything she asked.

With each visit, I would go deeper and deeper to sleep. I was starting to remember things I'd forgotten for over four years. She made me cry so hard I couldn't stop. I had heard of people who could put you to sleep, but I was so deep into what she was doing for me I kept going back. I couldn't believe the pressure that went away after I woke up, and couldn't wait for the next session.

* * *

It was about this time that the Gulf War started.

One night, the counselor called me. "Do you know where I can get a body bag?" she asked.

The question shocked me a little. "What do you need a body bag for?"

"Some people I know are getting up a group to protest the war," she said, and something about "no blood for oil."

I think I hung up on her; I'm not sure what happened after that.

The next thing I remember, I was sitting in my car, looking at the protestors and all their signs. I wasn't sure how I'd gotten there, or what I was going to do. Then I saw a friend of mine, a McMinnville policeman. He pointed at me, came over to my car, and told me to get out of there.

* * *

I suffered a very bad relapse and ended up having terrible flashbacks. All my old war wounds were hurting, as though I'd been wounded all over again, and the pain was so bad that I drove myself to the Veterans Hospital.

While I was sitting in the doctor's office, the doctor asked me why I was talking so fast and why I kept sniffing. I had no idea I was doing this.

The doctor was just starting his career, but had a lot of good advice for me. He'd learned from his father, who'd been a doctor during Vietnam, about guys like me who can never let go of the war. The doctor asked me to just write down whatever was bothering me. We would talk about it, and I could call him any time I needed to talk further.

I couldn't believe how much it helped me to write about my life. Things that used to be a big deal to me seemed to just vanish once I put them on paper. I would get up in the middle of the night and sit at my typewriter, only half aware of what I was doing. Page after page the words came out, sometimes misspaced, sometimes misspelled, sometimes not even knowing what half of them meant…I just kept typing.

I think this must have gone on for weeks…maybe even months. Then, one day, when I had nothing on my mind, I just boxed up all the pages, put them away and forgot about them.

* * *

I had made some bad mistakes with my gym and the club. I understood that now. The club was broke, but my wife didn't want to tell me we'd been losing money, so she was using our own money to keep things going. We were in deep debt—well over $100,000, as far as I could tell. I couldn't believe what had happened.

Most of the members had been run off by the guys who wanted us out of the club. They had a strong clique, and the damage had been done. If we couldn't get help, we'd have to shut down the club. The remaining members never wanted to help, so we had to close and take the loss with no money.

We also had to sell the gym and deed the building back. That was another big loss. We were now broke, and didn't even know if we could keep our home. I had no clue what I was going to do.

I got a phone call from a friend who asked me what I was doing, and wanted to know if I needed a job. It turned out he was going to have to take back a company he'd sold because the new owner wasn't making it. He gave me the guy's name, and I went to see him.

He assigned me the task of cleaning up the equipment he wanted to sell off. It was a tough job, and I worked many hours with an asphalt sealing company—what a messy job *that* was—but when I got it done, the owner offered me the chance to run the company. Otherwise, he would just sell it to get rid of it.

I learned the business fast, and found that if I worked hard there was plenty of money to be made. My boss was a great guy: after I'd worked for him for a while, he offered me the company. I even had a side job as a security guard, for the contractor building the Spirit Mountain Casino in Grand Ronde, the little town where I grew up. Within 7 years, I was back on my feet.

* * *

During this time, I often thought about what I'd written for the doctor, and how much it had helped me. I shared some of my writing with the members of a local writers' group, "Easy Writers"; they told me I should put it into print, so other people could read what happened to me.

I gave my manuscript to a lady who cleaned up the writing for me, while preserving all my four-letter words and some of the other stupid things I'd said. The resulting book, called simply "Gunny," was printed in 1995.

I was hoping for a happy ending…but my hell was just beginning.

* * *

My book woke a giant within me. I had five thousand copies made but had sold only 300 or so; the rest were piled in my storeroom. Meanwhile, working two 20-hour-a-day jobs was killing me, and something was going wrong inside: I was passing blood when I went to the bathroom.

A trip to the Veterans Hospital revealed I had bladder cancer. I was lucky it hadn't gone any further, but to remove it, they would have to go through my penis. I broke out in a sweat, thinking, *God is finally getting even with me.*

Once a week, early in the morning, I had to go to the hospital in Portland for treatment…then come home and *try* to go to work. I couldn't go to the bathroom without passing blood, and the pain was in the tenderest part of my body.

Six months later, the cancer came back. *Here we go again*, I thought: *"don't worry, you're going to be OK, we just want to check you once more because you have a lump on your prostate, but it's nothing to worry about, maybe it's just caused by your treatment, but we'll take a sample just to check."*

* * *

The doctor called me after I got home. "I'm sorry to tell you," he said, "but you have prostate cancer, and it has to come out—fast."

From what I knew, they'd just stick their finger up my butt to check it out, then a little snip, snip and I'd be sent home. How bad could *that* be?

Yeah, right. *Better say goodbye to Little Willie, put yourself out of business and take what's left of your manhood.*

* * *

After that, I had to go in every six months for a year or two, then once a year after that, so they could take a look and see if I was doing okay.

On one of my "routine" checkups, the doctor found a lump on my jaw. Sure enough, it was cancer.

* * *

I don't know or understand how my body keeps going when my mind gives out, but once again I pulled through. My company was doing well, and I was getting my life in order. We were able to buy a new factory home, and I was even thinking about selling my business and trying my hand at retirement.

We bought a computer and I began learning how the damn thing worked. When I went online, I started finding messages from all over. There were people looking for friends, military guys looking for old buddies. Until now, I'd only been in touch with the few guys I knew, but that was about to change.

* * *

One day, I got a message from a guy looking for people who'd known a Wallace Schmidt from F Company 2nd bn. 4th Marines in 1967 or 1968. I remembered several guys nicknamed 'Smitty,' so I had him send me a photo. It turned out I *did* know him. He was a little guy, just over five feet, but very brave and did his job well.

The next message was very sad news...five years after coming home from Vietnam, Schmidt had hanged himself. His family had been living with this memory for 25 years, and the guy wanted to know if I could help them understand what could have happened.

Mike Summers, a buddy of mine who lived here in Oregon, had also known Schmidt. Mike and I agreed to go to Schmidt's home in Minnesota and meet his family. General Weise, our commanding officer in Vietnam, would accomany us. Weise planned on having a memorial for Schmidt, in the hopes that the honors would help his family cope with their loss.

When I met Schmidt's family, I was not ready for the feelings I experienced. There was a sense of hatred, or some other hard, negative emotions. Initially, I thought it might be directed at us, but once we were all in the same room, it seemed more like something within the family...like a dark cloud hanging over the room. The family was in deep sorrow, and I felt that someone within the family was being blamed for why Schmidt had killed himself.

The general had to return to the airport briefly to pick up his luggage, and told me not to talk about what had happened in Vietnam until he returned. I had brought some memories and a few pictures to show the family, along with my Navy Commendation Medal. I thought I would give it to the family as my gift to them.

I couldn't hold it inside any longer, and handed them the book I'd brought for them to look at. They looked through it pretty quickly, until they came to the medal I'd placed inside.

Schmidt's mother paused and looked at it. "Oh my God," she said. "You're giving us *your* medal for *our* son!"

I was almost ready to cry. I wanted to tell them about their son, but the General had asked me not to say anything. Finally, I gave in and started to cry. "I have to tell you," I said, "it's not your fault that Schmidt killed himself. Your son and your brother was a brave Marine who should never have come home from Vietnam. I think his mind died there and he just took his body home to die in.

"He lost everything," I told them, "and he never got over the battles he fought. So many of his buddies died in his arms, and he couldn't accept the fact that *he* had lived. That's why he killed himself. There was nothing any of you could have done."

It was so quiet...and then everyone started to cry. I think they needed to hear that. Everything changed, and I could feel the weight being lifted from them. When the general returned, he noticed the difference, but never said anything. I think he knew I must have told them something.

The rest of the visit went well. We had a Memorial Service for our buddy, Wallace Schmidt, whom his family called "Skipper." After the service, we went back to the oldest girl's house for food and to visit some more. They had some videos of the family, and a Memorial they'd put together to remember him.

Somewhere that day, I saw a picture of Schmidt, and he was missing some fingers. "I saw Schmidt in one of my dreams," I told the oldest girl, "and by the way he held his gun I could tell some fingers were missing. How did he get in the Marines without all his fingers?"

She looked at me and said, "He lost them the day he was wounded: he got hit in the hand."

I was at a loss for what to say, because I hadn't seen him after he'd been wounded the second time, and she didn't know he'd been wounded on March 12, 1968.

They showed me the Memorial they'd made in his honor. "He should have two Purple Hearts," I told them, "and a medal for Valor. I'd written him up for an award and asked that he be awarded a Silver Star...but sometimes the people in the chain of command will change the award." I was upset over that, but was still trying to understand how I'd known he was missing the fingers.

* * *

We left for home the next day, and I made up my mind I was going to find out why Schmidt never got his medal. I knew, somewhere in my paperwork, I had a copy of the award request I'd put him in for. I also wanted to look at the picture one of my artist friends had drawn for me based on my memory of Schmidt.

I found the paperwork for the Silver Star award, as well as the picture of him...missing the fingers. I couldn't understand how I'd known that. It was driving me crazy...and the bad dreams were coming back.

I was going for treatment, still running my company, and fighting the Marine Corps to re-open Schmidt's records to find out why he never got the award. I was so mad, thinking that maybe if he'd *gotten* the award, he could have understood that what he did in combat was the reason he lived and others died.

I had to contact all the officers who'd been there when the award was put in, to see if they remembered it. They all believed me and agreed to sign off on the award, except for one officer who wanted to downgrade the award to a Bronze Star.

"Bullshit!" I told them, and went over their heads. "If you'd given him the award when I requested it, maybe he could have understood what had happened...and he might still be alive today."

The Marine Corps came through and approved the award. Schmidt's family would be awarded the Silver Star in his honor.

Schmidt's family wanted me and Mike Summers to join them at the award presentation, at the state capital in Minnesota. They were going to forego exchanging Christmas gifts that year, and put their money into plane tickets for us.

* * *

There were lots of people at the ceremony, including General Weise and Colonel Gavlick, and several officers from Vietnam.

Just before the award was to be presented to Schmidt's parents (who were no longer married), the family decided they wanted *me* to present the medal.

"I'm honored," I told them, "but that's not technically my job. The award should be presented by an officer."

General Weise sided with the family. "If that's what they want, then that's what will happen."

I had to pull deep into my mind to do it—I knew this was *not* the way it should be. But the family believed that, if not for me, this would never have happened. It gave them closure.

I'm still very close to Schmidt's family. They check in with me all the time and tell me about their family. One of the girls even came to Oregon for a visit.

* * *

I paid the price for what I did: I think the Marine Corps put a check mark by my name, and they'll probably kick my ass if I write to them again.

I know I stepped over the line when I wanted the family to get this medal, but I knew he had it coming. I also knew it would let the family come to terms with what their son and brother had gone through.

Another benefit: it cured my dreams about Schmidt. Somehow, I think those were his doing: he wouldn't get out of my dreams until his family could understand what happened.

All this came to pass because of the message on my computer…maybe it would have happened somehow anyway. Because of my book, I was now hearing from more and more families. Most had nothing to do with me personally, so I had no trouble dealing with them.

* * *

In March 2000, another message arrived, this one from an Army Sergeant looking for someone who knew his brother, a member of F Co. 2nd bn. 4th Marine who'd had been killed March 7, 1968.

We had five Marines killed that day, and several wounded, and I told him that in my reply. He told me his dad had been a Marine in WWII, and his older brother—a former Marine like himself—was an author who wanted to write a book about his brother's life and the men who'd served with him.

When we had the chance to talk to each other, he told me his name and I remembered who his brother was. He'd been blown almost in half by a rocket round…little did I know we were going to relive that day over many times. It would take me back to Vietnam, to the place where he died, and to meet the enemy soldier who fired the round that killed him.

But that's another story….

With Charles Swindell at Hai Van Pass, where many battles were fought...

Water buffalo grazing on the old battlefield: so many changes after 33 years...

Appendix A
Returning to the Battlefields of Vietnam
After More Than 33 Years!

It was never my intent to ever go back to Vietnam. The memory of the Vietnam War was too deep. What it has done to my life and many of the men I served with in the war, the memory of the men I saw dead and wounded....

I have seen the war up close and I was the Gunnery Sergeant of F Company 2nd bn. 4th Marines 3rd Marine Division. Our outfit was called "The Magnificent Bastards" and they called me "Gunny." I was wounded six times and awarded four purple hearts.

In March 2000, I responded to a message on my computer from a brother of a Marine killed March 7, 1968 that was looking for someone who may have known his brother who was killed while serving with F Company 2nd Bn. 4th Marines in Vietnam. That was my company and I remembered that we had five Marines killed that day. We had only been in this area three days and been in battle every day and night and up to now we hadn't lost a man, not even wounded.

The battle that day started about 7:30 in the morning with the first Marine shot through the neck and several others wounded. My job as Gunny was to get the wounded men out and I had spent the better part of the morning moving through the area to get them out.

I was moving forward of the area looking for a Marine who had been shot in the foot when I stopped to talk to two Marines smoking a cigarette. The two Marines were Pfc. Jeffrey Smith and L/Cpl. Jim Arnold. I asked them what they were doing and the man close to me was Pfc. Smith. He said they were just going to finish their cigarette and then get back to their platoon. I told them I was moving forward to find the Marine who was shot in the foot. I jumped up and moved when I heard the rocket rounds coming in so I dove for cover; one round landed beside the Marine I had just talked to almost cutting him in half killing him. I moved back to his side and the Marine beside him was calling for help. One of our Corpsmen got there about the same time I did and told me, "Gunny, he is dead."

Jim Arnold was crying. "He can't be, I just talked to him...I'm hit" he said. The corpsman was trying to cover him up, but Arnold kept saying he wasn't dead. I knew the corpsman well and he had been in combat for several months and knew his job well. He was from Hermiston, Oregon.

I called for a helicopter to come in and pick up our dead and wounded. Jim Arnold and I carried Jeffery Smith to the helicopter, he was the first Marine killed since we moved into this area.

I hadn't thought about this Marine's name since that day over 33 years ago, but not many days went by that the memory of that day didn't came back to me. It was the same helicopter I fell from when it took off before I could get off.

The person who put the message on the computer was one of Pfc. Jeffery Smith's brothers. He was from a Marine family...his dad and two brothers were Marines. That day, March 7, 1968, flashed through my mind as if it just happened. Why after all these years would this be coming back to me? What could I say? How would I tell them how he died?

I got a phone call just an hour or two after my many messages went on the computer. It was John Smith, a newspaper man from Atlanta, Georgia, and he told me Jeffrey Smith was his brother and he wanted to know if I could talk about what happened that day his brother died.

He told me he had written several books and was putting together information and hoping to write a book about his brother and planned to call it "My Brother's Keeper."

After talking for a few hours, he asked me if he came to Oregon could he talk to me more about the war. He had also found two other Marines who knew his brother and asked if I knew them and I told him I did. I also told him the Corpsman that was there when his brother died also lived in Oregon, but I wasn't sure if he would talk about the war because he was still having trouble dealing with what had happened.

John Smith came to Oregon and we spent three days together. We were able to travel to Hermiston, Oregon, and met Ken Fickel, the Corpsman that was there when his brother died. My feeling, at this time, was that I had told him everything I could about that day. I had some pictures of men from our company, along with a map that I carried over 33 years ago, on which I had recorded where we'd had men killed.

A few days after he returned home and to work, he called me and said that the company he was writing the book with wanted him to go to Vietnam and do a story and take pictures of the Battlefield and asked me if I would go back with him. Jim Arnold, the Marine who was beside his brother, said he would also go back, if I would go.

I agreed, hoping that it would never happen because it would be over a year before he would go and I had hoped I could get out of it somehow. For the next year my thoughts were never on the trip to Vietnam much. The day came when I had to say "Yes" I would go. It was going to happen and the memory of that stinking place came back to me and I couldn't sleep at night…my nerves were going wild. I had lost 20 pounds and one night just a week before we were to leave, my nerves got the best of me and I ended up at the emergency ward at the hospital at 2:00 am. Lucky for me the doctor on duty had been a flight doctor during Vietnam and when he heard I was going back he got me some medication that helped me settle down. I had made up my mind that I wasn't going back but I would fly to LA and meet the guys and tell them I was backing out.

Crossing the road through a bicycle gauntlet

Must've been something I ate…

Well, that never happened and after several hours at the Hilton Hotel Lounge, I was in line to get on the plane that would take me back to Vietnam... and for the next 17 long hours I paid for my stay in the lounge. We landed in Japan long enough to refuel and then 5 more hours to Bangkok Thi. A few hours layover and off to Vietnam and two more hours on the plane.

There it was after 33 years... Vietnam...overcast and raining. Our former enemy did not seem very happy to see us as we went through customs. *Keep your mouth shut and don't look at me* is what I saw in their eyes.

Once we were done with customs, it was welcome, hurry on to the bus, off to the hotel, drop off our bags and

Author and illustrator Ellen Keeland drew this portrait of us on the boat.

back on the so called air conditioned bus. I had forgotten how hot and muggy Vietnam was. Hundreds of bikes and motorbikes, some with three wheels, were everywhere. I would learn to hate the sound of the horn...beep, beep, beep, hour after hour and when we got off the bus the heat and vendors were there to meet us, on the Battlefield or in the mountains. They all knew the words Sir, Sir and the little girls sang "Don't worry, Be happy" and they were sweet as can be and we paid them $10.

Since we were with a tour group, we stopped at all the old battlefields and the bad news was that the Battlefield we were going to wasn't until the end of the second week. Four days into the trip I had eaten something that I shouldn't have and I got sick and nothing I took helped me. The food wouldn't stay down and the only thing I could keep down was Slim Fast diet bars, so to make them last I only ate two a day...great diet.

By day nine we made it to the area where I had fought my battles and we were told we would have to travel up river in a boat, a flat bottom boat we called San Pans when I was there.

We had to be at the river first thing in the morning and meet the boat. We got the news that the commander of the Viet-Cong Forces that we fought was

My friends, the boat crew

'O sole mio...

now the man in charge of all the area and all the villages that we wanted to visit
and he was going to be our guest on the trip.

By now my diet of Slim Fast Diet bars had taken its toll on me and I had
to dig deep inside to hold up. The boats took us up the river about three miles
and I could see the Battlefields that I had fought in. The boat let us off about
two miles from the village that I was to show John Smith where his brother died.
Up to this time Jim Arnold hadn't said anything about the battle and in fact he
told me he was sorry he did not even remember me. We had to walk about two
miles and it had rained almost all night, but the sun was up and it steaming. The
trails were deep in mud…all I needed was my rifle and I would be back 33 years
in memory.

John Smith had bought some flowers, some fruit and some pictures of his
brother along with a few other items. He had planned on saying a few things
about his brother but he could not…he started to cry. I said, "John, this is where
your brother died" and I pointed to the spot. Jim Arnold said that he remembered
the mound and walked over, sat down by himself and started to cry.

One of the members of the tour group was a retired Marine Col. who up
to this time had a lot to say. He had been telling all about all the battles he was
in and seem to always know about everything that happened wherever we went.
He stepped up and said, "I don't think John Smith is up to doing any service,"
and took out his Bible and said, "I will read several chapters and tell about the
battle." I walked up to him and said, "I will make this short and sweet and I will
tell the group about this battle."

When we finished, it had been short and sweet and the Vietnam guide
who was doing the talking said the Commander of the Viet-Cong wanted to
say something to us. He talked to us and told us all the good his people did and
several things I and the rest of the group did not want to hear, but we never said
anything and let him finish.

John Smith and Jim Arnold had brought with them three cans of fruit
cocktail, John was able to tell us that his brother and Jim Arnold had just shared
a can of fruit cocktail and were smoking a cigarette just before he was killed.
That was the only thing Jim Arnold could remember and that was about the
time I came up where they were.

One of the people in the tour group was a 30 year old girl who was a doctor
and was there because her father was a doctor who was in support of our
operation when I was there. She asked if I would tell her about the battle of the

My photo with Jim Arnold
and VC commander Mr. Han

Mr. Han and I checking the map I brought
with me—the same map I'd used in 1968

day John Smith's brother was killed. By now the old Gunny in me was coming out and I took charge and told about the battle. When I was finished, I told the group that John wanted us to share the fruit cocktail in memory of his brother and could we all have a moment of silence for his brother. The two or three Vietnam people who were with us started to talk and this girl walked up in front of them and put her finger to her mouth and said, "SHHHH!"

I was standing near the grave and the commander of the Viet-Cong walked up to me and in very good English said to me, "You are a great warrior. Will you—" and he pointed at Jim Arnold "—take a picture with me?" He told me a story about the village that our battalion was in. He said that they had a tunnel under it and his people would report to him what our activity was each day.

I pointed to the west end of the village and asked him if the tunnel was in that area and if so, was it still there. He said it was in that area, but the tunnel was gone now. I looked at Arnold and tried not to smile.

We met at the bus later in another village and we traveled to the village where Jim Arnold and I were wounded on March 12, 1968, just five days after Arnold and I carried Smith, our friend to the helicopter. Jim Arnold was wounded three times that day, all minor, but I wouldn't see Jim again until our trip. His memory was coming back after over 33 years that he had blanked out the two battles that he had lived through.

We talked more about the battle we had been in and he was starting to remember more about our times together after 33 years. He said he remembered two Marines pulling him over a mound of dirt or a bank near the creek. We walked up a trail and as we came to a mound near the creek I asked him if he remembered this area. He said the river was too big: 33 years ago it was just a small creek; now they had dams on all the rivers.

"This spot," I said, "is where the two Marines pulled you out of the line of fire and took you to the landing zone where the helicopter picked you up."

He said that he remembered that and told me the guy who was loading the wounded told them to put the worst wounded on the plane first and he said they put him on, but he didn't think he was hurt that bad. He had been shot through the arm, hit two or three times in the back. One hole you could stick a softball in. He couldn't believe I knew all that about him. I told him my radio man and I were the two Marines who got him out and he was hit badly. He told me he was in the hospital for over 18 months recovering.

Jim Arnold asked me why I was smiling when I talked to the Commander

Looking for the battlefield where John's brother Jeff was killed on March 7, 1968

Me, Jim Arnold and John Smith, standing on the spot where Jeff was killed

of the Viet-Cong. I told him I never knew about the tunnel, but I knew that the enemy was watching us because I had seen them, though I was never able to see where they came from or where they went. But I knew it was late in the day because I would see movement about the same time every day in the tree line.

One day I had the sniper's rifle and saw through his 20 power scope and who I saw had a rifle and I shot at him, but missed. So when he told me about the tunnel now after 33 years, I knew where the enemy had come from and my smile was because when he told me about them making reports to him, I was also thinking about a few things I know he never got reports on.

Our last meal together before returning home

* * *

One thing our tour guide had warned us about was that nothing could be removed from the battlefield...not even rocks or dirt. But I knew that most of the guys I'd served with would never be able to return to Vietnam, and I wanted to bring them back a souvenir. So I decided to take some dirt from each battlefield we visited that we'd fought on.

Taking dirt from the battlefield... despite being told not to

When I got home, I had an artist named Victoria Littlejohn make me some special ceramic plates. Sealed in the center of each was a transparent container of battlefield soil.

I sent the plates to some buddies I was in touch with. Most of them knew I'd taken a big chance in removing the dirt, but I felt we saw too many good men die there. It was a memory I never wanted to forget.

Taking another "soil sample"

Victoria's finished plates with soil inside

Appendix B, Part 1
"A Big Man with an Even Bigger Heart"

Written by John Smith, author of "My Brother's Keeper" and brother of Pfc. Jeffrey Smith, with whom I served in Vietnam. In 2001, John went with me to Vietnam.

I had a fairly good idea of what would be waiting for me as I got off the plane at Portland International on Friday evening, May 26, 2000. Gunny Brandon said he would be easy to recognize: "I'll be the ol' fart wearing a Marine Corps T-shirt, the big guy held together with duct tape." I thought he was joking.

Percy Eugene "Gunny" Brandon is the face of war. Shrapnel pocks his cheeks and forehead, and four fragments embedded in his right eye cause double vision. Shrapnel fractured his left wrist on March 4, 1968, and an enemy mortar round blew off his left thumb on March 12, 1968. He received a concussion from an NVA artillery blast on March 30, 1968 and two days later another enemy artillery round again knocked him out. When he finally regained consciousness, he coughed up blood for three hours.

"I was in charge of about 70 riflemen and none of them wanted me near them, they said I was just a magnet for enemy fire," Brandon said as he and his wife Shirlie escorted me out of the airport to the parking lot. "Course, everyone knew the body bag hadn't been made that could hold my sorry ass. Well, almost."

On June 28, the day before his 33rd birthday, Brandon tripped an enemy Claymore mine...what his Marines appropriately called a "Hellbox" an explosion with such horrible consequences that Brandon was left for dead inside a rubber body bag. When he regained consciousness 11 days later, he was told that his body had been punctured 43 times...in both eyes, both arms, both legs, and the right testicle. The right side of his face was sliced open in three places, and his left eardrum and his right lung was punctured. The worst of the wounds were to his stomach, which was ripped from his breastbone to groin, exposing his intestines. Brandon said he would have bled to death within that body bag had it not been for Captain Turley, who was asked to make the final identification of Brandon's body at graves registration and noticed that Gunny was still breathing, which resulted in Brandon being immediately medivaced to the hospital ship sanctuary.

Gunny recounted this near death experience with a burst of laughter as he patted his wife's hand. Shirlie looked at her husband, then at me in the back seat of their van. She raised her eyebrows, failing to see the humor. She could only remember the horror and helplessness, as she prayed at Gunny's side in 1968 as he drifted in and out of consciousness, screaming all the while, from his bed at Bermington Naval Hospital in Washington.

Brandon spent less than five months in Vietnam, his tour beginning in December 1967 after spending three years as a drill instructor at Paris Island, South Carolina. He was discharged after 20 years in the Corps, the last four of which were spent on medical leave as he underwent a seemingly endless series of excruciating bone transplants and skin grafts. That should have ended his ties to the Marine Corps. "But it didn't," said Shirlie. As she cautioned me as we made the 40-minute drive southwest to their home in McMinnville, "Gene has never really taken off the uniform." Whenever there's a Marine who needs help, no matter what part of the country's he's from, Shirlie said her husband are quick to lend a helping hand. Even now, approaching age 65 and still recovering from prostate cancer surgery, he has opened up his home and his heart to a complete stranger.

"Well almost a complete stranger," said Shirlie, smiling warmly. "You are, after all, the brother of one of Gene's young Marines. He's never stopped caring for his men. He's never stopped being a gunnery sergeant."

* * *

Gunny and Shirlie live in a quaint ranch home on a sprawling farm in the heart of Yamhill County, three miles outside of McMinnville, population 27,500. The local Chamber of Commerce calls this part of the state "Oregon at its best," which is not a stretch. This is wine producing country, nestled in the Willamette Valley. Downtown McMinnville, with its many buildings built in the 1880s, feels like a time warp. The locals do not hesitant about boasting that this is an old-fashioned community with old-fashioned values, and that Gunny Brandon is one of its heroes, its heart and soul, the embodiment of the community's patriotism.

Gunny and Shirlie grew up here. They were married in 1956; three years after Gunny joined the Corps. Since his induction in January 1953, Brandon has lived and breathed the Marine Corps. Shirlie willingly moved their son and two daughters from base, in essence being the sole parent while Gunny toiled endlessly at being the perfect Marine, testifies to her character. The sacrifices made by military spouses, especially of enlisted men, are too rarely noted. If further testimony to her devotion is needed, it can be found in her staying with him after Vietnam through seemingly endless surgeries and bouts of depression. "I knew what I was getting myself into when I married Gene," she said. "He was all Marine, but he was my Marine-faithful, loyal and true. Everyone makes mistakes; we've had our good moments and our bad. And Gene could have been a better father, spending more time with our children. But ours has been a good life. I married a good man, with a big heart, who wanted to be a good Marine."

She said this at her kitchen table shortly after we arrived from the airport. Gunny was busy sorting through his memorabilia-combat maps, souvenirs taken off the dead enemy, and snapshots he'd taken in Vietnam laying everything in his semblance of order, of fractured time and place, which he admitted without embarrassment was a bit jumbled. His memory lapses are because of a combination of concussions sustained in combat and posttraumatic stress. "Damnedest thing," Gunny said. "I'll be working, up to my knees in asphalt or whatever, and then all of a sudden I'm back there, seeing this guy getting a direct hit from an NVA mortar. And then I want to run and help him, knowing it's no use, that he's dead; and then I realize he's not even there, that I'm not even in Vietnam, but he's still gone and... ah, I don't know. I lost something like 56 of my 68 riflemen killed in such a short time, between March 7 and May 2. I guess I see too damn many faces."

There was an uncomfortable silence, then Shirlie said that Gunny has no recollection of being sent home from Vietnam in May 1968, shortly after his fourth wound. "He played with the children, mowed the lawn, and drank a lot of beer with friends and neighbors, acting as normal as anyone else who'd seen as much as he'd seen," she said. "And then he signed a waiver, allowing him to go back into combat, and the next thing he remembers is being back in that place. In his mind, he wasn't at home at all."

Gunny simply smiled as he sorted through his yesterdays, oblivious to our conversation. Shirlie gave me a hug, and then excused herself, cautioning her husband not to stay up too late embracing the past.

Between the time we first connected via the Internet and the moment we met face to face, Brandon and I were in constant communication. There were letters and emails, sometimes twice a day. And the telephone conversations seemed endless, weekly sessions that stretched into the wee hours of the morning. Gunny told me up front that he wasn't looking for anyone's sympathy, that he only did his duty and did it well, and that he would answer all of my questions as honestly as possible. He told me how much he loved his wife and children, that without their support he would never have fully recovered from his wounds. "Even as chewed up as he was when the Corps finally retired me, I've never been able to sit still," he said, then rattled off the jobs he's held over the years, some of which were owning and operating restaurants and bars. Now he has his own asphalt business, working a minimum of 14 hours a day, six days a week. "Business has been good because everyone knows that I don't make excuses, and I don't sit around on my butt and let the work pile up. I've got more work than hours in the week to complete it." And when not paving driveways and parking lots, he spends his off hours putting up flagpoles for the community's residents. "You can never have enough American flags flying," he said, laughing.

But more often than not, we talked about Vietnam. In truth I learned more than I care to about Brandon and the hell he and his Foxtrot Marines endured there, mainly because the majority if it was gut-wrenching and nauseating. Having read almost everything written about that war in hopes of clues, how ever small, to what happened to my brother.

I can't even remember any newspaper guys linking up with us," Brandon said. "Maybe it wasn't glamorous enough because we were stuck way up north, right along the DMZ. What we did was search and destroy, which today doesn't seem to make a great deal of sense. We were surrounded all the time. We had the DMZ to our north, and plenty of NCA and hard corps VC completing the rest of the 360 degrees. We'd hit them, and then they'd hit us. That was our war."

For almost three months I shared Gunny Brandon's nightmares via long distance, sharing anger, frustration, tears, and an occasional laugh, but most of all hearing a helplessness that bordered on desperation, his guilt that, despite his over powering size and strength, despite his dedication and risks, he was unable to prevent the death of so many of his young Marines. Sometimes his memories felt like a knife scraping against bone, yet I found it impossible to end the communication because of the early remark, "It is really healing for me to get this off my chest, buddy. Gunny, I really didn't know how much of this shit was still trapped inside me."

* * *

Gunny Brandon is a huge man standing 6-foot-2 and weighing 276 pounds. He is not particularly articulate nor well educated, the result of his quitting high school midway through his sophomore year in January 1953 to fulfill his ambition of being a Marine, which was a matter of honor…tribal honor, the blood mix of his Rosebud Sioux and Cree Indian warrior tradition; military honor, because his older brother, Howard, was killed at Iwo Jima while helping pin down Japanese snipers as fellow Marines and Navy corpsmen raised the flag on Mount Siribachi.

That Brandon achieved the most honored and respected rank within the Corps, Gunnery Sergeant, which is the closest thing to being God among enlisted men which qualifies him to be called a Marine's Marine. But to describe him only in this manner is to greatly shortchange the man. His presence fills a room and his voice commands respect not because he is a Marine, but because he's Percy Eugene Brandon…rock-solid, true to his word, his wife, his family, his country and his friends, whether they are those who survived Vietnam or a blood relative of one of Brandon's young Marines who didn't. Pointing out Brandon's academic shortcomings is not meant to be an insult for when people are shooting at you, you would swamp the faculties of all the Ivy League schools and the state university system of California for one warrior like him, a gunnery sergeant or not.

But even Brandon has a weakness; he's haunted by what he's seen but even more because he could only be one Gunny and not Superman, which brings him down to the level of the most petrified private in the combat ranks, because Brandon is haunted that perhaps he wasn't good enough. And while he likes to joke about all the "zippers" that decorate his body, those horrid surgical scars from hundreds of stitches, the worst of these are only visible during the ghastly remembrances shared with trusted friends as Brandon fights back the tears and exposes the scar tissue that calcifies his heart.

And that's exactly what he did as we sat face to face at his kitchen table, with only his memorabilia separating us, as the clock on a nearby wall slowly advanced toward midnight, and Brandon's mental clock spun wildly in reverse to Vietnam 1986…jumping from combat in June to incidents that happened in February, then to his surgeries in Japan in August and then back to battles that happened in May. It was impossible to keep his story-telling in chronological order, for one story always led to another and another, all without rational rhyme or reason, making little or no sense at all, I simply listened, interrupting with a question only sparingly, being the sponge that soaked up his agony, listening to stories that all had a sameness, a profound sadness, the closeness only those thrown into combat feel; men of various faiths and race, with little in common except the circumstances in which they were trapped, becoming brothers in blood, terror, and anguish. "The hardest part," Gunny said, "was moving back down the line to one of my Marines and having to tell him that his best friend just got killed. They'd say 'can't be, Gunny; we just had a cigarette together a few minutes ago.' That's the way it was with Jim Arnold; he really took your brother's death real hard. He just didn't…"

Gunny looked away, his fingers unconsciously moving around his war souvenirs before pausing at the combat map in front of him, the map once carried by 2nd Lieutenant Richard Sisk, the commander of Fox Company 2nd Platoon. It still bears traces of Sisk's blood. He was the first casualty, suffering a gunshot wound to the neck he would recover from, during the battle in which my brother was killed.

Silence, for I felt guilty putting Brandon through this once again. Before I could summon the courage to ask about my brother, Gunny told me about the night Jeff and his fire-team were attacked by three-foot-tall apes while manning an observation post near the Rock Pile. Damnedest thing you'd ever want to see, said Gunny, getting the call on the radio that monkeys were overrunning Jeff's fire-team. "So tell 'em to throw some fuckin' bananas at 'em," thinking they were pulling my leg. Then they called back and said, "Hell with the bananas, Gunny. They're throwing rocks at us." When Brandon checked on their position at daylight, sure enough, there was some of the damn apes screeching and jumping up and down on the rocks. Vicious little bastards, looking more like gorillas than monkeys. Jeff and his buddies were pretty well scratched up from when the apes jumped into their fighting holes and started clawing at them, so I fired a .50-caliber machine gun at the damn things. Them apes didn't bother us again."

We laughed together, but it was short-lived because as the night wore on Gunny's depiction of Vietnam took on a darker tone. His visual aides enhanced this darkness; pictures of enemy dead and letters and family pictures taken off the bodies of slain NVA and VC. There were also pictures of some of Brandon's own men, who proudly mugged before the camera before the assault toward Bac Vong on March 7, smiling Marines with their weapons poised for combat.

"Ever since we first talked on the telephone, I keep wondering if any of this really happened," Brandon said. "Vietnam was so damn crazy, there were so many mistakes made in that war. Course, back then you couldn't tell me our tactics didn't make sense. We were told to take an area and we took it, we found the enemy and killed him, and we lost Marines. We took villages, stayed a few days and then left. Then we had to take that same village a week or so later, losing more Marines. They were like family. It hurt so much…"

It hurt so much that whenever Brandon closed his eyes, the faces of these young men haunted him. This went on for years after he'd left Vietnam. Gunny's sleep was fitful, if he slept at all. He would lie down and close his eyes, and David Bingham would visit him. Bingham, whom everyone called "Gunny's Shadow," the kid who was captured by the NVA at Dai Do, his hands bound behind his back with barbed wire, and executed. Gunny would close his eyes, and Skip Schmidt would visit him. Schmidt, who was a hero at Lam Xuan East, survived Vietnam and killed himself four years later. Faces, an endless parade of faces darting in and out of Brandon's sub consciousness…David Rogers, Richard Bartlow, Thomas Fleming, James Bettis, Jeff Mead, Gary Hill, Walter Cleveland, Adolph Martinez, James Burke, Robert Weeden, John Malnar, and Ken Watkins; faces with only nicknames attached; Giant, Frenchy, Rat, Baby Doc, and Feather Merchant; and faces without names.

"We had three or four Smittys and all of 'em was killed," Brandon said, then stared at the map in front of him for the longest time. I said nothing, waiting with a cold dread in my heart. "You know, when I returned home and had all the surgeries…damn gangrene, boy is that a bitch, that stuff liked to have killed me, anyway, the pain just would never go away, no matter how much the doc cuts into me. So it was years later, and I'd be drinking and hurting, and I get in my car and steer onto an isolated stretch of road and then I'd just close my eyes and hope the pain would go away. Yeah, I'd close my eyes and drift off, then wake up with the car in a ditch, the front caved in and me not knowing if maybe I'd just played around with suicide, not knowing how the hell I'd ended up in a there, but knowing sure as hell that my head hurt and my heart hurt and that I'd have to spend another goddamn day with this pain. I did that a few times, and then got help from the VA. They helped me get my head screwed back on properly."

Gunny stared deep into my soul and said he hoped I wouldn't walk away with the wrong impression of him, that he wasn't nuts or a borderline psychotic, that he was just a simple man who tried as hard as he possibly could to complete his mission. Yet, when the last echo of gunfire had drifted away and all the smoke had cleared, too damn many of his boys were no more.

"I spent the first 12 years in the Corps preparing myself for war, then the next three preparing Marine boots for war. And then when it looked as if Vietnam would pass me by, I pulled every string I could, called in all my IOU's in order to get sent into combat," Brandon said. "Didn't seem right being a Marine and never having tasted war. So now I have seen it, survived it, and now here I am, knowing I shouldn't be thinking about that shit anymore, but being unable to stop myself, lifting the lids of a lot of coffins and looking in."

And what Gunny saw when he lifted the lid was my brother; not Jeffery or Jeff, but Smitty. Seeing the yellow-orange muzzle flashes coming from my brother's fighting hole on the night of March 5, he knew Jeff was holding up okay despite the terror that a reinforced company of NVA regulars tried to overrun the battalion headquarters at Mai Xa Thi. At first light when Gunny carefully checked the enemy dead in front of the 1st Platoon's position, he felt damn proud of what his men had accomplished.

"Everyone in your brother's platoon had at least one kill," Brandon said. "I counted 26 dead gooks in front of our position alone, but shit, they kept coming at us in waves, yelling and screaming. Not that this bothered Jeff, your brother was really cool under fire, not excited in the least. He held his ground, an outstanding Marine, that's what he was. And once the attack was over, we stripped the dead, emptied out their pockets and took souvenirs, and snapped a lot of pictures. It was a pretty big deal. In some instances, it was the first time some of these guys had actually seen the enemy face-to-face."

It was almost 3 o'clock in the morning when I finally gathered the courage to press Brandon further on the details of my brother's death. Gunny hesitated, then retread the ground he had traveled in earlier telephone conversations. Finally, he looked across the table and extended his right hand, which I clenched without hesitation. His eyes never left mine when he said, "Don't know if you're up for this or not, but I made a lot of telephone calls before picking you up at the airport. Like I said, almost all of the guys who knew your brother are dead. But there's one guy that was our Corpsman for the lst Platoon, who lives about four hours across the state, over in Hermiston. The guys name is Ken Fickel and he tried to save your brother's life that day, but couldn't."

He paused, then smothered my hand with both of his, and said, "Anyway, Ken knew Jeffery, and he says he'd really like to talk to you. He's been trying to track you down now for the past 32 years."

Appendix B, Part 2
Corpsman Up!

Written by John Smith, author of "My Brother's Keeper" and brother of Pfc. Jeffrey Smith, with whom I served in Vietnam. In 2001, John went with me to Vietnam.

Fickel closed his eyes, almost as if he were trying to black out the faces. But to no avail, for the images are just as endless today as in those long ago yesterdays. There's Lonnie Morgan, tough as nails and oblivious to the bullets whizzing past his head, directing fire at the seemingly endless waves of charging enemy. And after the battle, the eerie silence is broken only by squealing pigs as they feasted on NVA. And there are the three new guys, brought in during the heat of the battle, jumping out of the chopper's hatch and being killed before they could fire a shot, preacher losing his leg when a shell casing fell on it, and Giant getting shot through the hip. There were Marines with head wounds, sucking chest wounds, and self inflicted wounds. Steve Klink seemed to be stumbling around in the dark, his back blown open by a rocket propelled grenade. And Gunny Brandon… my God, he was bleeding from every part of his body. Lieutenant Richard Sisk was the first to get shot, an enemy round ripping through his neck. Three other Fox Company Marines sustained minor leg wounds, while farther to the west, Hotel Company was also pinned down in the ambush-opening volley, and five of its Marines were killed. Ignoring intense enemy gunfire, Gunny Brandon raced to the head of the column and was the first to reach Sisk. Brandon inserted his forefinger in Sisk's wound and slowed the bleeding. Within minutes an evacuation chopper landed, and Sisk was medivaced to a field hospital in the rear, accompanied by Fickel.

Ken Fickel did all he could to save my brother, but his efforts were to no avail. Jeff was cyanotic. When Fickel could not find a pulse, he filled out a wound tag and attached it to the laces of Jeff's left combat boot, the leg that was still intact. All the while, Jim Arnold screamed at Fickel to do something to save my brother.

"That was always the worst part, knowing one of your Marines were dead or he was so damn busted up that there was nothing humanly possible that anyone could do to save him," Fickel said. "I know Arnold took it hard, and I'm sure he's still pissed at me to this very day. But you've got to believe me; there was nothing I could do for your brother except cover him with a poncho."

Approximately 20 minutes later, Brandon and Arnold carried my brother's body, using that poncho as a stretcher, through the paddies waist high muck and a hail of enemy gun fire, to an evacuation helicopter. So intense was the enemy fire that as soon as Brandon secured my brother onto the chopper, it lifted off so suddenly that Brandon did not have time to clear the hatchway. Hanging by his fingertips, he fell 100 feet onto his back into the paddy…greatly winded and bruised, but intact enough to continue fighting for another two hours.

"And just like that, at around 4 p.m., everything stopped. The fighting ended just as suddenly as it had started," Fickel said. "So we gathered the rest of our dead and wounded, and then returned to Mia Xa Thi. That's about all I can tell you, except that I'm sorry. Your brother was a good Marine and…well, those of us who made it out of there alive with the sense of guilt. There's not a day that goes by that we don't ask ourselves why we lived when so many others didn't."

Ken Fickel and I embraced. There was nothing left to say.

Appendix C
Story About Skip Schmidt

Written by Christy Sauro, author of "The Twins Platoon" (2006), from an interview he conducted but did not include in his book.

"I hated to leave those bodies, even temporarily. It went against everything the Marines stood for, but I couldn't see killing more of my Marines to pull back Marines who were already dead" (pg 40 Magnificent Bastards)

Skip Schmidt was one of the few to survive the ambush. Later that same night one Marine in particular was having a real rough time. It was the new guy named Martinez. Skip got him through it by having enough sense to realize Martinez needed more help than he could provide. PFC Schmidt brought Martinez to his commanding Officer who saw to it that severely traumatized Marines got the help he needed. A short time later Martinez was back with his unit and he and Schmidt became friends.

The Foxtrot Company Gunnery sergeant was a 33 year old career Marine and former Drill Instructor. He was a large man who once tried out for the Chargers Football Team as a 278 pound nose guard. Trimmed down to 239 pounds, the 6 foot 2 inch tall "Gunny" Brandon was a hard charging Gung Ho Marine who set a high standard for others to follow. It was his job to look after the enlisted men and keep them in line. His years on the Drill field left him with some hard to break habits. If someone got too out of line, the Gunny could get physical. He took his job seriously and was determined to keep "his" men alive. His concern for their welfare was sincere. The Giant sized man enthusiastically guided his men and took a keen interest in helping them with their personal problems, which boosted the morale of his men.

Gunny took special notice of PFC Schmidt. The young PFC knew his job well and was always there and ready to do it. Gunny Brandon never had to worry about Schmidt, other than he might do more than his job. He wished he had a 106 Marines like Schmidt.

Then there was PFC Summers, the corrigible from 3 Platoon. Summer was the product of a stormy upbringing. The last name on his Birth Certificate didn't match the last name on his four year enlistment papers, because he was adopted at age 14. The short, stocky, thick necked, baby faced, Summers had great upper body strength from lifting weights as a teenager. As a teen he was a fair skin cowboy and idolized the family of American Indians that had taken him in. In no way did he match them in physical appearance. He was a pale face of Irish decent with near red hair.

The way Summers boasted about the American Indians, and life on the reservation, didn't hurt his relationship with Gunny Brandon, who had Rosebud, Sioux, and Cree Indian blood running through his veins.

Summers joined the Corps to be a fighting Marine. Not to clean toilets or cook! When it came his turn to pull that kind of duty he used extreme measures to finagle his way out of it. Trying to out smart the system, he mostly out smarted himself and from his NCOs' he got lectures and demotions. But when it came to those things that pertained to being a "Combat" Marine, he took great pride in his proficiency.

Summers was a free spirit. He would wonder off and go visit people in other Platoons. Today he had a yearning to see Martinez, who was a good friend. Summers left his 3d Platoon and went through an unsecured area, to see his buddies in 1st Platoon.

"Hi Wally!" Summers said to Schmidt as he approached. Summers sense of humor was a bit warped and he unmercifully teased the people he liked by deliberately calling them by the wrong name. "Wally" wasn't Schmidt's first name. Schmidt turned to Martinez and said loud enough for Summers to hear.

"I ought to kick his ass for calling me Wally!"

Summers grinned and said with flavor, "OK! WALLACE!" That was Schmidt's real first name. Skips face crunched up and after a brief pause, he looked at Martinez and said; "Now I know I'm going to kick his ass!"

Gunny Brandon did a double take. What the hell was PFC Summers doing in 1st Platoon! The only way he could have gotten there was to have traveled through enemy territory!

Summers and Schmidt had just started to playfully kick dust at each other, when a distraught Gunny Brandon appeared on the scene, harboring visions of Summers strolling through the bush by himself to get there.

"YOU TWO FEATHER MERCHANTS KNOCK IT OFF!" Gunny Brandon bellowed. The two Marines, both much smaller than the Gunny, froze. Looking Squarely at Summers, Brandon accused, "WHAT DO YOU THINK YOU ARE? A GODDAMN TOURIST?"

Summers looked down. Once again he had run afoul. Surely the Gunny would think he was short on brains for venturing off all by himself.

"You're lucky you didn't get blown away!" Gunny reprimanded. That was it! Gunny left Summers to reflect on the errors of his ways. What Summers lacked in discipline he made up for in fortitude. Gunny knew knocking Summers around wouldn't do any good. He had been knocked around all his life. What Summers needed more was people who cared about him, and that's what

1997: Friends and Family of PFC Wallace Robert Schmidt of Minnesota.
Born November 1948 – Died November 1972 – A very brave Marine.

Summers would find in 2/4…people who cared about him.

After Gunny left, Summers turned and said to Martinez, "JOSE! What are you looking at?!" Martinez laughed. His first name wasn't "Jose" it was "Adolph" and he hated it. He'd leave well enough alone.

"Mail Call!" Everyone hurried out hoping to get a letter from home. There were all these letters from Shannon Schmidt's fourth grade class! Skip smiled when he saw them. He had written to his little sister Shannon and asked her to see if her class would write letters that he could share with his outfit. Shannon came through for him with flying colors!

In April the photos Skip had taken reached his family back home. Under each photo we wrote what the picture was of. One picture stood out from all the rest. It was the photo of a young male Asian, in his late teens, lying face up on the ground with his eyes closed and his arms pulled up.

"Yes!" Eugene agreed. What he didn't say was that not a day went by that he wasn't thinking about Skip. When he returned from World War II there were many things he really did not care to talk about. He figured Skip felt the same way, so he never pushed him to talk about his combat experiences. He was painfully aware that he knew so little about Skip's combat duty and to think now he might never know how deeply it saddened him. "I should have been more of a hugging father instead of a Gunny Sergeant Dad."

The chances of the Schmidt's ever hearing from somebody who serves with Skip seemed most unlikely.

Adolph Martinez was one Marine who knew Skip well. In March when 1st Platoon was nearly wiped out, the ambush occurred on Martinez's first day in Vietnam. Skip helped get him through the ordeal and afterwards they became friends. Both had first names that PFC Summers, the incorrigible from 3rd Platoon, loved to make fun of. Martinez and Skip fought together at the Battle of Dai Do. On the same day Skip was wounded and medivaced out, May 2, 1968, Martinez was killed in action. He was one of the many Marines who served with Skip that the Schmidt family would have no chance of ever hearing from. Many of the Marines who knew Skip never survived their Tour of Duty.

Saying goodbye, 25 years later…

Robert Schmidt's family

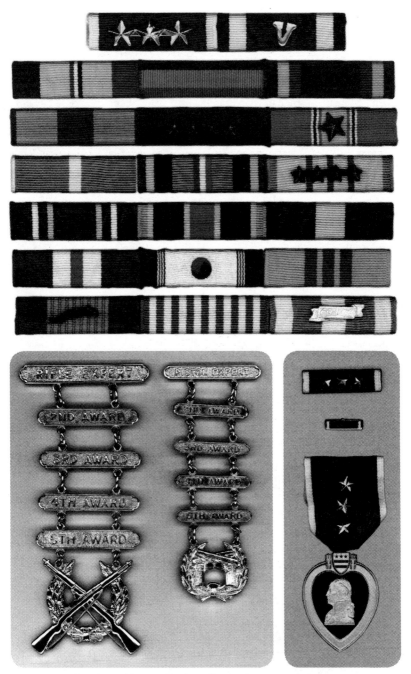

Just a few of my ribbons and badges. The Purple Heart with three stars was awarded for the wounds I received in 1968 (on March 4, 12 & 30, and June 28).

Appendix D
Honors, Awards & Commendations

"He is the prototype of the fighting career soldier and a Marine. He is an unparalleled drill instructor, leader, influencer and motivator of men—unique in my experience. Talents: extremely upright and wholly reliable. Application: vigorous and enthusiastic, no matter what the assignment. Half a Brandon is worth more to a unit than most whole Marines."

— DI Commander, Parris Island

THE SECRETARY OF THE NAVY
WASHINGTON

The Secretary of the Navy takes pleasure in presenting the NAVY UNIT COMMENDATION to

BATTALION LANDING TEAM
SECOND BATTALION, FOURTH MARINES

for service as set forth in the following

CITATION:

For outstanding heroism in action against insurgent communist forces in the northern I Corps Area, Republic of Vietnam, from 5 March to 31 May 1968. Assigned the mission of keeping the vital Cua Viet River open from Dong Ha to the coast, the Battalion Landing Team was heli-lifted on 5 March to the vicinity of Mai Xa Canh, a village in the coastal area east of Dong Ha. An operation was immediately launched to seek out and destroy certain North Vietnamese Army forces which had been interrupting the flow of logistics traffic on the Cua Viet. Aggressive patrolling and extensive sweeps resulted in numerous engagements with the enemy and a decrease in his overactivity. The Battalion Landing Team's Area of Responsibility in the Mai Xa Canh vicinity was the operating and infiltration route for six enemy units. Avoiding a direct confrontation with the Marines, the infiltrators skirted the Battalion Landing Team's Area of Responsibility and established themselves to the west at the village of Dai Do. Learning of the enemy's plan, the Team advanced on Dai Do on 30 April and was met by a well equipped adversary, firmly entrenched in heavily fortified bunkers, supported by heavy artillery, and determined to fight to the last. In the three days of savage fighting that ensued, the stubborn enemy was slowly and painfully driven from his defense positions. During the Battalion Landing Team's three-month stay in the Cua Viet area, the river remained open, having been closed only during the battle for Dai Do. The Battalion Landing Team successfully accomplished its assigned mission while inflicting devastating losses on the enemy in terms of men killed and equipment lost. By their effective teamwork, aggressive fighting spirit, and individual acts of heroism and daring, the men of the Battalion Landing Team and supporting aviation units not only achieved significant results, but in doing so exemplified qualities of courage and skill which were in keeping with the highest traditions of the Marine Corps and the United States Naval Service.

DEPARTMENT OF THE ARMY
U. S. ARMY COMMAND AND GENERAL STAFF COLLEGE
FORT LEAVENWORTH. KANSAS 66027

13 September 1968

Statement of Lieutenant Colonel William Weise, 057704/0302, U. S. Marine
Corps concerning Gunnery Sergeant Percy E. BRANDON, 1372356, U. S. Marine
Corps.

Gunnery Sergeant BRANDON served in my command, Battalion Land Team
2/4, during a period of extremely heavy combat against regular North
Vietnamese Army Forces in Northern I Corps Zone, Republic of Vietnam
from February 1968 until I was medically evacuated in May 1968. Gunnery
Sergeant BRANDON served as gunnery sergeant, Company F during the period
and I am well acquainted with his performance both from personal observation and from reports of his company commander and other officers and
noncommissioned officers.

Gunnery Sergeant BRANDON was a definite asset to the command. His
performance was far superior to the average gunnery sergeant of equal
experience. He was dedicated, selfless, efficient and extremely cool and
brave under enemy fire. His men responded to his leadership willingly.
He always sought responsibility. On several occasions, when his company
suffered heavy casualties, including officers and other key personnel,
his aggressive and rapid assumption of responsibility kept his unit
functioning effectively.

Gunnery Sergeant BRANDON was recommended twice for combat decorations
for heroic performance while I was battalion commander.

Understanding that he is being considered for retirement due to disability from wounds received in action, I respectfully recommend that he
be retained on active duty. I make this recommendation not only because
of his outstanding record in combat but because I feel he has definite
potential for future growth within the Marine Corps, despite his handicaps.
There are many duties that he will be capable of performing and I am
certain that he will apply himself to any assignment with vigor and
enthusiasm. I would particularly desire to serve with Gunnery Sergeant
BRANDON in any future assignment.

William Weise
WILLIAM WEISE
LTC, U. S. Marine Corps

AWARD RECOMMENDATION
NAVPERS 1650/6 (8-67) S N-0105-902-8160   DATE 10 Feb 1969

INSTRUCTIONS
(Originating command fill in all information available and forward to immediate superior.) — (In addressees utilize fill-in endorsements. Attach additional sheets as necessary to amplify recommendation.)

1. From: LTCOL William WEISE 057704 USMC Marine Corps Section, USACGSC Fort Leavenworth, Kansas 66027 (Former CO, BLT 2/4)	2. To: Commanding General Fleet Marine Force Pacific

3. FILE/SERV. NO. 1372356	4. NAME (Last, first, initial) BRANDON, Percy E.		5. RANK/RATE GNY SGT	6. OFF. DESIG/MOS 0369	7. BR. OF SERV. USMC

8. STATUS [x] REGULAR [ ] RESERVE	9. SOCIAL SECURITY NO. 544-34-3603	10. EXP. OF ENL. OR OBL. SERV. 29 April 1970	11. ESTIMATED DETACHMENT DATE UNK

12. PERMANENT ADDRESS 142 E. 7th Street McMinnville Yamhills, Oregon 97128	13. PLACE OF BIRTH Tarmalee Todd South Dakota

14. NAME OF PRESENT UNIT G-3, HQ CO, HQ BN, HQ REGT, MCB, Camp Pendleton, Calif.	DUTY ASSIGNMENT NCOIC Base Swimming Pools

15. NAME OF UNIT AT TIME OF ACTION/SERVICE CO "F", BLT 2/4, 9th MAB, FPO 96301	DUTY ASSIGNMENT Company Gunnery Sergeant

16. NAME OF AWARD RECOMMENDED Bronze Star	17. [ ] HEROIC [x] MERITORIOUS	18. [ ] POST HUMOUS	19. HAS SERVICE BEEN HONORABLE? [x] YES [ ] NO

20. COMBAT "V" RECOMMENDED [x] YES [ ] NO	21. AREA WHERE ACTION TOOK PLACE I CORPS ZONE, RVN	22. DATE OR DATES OF ACTION/SERVICE 9 February 1968 - 2 May 1968

23. PREVIOUS DECORATIONS RECEIVED AND DATES OF ACTION (Unit Unit Awards, campaign and service medals)

Purple Heart, Date Unknown

24. DECORATIONS RECOMMENDED BUT NOT YET ACTED ON INCLUDE DATES OF ACTION/SERVICE COVERED

None

25. OTHERS BEING RECOMMENDED FOR SAME ACTION/SERVICE (Name, rank, service number, branch of service and award recommended)

None

26. EYEWITNESSES (Name, rank, service number, branch of service. Attach statements as required)

GAVLICK, Michael H., 1st LT, 095401, USMC (statement attached)
WEISE, William LTCOL, 057704, USMC (originator of recommendation—statement included in summary of action)

27. SUMMARY OF ACTION (Include dates, assignment, location, weather, enemy and friendly strength and disposition, casualties, action justifying the award. When Medal of Honor is recommended append free hand sketch of area.)

During the period, Gunnery Sergeant BRANDON, while serving as Company Gunnery Sergeant, CO "F", BLT 2/4, 9th MAB, made significant contributions to the success of his unit during numerous contacts with regular NVA forces in the DMZ area of I Corps Zone, RVN.

Although only a staff sergeant at the time, Gunny BRANDON effectively and positively influenced the action of the platoon sergeants and other subordinates. During several vicious engagements when his company suffered heavy casualties, including key personnel, he moved fearlessly through heavy enemy small arms and supporting arms fire to direct reorganization of units and the evacuation of casualties. These actions included the battle for Vinh Quan Thong, 18 March 1968, when BLT 2/4 accounted for 130 enemy killed and the battle of Daido, 30 April - 2 May 1968, when more than 600 enemy were killed.

NAVPERS 1650/6 (8-67) (BACK)
28. SUMMARY OF ACTION (Cont'd)

Two different company commanders were enthusiastic in their praise for the actions of Gunnery Sergeant BRANDON. Between combat actions, he energetically guided and supervised the training of junior NCO's. He also took an active and tireless interest in the personal problems of his men thereby contributing to the high morale so prevalent in his company.

During the above period, the undersigned was Commanding Officer, BLT 2/4, and personally observed the actions of Gunnery Sergeant BRANDON on several occasions in combat.

29. I certify that the facts contained herein are known to me.

NAME, RANK, etc William WEISE, LTCOL (Former) CO, BLT 2/4	SIGNATURE

30. FIRST ENDORSEMENT
From:

DEPARTMENT OF THE NAVY
HEADQUARTERS UNITED STATES MARINE CORPS
WASHINGTON, D. C. 20380

IN REPLY REFER TO
DLC-cas

MAY 9 1969

From: Commandant of the Marine Corps
To: Commanding Officer, Regt Hq Co, Hq Regt, MCB, Camp
         Pendleton, Calif. 92055

Subj: Purple Heart and Gold Stars in lieu of a second
         through fourth Purple Heart; case of Gunnery Sergeant
         Percy E. BRANDON 137 23 56 USMC, verification of

Ref: (a) Yr ltr AEA:rms over 1650 of 23 Jan 69
         (b) CMC ltr DLC-gvl of 8 Apr 69

Encl: (1) Purple Heart Certificate

1. The records of this Headquarters now show that Gunnery
Sergeant BRANDON is entitled to the Purple Heart and Gold
Stars in lieu of a second through fourth Purple Heart for
wounds received in action insurgent Communist Guerrilla
forces on 4, 12, 30 March and 28 June 1968 in the Republic
of Vietnam. The Certificate is enclosed with the request
that it be delivered to him.

                                    E. F. Schurman
                              for A. GARDONI
                                    By direction

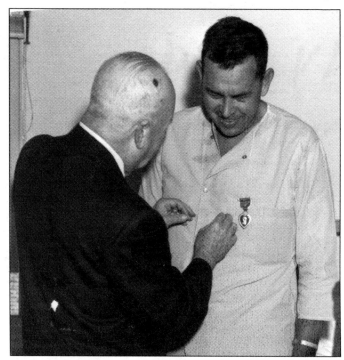

Retired General Robertson presenting me with my third Purple Heart

UNITED STATES MARINE CORPS
MARINE CORPS BASE
CAMP PENDLETON. CALIFORNIA 92055

IN REPLY REFER TO:
7/BCB/bcb
1800
29 Aug 1969

From: Commanding General
To: Gunnery Sergeant Percy E. BRANDON 137 23 56/0369 USMC
Via: Commanding Officer, Headquarters Regiment

Subj: Transfer to the Temporary Disability Retired List

Ref: (a) 10 USC 1202
        (b) CMC msg 281910ZAug69
        (c) MCO P1070.8, IRAM, par 2004

1. The Secretary of the Navy has determined that you are physically unfit
to perform the duties of your grade and has directed that you be temporarily
retired by reason of physical disability under the provisions of references
(a) and (b). You are released from all active duty at 2400 on 11 Sep 1969 ,
and transferred to the Temporary Disability Retired List effective 12 Sep 1969 ,
Your active duty pay accounts will be settled to include 11 Sep 1969 . Your
pay entry base date is 5 Apr 1953 . On 11 Sep 1969 you will have completed
 16   years, 4 months and 22 **days of** active service.

2. Your disability is rated at 70 percentum in accordance with the standard
schedule for rating disabilities in current use by the Veterans' Administr-
ation; VA Code(s) 5222077069-5099-5003-5294-5010-5003 apply.

3. You should receive orders to report to a military medical facility for a
periodic physical examination at least once every 18 months to determine whether
the disability for which you are temporarily retired has stabilized or changed.
Your failure to report for a scheduled physical examination may result in term-
ination of your retired pay unless you can establish good and sufficient reasons
for not reporting. Detailed information based on provisions of law which are
applicable in your case will be forwarded to your home address by the
Commandant of the Marine Corps (Code DMB).
                                        142 E. 7th St,
4. Your home of record is shown as   McMinnville, Oregon 97128

5. Please keep the Commandant of the Marine Corps (Code DGH) informed of
any change in your mailing address. This report is in addition to that
required to be submitted for retired pay purpose.

6. An identification card has been issued to you in accordance with ref (c).

7. Two copies of these orders will be furnished to the disbursing officer
carrying your accounts. Your records indicate unused leave in the amount of
 00 days on date of separation.

8. Expenditures under these orders are chargeable to appropriation 1701105.
2754, MPMC- 70.0C 21, BCN 45690, AAA 27, TT 2D, CC 74123, 74160, HHE 74162.

                              DONN J. ROBERTSON

Copy to:
CMC (Code DMB)
DisbO MCB Cmdren (3)
MCFC KSC (2)

CERTIFICATE OF APPRECIATION

FOR SERVICE IN THE ARMED FORCES OF THE UNITED STATES

PERCY E. BRANDON 137 23 56
Gunnery Sergeant U. S. Marine Corps Retired

I extend to you my personal thanks and the sincere appreciation of a grateful nation for your contribution of honorable service to our country. You have helped maintain the security of the nation during a critical time in its history with a devotion to duty and a spirit of sacrifice in keeping with the proud tradition of the military service.

I trust that in the coming years you will maintain an active interest in the Armed Forces and the purpose for which you served.

My best wishes to you for happiness and success in the future.

Richard Nixon

COMMANDER IN CHIEF

DD . FORM JAN 70 1725

```
                              *** ELIGIBILITY ***
BRANDON, PERCY E              SSN: 544-34-3603            DOB: JUN 29,1935
================================================================================
C#         : 24328506                          ELIG: SERVICE CONNECTED 50% to
C-Folder Loc: PORTLAND-RO
                                               1010F:
                                      ADD'L ELIG: SERVICE CONNECTED 50% to

SERV RECORD:    Branch      Service #   Entry      Separation  Discharge
      1         MARINE CORPS 1372356    04-29-68   09-11-69    HONORABLE
POW: NO

Environmental Health Risks
AGENT ORANGE: YES (Reg #: )
RADIATION   : YES (Registered on: -- Method: NUCLEAR TESTING)
--------------------------------------------------------------------------------
Service Connected: YES  100%      Fee Basis ID: 107326     Expires:
Fee authorization Periods :
            DEC 2,1982 to DEC 2,1988

Disabilities:   100% SC    CONDITION OF THE SKELETAL SYSTEM
                 70% SC    LOSS OF USE OF HAND
                 30% SC    REMOVAL OF SPLEEN
                 20% SC    TRAUMATIC ARTHRITIS
                 10% SC    LOSS OF MOTION OF MIDDLE FINGER
                 10% SC    SCARS
                 10% SC    BRAIN SYNDROME
                 10% SC    IMPAIRED VISION
                 10% SC    CONJUNCTIVITIS
                 10% SC    MUSCLE INJURY
                 10% SC    BACK STRAIN
                  0% SC    MUSCLE INJURY
                  0% SC    SINUSITIS
                  0% SC    IMPAIRED HEARING
                  0% SC    RESIDUALS OF ABDOMINAL WOUNDS
                  0% SC    SCARS
                  0% SC    FACIAL SCARS

 Eligibility Status: VERIFIED
Verification Method: HINQ/348 7131 DTD 9-11-92    Date: 08-09-94
```

EDWARD J. GORMLEY
MAYOR

PROCLAMATION

GUNNY BRANDON EVENING
JUNE 29, 1995

WHEREAS, The Citizens of the State of Oregon and Yamhill County have a proud history of serving our country faithfully,

and

WHEREAS, the City of McMinnville is home to many members of the U.S. Marine Corps and recognizes "once a Marine, always a Marine",

and

WHEREAS, many of us have come to associate the word "Marine" with one individual, Gunnery Sergeant Percy E. Brandon,

and

WHEREAS, McMinnville and Yamhill County are better places because of the contributions made on behalf of active duty servicemen and veterans by Gunny Brandon;

NOW, THEREFORE, I, Edward J. Gormley, Mayor of the City of McMinnville, Oregon, in recognition of Gunny Brandon's contribution to our community do hereby proclaim the evening of June 29, 1995 as

GUNNY BRANDON EVENING

and I call upon all those attending this event to join with the other Citizens of McMinnville in wishing Gunny a "Happy Birthday" and much success in the publishing of his autobiography.

Dated this 29th day of June 1995.

Edward J. Gormley, Mayor

230 East Second Street • McMinnville, Oregon 97128 • 503-472-9371

The Heart of the Oregon Wine Country

Certificate of Upgrade
to
Complete Asshole
is awarded to

Percy Brandon

In Recognition of Your Obnoxious Attitude, Ability to Piss People Off, Completely Asinine Juvenile Behavior and Total Dedication to Personal Gain Without Regard to the Many Hardships You Have Forced Upon Friends, Family, and Others During Your Lifetime. You Have Become a Legend In Your Own Mind.

To Recognize Your Upgrade From **Half Assed** to **Complete Asshole** Gives All Concerned Great Satisfaction If Anyone, For Any Reason, Doubts Your Status

JUST BE YOURSELF

Effective Date: 27 April 2000   Signed:

Dan W. Showalter, Jr.
Commanding Officer of Assholes

My Pay in Vietnam

I was a Staff Sergeant when I reported to Vietnam. My job was Gunnery Sergeant of Fox company second battalion fourth Marine third Marine Div. I had only a few months left in the Marines. I had over sixteen years in by then and only had to sign up for three more years, then I could retire and go home to my wife and three kids.

They gave me a little card to show me what my pay would be while I was in Vietnam. As I was writing this book, I came across the card and was looking at my pay. After deductions, I would be getting $424.99 per month, which included $115 for combat pay, over sea duty, and family separation. I tried to break that down to see what I'd been making per day or per hour...while the VC took turns shooting at me. Close as I could tell, it came to $14.00 a day, or about 60¢ an hour. And we only had to work 24 hours a day, seven days a week. Well, I lied a little: we got an hour off for church.

I did end up making a little more money by May 1968 when I picked up Gunny, but I got shot on June 28, 1968. I think there was enough money for two fifths of Jim Beam, and a half case of beer...give or take a can or two.

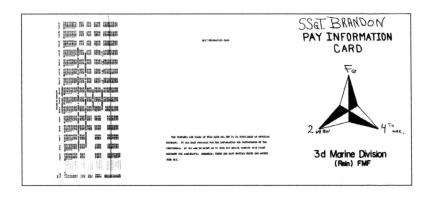

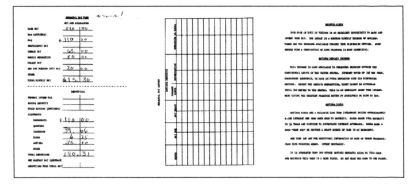

"The Ballad of Gunny Brandon"
by Al Wimer, from "The Traveler"

He grew up in Grand Ronde
Just a few miles away
He rode the local school bus
To a country school each day
He'd read of all his heroes
And all the things they'd do
He couldn't wait to grow up
So he could be a hero too

He was a laid back fight back
Rifle totin' son of a gun
When most men would tremble old Gunny was just havin' fun
When America got in trouble
Old Gunny was to the scene
He was a laid back fight back freedom lovin' American Marine
(Music only) Wait!!!!!!!
He crawled the swamps of Vietnam
And fought in Korea too
Where ever the call of freedom
Rang out for me and you
Some folks done ask old Gunny
Why you do the things you do
He heard the call of freedom
And he just had to see it thru

He was a laid back fight back
Freedom lovin' son of a gun
When most men would tremble old Gunny was just havin' fun
When America got in trouble
Old Gunny was to the scene
He was a laid back fight back freedom lovin' American Marine
He was a laid back fight back
Rifle totin' son of a gun
When most men would tremble old Gunny was just havin' fun
When America got in trouble
Old Gunny was to the scene
He was a laid back fight back freedom lovin' American Marine
He was a laid back fight back freedom lovin' American Marine

"Left! Right! Left! Right! Left! Right! Left!"

"Around the Corner I Have a Friend"
by Jim Norris

Gunny's Note: Jim Norris was my right hand man in Vietnam, and one of the few Marines brave enough to call me "Percy"! Jim fought beside me during some of our worst conflicts. As rumors go, he heard I was killed later in battle, and never forgave himself because he had not been with me. Over 35 years later, we finally made contact. This is a poem he wrote about me.

Around the corner I have a friend,
In this great city that has no end,
Yet the days go by and weeks rush on,
And before I know it, a year is gone.

And I never see my old friend's face,
For life is a swift and terrible race,
He knows I like him just as well,
As in the days when I rang his bell.

And he rang mine but we were younger then,
And now we are busy, tired men.
Tired of playing a foolish game,
Tired of trying to make a name.

"Tomorrow!" I say. "I will call on Percy
"Just to show that I'm thinking of him."
But tomorrow comes and tomorrow goes,
And distance between us grows and grows.

Around the corner, yet miles away,
"Here's a telegram, sir": "Percy died today."
And that's what we get and deserve in the end.
Around the corner, a vanished friend.

Remember to always say what you mean.
If you love someone, tell them.
Don't be afraid to express yourself.
Reach out and tell someone what they mean to you.
Because when you decide that it is the right time, it might be too late.
Seize the day. Never have regrets.
And most importantly, stay close to your friends and family,
For they have helped make you the person that you are today.

Appendix E
Correspondence

Dear Gunny,

I have received the packet that you sent. I want to take this opportunity to thank you from the bottom of my heart. It certainly is pleasant to know that there is one special Gunnery Sergeant that would sacrifice a portion of his valuable time to help with my endeavor to fight for resolution. The personal letter that you included with the packet was a great inspiration to me. Thanks ever so very much! I have discovered one operation already that was not credited on my DD214 (operation task force key low, phase 1) in your declassified packet. I will now give the packet to the veterans for processing.

I do not know if you are back from your long trip across the Pacific but I hope that you were able to find some restitution. I know from your experience that it must have been a surreptitious entry and departure for you. I sincerely hope that it was not too hard for you.

Richard Tyrell called me again tonight. It is really amazing that his voice sounds exactly the same as it did 33 years ago. I was very excited to hear from him but it is hard to find common ground without revisiting the past, especially over the phone. He indicated to me that he has also had a very hard and trying time over the years. I certainly hope that he can find peace, and it sounds like his wife is very supportive.

Gunny, I want you to know that you are indeed one true friend to me and I shall never forget what you have done for me and the troops. If there is ever anything that I can do to repay you, please let me know. Well I guess I had better send this before I get to sentimental. Again thanks so very much!

Sincerely,
Ken Fickel

* * *

Dear Dave Leverone,

Been over 33 years ago since we served together in Vietnam with F Co. 2/4 seems like a life time but our memories are still there when you left April 1968 to go Home 1 wondered if the Marines coming in to take your place would be as good a Marine as you were.

I know we fought some tough battles and you guys in the Platoon did a hell of a job, I know you never got hit in but I know in your mind you must have been wounded bad as we all did who could go through what we had to do and not have to relive it over in our minds, we seen to many good men die, very close friends...what I can say Dave. I know you had a hell of a job and our only thanks was a free ride home and nobody here to thank us for the shit we had to do.

I have never met anyone out here in civilian life that could even cone close of being like you or any of the men we served with. I was honored to be your Company Gunny and please except this little bit of Dirt I took from the battlefields we fought on. I know we can't see the blood; but I know we shed more then anyone will ever know.

Take care of yourself Dave. You will be in my mind and heart as one hell of a Marine who served your country with pride and guts.

Semper Fi.
Gunny Brandon

— Dave's Reply: —

Hi Gunny,

Just a few lines to say hello and keep in touch. It's hard to find the words to say what an honor it is to have something in common with someone from the (old corps), an experienced warrior such as yourself. For me it's a blast from the past, if you will. Thirty or more years are a long time, so they say but, in many ways it seems like yesterday 1967-68.

It's a young marine in Vietnam serving with 2/4 I for one and as did so many others looked to you for guidance and support to get us through every battle big or small. It was because of your leadership and skill and others like you from Parris Island to Camp Pendleton that instilled discipline and training that enabled us to meet the challenge we faced.

Gunny your career in the Marine Corp was a lot more extensive than mine- one hitch for me. I'm sure its something you can look upon with great pride and accomplishment.

Many years ago in Vietnam the Gunny said to the troops "Make sure you write home" and we did. Thirty or more years later the Gunny said make sure to write- and I am (some things never change).

The plate you sent with the soil "you so boldly took" from the battle ground on your return trip Nam was greatly appreciated, and has a lot of meaning to me.

I'm looking forward to the next 2/4 reunion, hope to see you and many others there.

Semper Fi,
Dave Leverone

* * *

Well Gunny,

I know that it is about time I got off my dead butt and responded to your letters and cherished package. It seems I have been so very busy with appointments and we have had the grandchildren off and on through the summer. I was very surprised and elated to receive such a special gift. Vicki began to read the letter enclosed. I stopped her immediately and explained that I wanted to read the letter and examine the contents of the package when I could be alone. It was a special and sentimental time for me. After I had my special time alone, Vicki proceeded to review the contents and contact all members of my family to share the moment. All my family was deeply touched and I think they feel that they know you as well as I do and asked me to thank you from the bottom of their hearts. My family and I shall cherish your gifts and words forever.

You may be interested to hear that my retirement company was granted 100% disability. I still have not heard a word from the Veteran's or SS. Your help, letters and information packet that you provided me really helped thanks again, so very greatly.

I hope you, Shirlie and your family are doing well and that the trip to Vietnam was a positive experience. By the way Gunny, did you get your business sold so you can begin taking it easy? I think of you often and wonder what you are up to!

You are indeed loved for your gentle humor, devotion to your fellow comrades, and selfless devotion to our country, all of which carry with it a refreshing breath of honest soil from which you sprung. Your family must be very proud indeed. "OH IF ONLY I HAD THE POWER TO IMPOSE ALL THE GOOD THAT YOU DESERVE"

Your Friend Forever,
Ken Fickel

* * *

My Dear Gunny,

Well you did it again. I still am floating somewhere on up on a cloud. When I think about what happened last weekend and the chances of Skip getting the Silver Star after so many years it felt like we won the lottery. Like Col. Gavlick said, you are a mover and a shaker.

With all the attention and concern for Skip and my family, I can't help but wonder how all of this has affected you. I truly hope this has helped heal your wounds. Thirty years is a long time to be in pain and it's time for those wounds to heal. I hope you've known how important you are to us and that we would do anything for you.

When we were driving to the airport to pick you and Mike up, I said to Finn, "it feels like we are going to pick up Skip." The two of you bring Skip home for us. So having you stay at our home was a very special treat for me.

I find myself lost for words, a chapter in our lives has ended and if I had to put a title to it I guess I would call it "The Power of Love". Now a new chapter has begun, with a bigger family to share it with. You and Mike are like family to us, and no matter how many miles there is between us you will always be in our hearts.

Finn is serious about coming to Oregon and I think it is going to happen. I especially want to meet Shirlie. I just know she is a woman I would really like. Like I told her on the phone, "behind every good man there's a great woman."

I'm sending a copy of our local paper; Cliff did another great job writing the article. I'm also sending you a copy of the video from the ceremony, you will need to have the volume turned way up so you can hear everyone, but I think it turned out great. I am anxious to hear what your family thinks of it. Please stay in touch with us; we don't want to lose you.

Thank you again Gunny, from the bottom of my heart,

Diane

* * *

Dear Gunny,

Thanks so much for the package. It arrived last Friday, and I'll admit that I let it sit there on my table for the weekend before I worked up the nerve to open it.

When I finally did pry it open, it released a flood of memories. I had forgotten how big it was, but I recalled every inch of it, and the terrain the map depicted instantly came back to me.

I know some of the troops used to get a laugh at how I'd go around with my head buried in that map, bumping into things and people. But I felt it was probably my biggest responsibility to know that thing like the back of my hand, and I was constantly trying to figure out how we'd move and deploy if we had to cross certain areas.

I know I had shortcomings, and to this day I can still cringe at some of the things I did and said, and some of my decisions I made. I can only hope Gunny that you and the others can try to understand that I was giving my best, even when my best effort seemed to make no sense.

I can't tell you how much your kind letter that accompanied the map means to me. To have a senior Marine NCO even suggest that maybe I wasn't the worst brown bar the Corps had ever had. Well, that's something to cherish.

Once again thanks Gunny, and…

Semper Fi,
Lt. Richard Sisk P.L.T leader
F-2/4 Vietnam 1968

— *Gunny's Reply:* —

Dear Lt. Sisk,

It was good talking to you after all these years I know us troop and Officers never got to be that close but me being a Gunny I had to look for both sides.

You Officers had a tough job to do with half the men you needed and never having the times to train the replacements most of them coming to us fresh out of booth camp with very little combat training.

The day you got hit March 7th 1968 we hit a well trained enemy who was ready for us and were taking out our Officers and the other key men. Three men were trying to get you out and when I got to you the bullet went through your neck and you were bleeding bad and having trouble getting air. Our Corpsman about 19 years old from Hermiston, Oregon, Ken Fickel was able to get a tube into your neck to help you breath, but we were scared to put you on the helicopter by yourself so I sent our Corpsman Ken Fickel back to D med at Dong Ha. He did a good job and got you there. When he came back in the same helicopter it started to land and we got hit and it banked to take and Ken Fickel was thrown out the door about 20 feet off the ground landing on his back.

It took us a few days before we knew you had made it okay and I never got to see you again until you got back and got hit the second time. I came to see you on the ship while you were on the hospital ward. Do you remember giving me hell the day you got shot in the neck when we were in a rice patty and you were almost going into shock from your wound and the heat and I was dumping water from the rice paddy on you. You were trying to talk to me, but your mouth kept filling up with blood and I could not make out what you were saying. When I did see you after you got hit the second time I asked what was you trying to tell me and you said "Damn it Gunny don't put that water on me it's got leeches in it."

Before I put you on the helicopter I took the map you had in your pocket, it was soaked in blood but I knew you would not need it and I needed one. I have had your map now for over 33 years still got some stains on it from your blood and maybe some from me and I want to give it back to you. So don't ever say Gunny didn't return what he borrows.

I'm glad I was able to find you after all these years; you have been on my mind so many times as you see I even wrote about you in my book. Please stay in touch. I had hoped that someday I could hand deliver the map back to you. I don't know if I will ever get to see you before I got to make that last big formation but when I get there I'm taking over as the company of Gunny and I'm saving a spot for you okay.

In the center of this plate is the dirt from the battlefield where you and the men from F 2/4 fought. They told me when I was over there March 2001 we could not take anything not even dirt. We paid a hell of a price for this dirt and I took some any way to honor the men from F 2/4.

Semper Fi Sir
Your Gunny,
Gunny Brandon

* * *

Dear Sir,

During the spring and early summer of 1968 I had the pleasure to serve with Gunnery Sergeant Brandon while serving with Foxtrot Company, 2nd Battalion 4th Marines in the Northern I Corps Area in the Republic of South Vietnam, including the period of time in which the Battle of Dai Do was conducted.

Prior to that specific battle, April 30th, 1968, we had encountered several earlier substantial contacts with the North Vietnamese Guerilla Forces. During these contacts I was serving as the Weapons Platoon Commander and was in a position to personally observe the actions of Gunnery Sergeant Brandon. At all times he performed in an exemplary fashion. On one occasion he advanced under fire in order to assist in the return of a new lieutenant that had taken a serious wound in the neck. As always, extraordinary courage and devotion was common and expected among the Marines serving in 2/4.

At all times, while serving with Foxtrot Company, Gunnery Sergeant Brandon performed his duties in an exemplary fashion. He was adamant that the Marines carry out all of their duties. As a result of his attention and insistence on detail and discipline, I have no doubt that many Marines lives were saved. Simple items were insisted upon such as cover and concealment, clean weapons, additional training and conditioning of the troops which enhanced not only their performance, but also their survivability in War.

During the Battle of Dai Do, I do not recall that I was in a position to personally observe the actions of Gunnery Sergeant Brandon. I have been informed, and thereupon believe, that Gunnery Sergeant Brandon was onboard ship and administratively not required to join us during the Battle. Despite the administrative exclusion, he voluntarily left the ship to return to his unit to be part of the battle and to assist in the leading of troops. Due to the nature and complexity of this battle, I do not recall his return, but was advised shortly thereafter that he had returned and served in various functions as the Battalion reorganized and consolidated.

This was an extremely complex and protracted Battle. In my opinion every Marine, after three days of non-stopped fighting which often resulted in hand-to-hand combat, deserves significant recognition for his conduct. I have no doubt in my mind; based on my previous experience with Gunnery Sergeant Brandon that he deserves significant recognition for his extraordinary services during this Battle. Many awards were given to those who performed as did Gunny Sergeant Brandon; deserve a higher recognition than an administrative type of award.

I hope that my recollection of the services provided by Gunnery Sergeant Brandon will assist in his receiving the appropriate recognition that he deserves.

Thank you in advance for your prompt and courteous attention to this matter. If you have any questions please do not hesitate to contact me.

James A. Wainwright
Major USMCR (discharged)

* * *

Dear Gunny,

Just a note to let you know how much I truly appreciate and value the things you have recently sent to me. While I have not begun to read your book, the pictures are great. You really looked good as a young Marine! I will treasure the commemorative dish with the Vietnam dirt that you made. Not only are you quite an artist, you are a particularly clever one at that! Truly unique

Warmest regards,
Col. Michael Gavlick
F/2/4 Vietnam 67-68

— *Gunny's Reply:* —

Dear Sir,

I returned to Vietnam March 2001 and on the 23rd about 8:00 we headed up to the river to the villages where we fought over 33 years ago. It didn't take me long to remember once I saw the area and had been in it, looked about the same, the little creeks were now big rivers from being dammed up.

Got to think about the first time I met you at the bridge just below camp Carroll, God did I feel like the new guy, all you were wearing old worn out jungle uniforms, long hair, mustaches and me clean jungles close hair cut; I can still see you with the tomato sausage or something in your mustaches.

I wanted to be the best Gunny I could and you gave me a free run to do my job and you chewed my ass whenever I needed but one ass chewing was all I needed. I wanted you informed on what was going on and after 30 years I seen my fitness reports from Vietnam and that is what you said about me, I did my job and kept you informed.

When I got to the village we fought in I wanted to do something to remember the men from Fox 2/4 when they told us we could not take anything, not even dirt I knew that's what I would do. We paid a hell of a price for that dirt and I was going to bring some home for the guys.

I want to thank you for being my commanding officer we both had a hell of a job to do and I was very proud to be your Gunny and still so very proud to be your friend. If you ever need an old Gunny all you got to do is say "Gunny Up" and I will do my best to be there, Thank you sir!

* * *

Gunny,

Hey I went to the mailbox yesterday and had a package there from you. What a great idea you had about this plate with the sand in the middle, that's why you're the Gunny coming up with good ideas all the time. I want to thank you for the plate and being there when Jeff and I needed you and John also. You are one GOOD MARINE and a fine person in my book. I was glad to have served with you and to have been able to return to Vietnam with you was an honor, and I mean that with all my soul. If for some reason we can't get together for a long time. You may just get a visitor out there in a year or two. So I can guarantee we will get together again.

John sent me a picture of the three of us together I think it was taken the day we went to where Jeff was killed. I have it framed and on my wall over by my bar. I plan on getting that map framed and putting it over there also along with the plate that you just sent me. Hell if I keep this up I won't have any more room left for my alcohol over there. Well shit it doesn't last that long anyway, so what the hell.

Take care Gunny, say hi to your wife for me and keep in touch.

Semper Fi
Jim Arnold
L/cpl F 2/4 1986

Note: We went back to Vietnam in March 2001.

* * *

Gunny,

Just got off the phone with my father and he was almost in tears. His exact words, "You won't believe what Gunny Brandon sent me...the greatest present any father could get" Gunny you are the most wonderful person I have ever met. I am not kidding when I say that it is an honor to know you, to have spent time with you, to be considered your friend. In truth, you are my brother in spirit. When I opened your package Saturday, I was stunned by what you had done for my dad. I wasn't surprised that you could have done such a wonderful thing, because I truly believe I know your heart. Gunny you are the greatest. As I told my dad, the Marine Corps needs to clone you and have a Gunny Brandon with every Platoon in the Corps. If that were possible then I know every Marine from here to eternity would be in the best of hands. God bless you, Gunny. I will write more later. Gotta hit the rack. Reveille at Oh-dark-thirty.

Semper Fi
John Edwin Smith

Note: John Smith Sr.'s son Jeff was killed in my company in Vietnam on March 7, 1968. His son (Jeff's brother) John went back to Vietnam with me in March 2001.

* * *

Dear Sergeant,

My CONGRATULATIONS to you on being named 1984 Oregon State American Legion Legionnaire of the year.

The story about your efforts in establishing the American Legion Post 21 and raising its membership from 13 paid members to the present 400 is a success story which is amazing and outstanding, and from what I learn it was your enthusiasm and real effort, some of your own money- and hard work, that established the new Post. At the same time I read that you are the man of many talents; cook, auctioneer, fundraiser, and even a Santa Claus, and you are indeed to be commended.

Keep up the good work. My warmest wishes go to you.

Sincerely,
Mike O. Hatfield
United States Senator

* * *

Sure, Santa will give you a kiss...
now get the heck out of here!

Sorry, you're too young to kiss Santa.
Have a candy cane instead!

Bob Crider,

How have you been buddy, sorry I have not been in touch? I sent you a package let me know if it gets there in one piece okay, we are fine we have had a few bad days but what's new,

Take care,
Your buddy Gunny.

— *Bob's Reply:* —

Gunny,

Thank you is just not enough!

I returned Saturday afternoon from our National Convention in Milwaukee, Wisconsin to find a package from "My Gunny"!

And as always, you continue to amaze and humble me. Ever since I met you in 1968, you have always been my Marines-Marine. All the good and bad times we shared came rushing back as I read your letter. I only hope I was able to meet the expectations on those I had the privileges to serve, and I have always taken pride in my service with the finest fighting force the world has never fielded. Only you would take dirt when they tell you not too! Thank God you were discrete; prisons are real in North Vietnam.

Have a ton of work to catch up on, will write in the very near future. Again, thank you for thinking of me. You are a very special friend.

And leave the Monkeys alone!

Doc

I was that what others did not want to be; I went where others feared to go and did what others failed to do.

I asked nothing from those who gave nothing and accepted the thought of eternal loneliness...should I fail.

I have seen the face of terror; felt the sting of a bullets and the cold sweat of fear.

I have enjoyed the sweet moments of love.

I have cried pain and hoped but most of all, I have lived times others would say were best forgotten.

But I can say I was proud of what I was...A MARINE!!!

* * *

Dear Sir,

I am writing in regard to Gunnery Sergeant Percy Eugene Brandon, USMC retired, and his 10th February 1969 recommendation for the meritorious award of the Bronze Star Medal. Initial recommendation of this award was made by Brigadier General William Weise; then Lt. Colonel commanding 2/4, and Colonel Michael Galvick; then 1st Lieutenant commanding F Co 2/4. The award recommendation made a General Weise and Colonel Galvick; two of the best qualified to observe and evaluate Gunnery Sergeant Brandon's performance in the field and in combat, was later downgraded to the Navy Commendation award that was ultimately presented.

It is in my opinion that this is an injustice that deserves to be rectified. It is entirely beyond my understanding how an Awards Panel, or whoever it is that controls the medals award process, can downgrade citations that are earned on the field of battle. The people best able to judge a man's worth in battle are those who served alongside of him. It is when someone, who was not present on the battle field and was not a witness to the events under consideration can override the judgment of the witnesses on the scene, those mistakes can occur.

I was a 19-year-old PFC Rifleman, with barely six months in the Marine Corps, when I reported to 2/4 in the beginning of 1968. While assigned to F Co. I came into contact with Staff Sergeant Brandon, then acting company Gunnery Sergeant.

The early months of 1968 were damn hard on the Marines in RVN, especially on those of us operating along the DMZ. During those months our battalion was almost constantly in action, engaged in everything from squad sized firefights to company sized pitch battles; to a 4-day hand to hand fight to death with the reinforced 320th NVA Division at the battle of Dai Do. These events gave me an unparalleled opportunity to observe Gunnery Sergeant Brandon in action. It was there, under the most difficult circumstances imaginable, that Gunny Brandon earned my respect and admiration.

My view of Gunny Brandon was from the ranks. As one of the rank-and-file of F Co. my life and well being were often quite literally, in his hands. And I can say, without reservation, I was always confident of Gunny Brandon's leadership. Unlike some seniors NCOs in Vietnam Gunny Brandon led, up-front and by example, and well beyond the required high standard.

A singular example of Gunny Brandon's extraordinary courage and dedication to duty occurred sometime in March 1968 in the area of the village of Nhi Ha, during a vicious, grenade range, battle with NVA regulars F Co. suffered heavy casualties, including the loss of key personnel. At the time F Co. made contact with the enemy, Gunny Brandon was in the Battalion Command Post area, dealing with administrative duties.

When he learned that F Co. was in contact Gunny Brandon rounded up his radio operator and the company clerk and, determined to reach our beleaguered company, set out on foot across 2000 meters of unsecured terrain. Gunny Brandon carefully maneuvered his small party through heavy enemy, small arms and artillery fire, until he reached F Company's lines. Immediately upon arrival Gunny Brandon set about reorganizing the company. Despite the heavy volume of enemy fire Gunny Brandon moved about the area directing the reorganizing of the company's tactical units and the evacuation of our numerous casualties.

When one young Marine was critically wounded and needed immediate medical evacuation Gunny Brandon, unhesitatingly, took personal charge of moving the casualty to the medical evacuation helicopter. With some help from two young, F Co. Marines, Gunny Brandon carried the wounded man across approximately 200 meters of fire swept terrain to the waiting helicopter.

The daily conduct of Gunny Brandon on the battlefields of Northern I Corps RVN provided a powerful example of leadership-in-action to the young Marines of our battalion. Gunny Brandon demonstrated to us, in clearly defined terms, the true meaning of the words, SEMPER FIDELIS.

It is time that Headquarters Marine Corps remembers the meanings of those words, and keeps faith with one of its own.

Sincerely,
Michael L. Summers

* * *

Hi Gunny,

I hope all is well with you and your family. I haven't heard from you in a while and I was thinking about you. How did you make out at the reunion? I hope you had a good time. I can't tell you how mad I am about these terrorists. I wish I could get my hands on them. They really hit us hard Gunny. The financial district won't ever be the same. We lost as many people here in 1/2 hour as the Marines lost on Iwo Jima in 1 month.

My son turned down a job at the Twin Towers 7 months ago and at the time I was a little disappointed because I felt it was a good opportunity. Well, I don't have to tell how scared I was thinking he could have been inside. At the time it happened he was about 2 miles north of there. How are things in McMinnville? Gunny keep your eyes open, these are truly people we cannot trust. I wish we could muster up our old "F" company. I bet we can still kick some butt! Those of us that are left that is.

Well you take good care buddy and God bless you.

Your friend and brother Mike.
"Semper Fi"

* * *

Dear Sir,

My name is Mike Vassallo. I served with "F"- Co. 2nd Battalion 4th Marines in 1968 in the Republic of South Vietnam. While with the 2nd Bn 4th Marines, Gunnery Sergeant Percy E. Brandon was in the company of Gunnery Sergeant.

First let me state that I am appalled by the fact that this and other letters have to be written. This Gunnery Sergeant is one of the finest leaders that I have had the privilege of knowing in my life. In combat he was everywhere you looked. He was always there to calm someone down or convince someone else to advance. He constantly exposed himself to hostile fire and did all that he could to ensure the safety and well being of every man in his company. He was responsible for many acts of bravery that went unrecorded. God knows he didn't do these things for the medals, and he would never consider himself a hero, but to many of us he is. I have seen men do less than him and receive higher decorations.

I am asking you as a patriot and former Marine to take a much closer look at the once in a lifetime Gunnery Sergeant and give him what he so truly deserves. This man was put up for a bronze star with Combat V and he deserves NO LESS. I am hoping that you do the right thing in regard to Gunnery Sergeant Percy Brandon USMC.

Respectfully submitted,
Mike Vassallo

* * *

Dear Gunny,

When I reported to Fox 2/4 in Vietnam I was greeted by First Sergeant Duke (DO NOT MESS WITH HIS COFFEE) Dutchateu and assigned to a fire team. Gunny Brandon was the next senior noncom that I met over the course of my stay in Vietnam. Gunny took me under his wing and taught me what leadership is, what respect is, what camaraderie is, why sacrifice is necessary, why orders are followed exactly unless they would place your unit in danger. (You had better be fully prepared for the shit storm that such action would dump on you)

Gunny taught to always provide the care and safety of your men before yourself. Over a short period of time Gunny became my friend which to this day continues to astound me. Gunny never cut me any slack as he continues to fold me into the Marine Corps tradition and responsibilities. When we ran into any action that was not Company size Gunny was on the first chopper to land (Gunny always lead from the front) Gunny is fearless without being reckless. Gunny shaped me into the man I am today and my successes all go right back to the lessons he so patiently taught. I have no doubt that without his friendship and tutelage my career would have ended differently. Gunny suffered what I consider a disgrace to the Corp when he was not awarded the medals he earned, deserved because of the REMF's (enlisted and Officer) that he challenged (and provoked) to provide all that was necessary for his troops survival.

I still proudly call Gunny a friend and mentor. Gunny enabled snot nosed kids to survive and prosper with his leadership, discipline; compassion and his undying devotion to each and every one of his charges. Gunny allowed with his deeds and actions for more of us to survive Vietnam. Gunny never slacked off and lead by example.

When I left Vietnam (medivaced) as a Sergeant and returned to the United States. My time spent with Gunnery Sergeant Percy Brandon provided me with a sound foundation to move successfully through life. Thank You Gunny for the continuing friendship, guidance and for taking the time and effort you gave to shaping my life!

Semper Fi
Jim Norris
(I was a CPL at the time I served with Gunny Brandon)

* * *

To Whom It May Concern:

Gunnery Sergeant Percy Eugene Brandon is my personal hero from my time spent in Vietnam. He embodies the spirit of Semper Fidelis as well as any other Marine I know.

Gunny was big and bad and didn't need anyone to run interference for him, except for a few guys everyone knew came to like and respect him. I know I did and my respect began the moment Top introduced him to us. He put out his hand and shook with each of us and shared little about himself then I said, "If there is ever anything you think I need to know that will help make this the most squared away outfit in the Nam, as well as get home in one piece a year from now, don't be afraid to tell me. I lived through the Dominican and I really don't want to get killed here. Or words to that effect—words that if spoken in earnest are sure to endear a leader to any body of men.

Gunny came to Vietnam, straight from MCRD Parris Island, South Carolina, where he served several years as a senior drill instructor. I personally was never the target of his wrath, and I felt sorry for those who were. As a matter of fact I remember thinking what a gentle and soft-spoken man he was at our introduction. On getting to know him better, I learned that his size and deftness on the football field (287 pound nose guard) had earned a try out with the San Diego Chargers when Jack Kemp was quarterbacking the team.

Over coming weeks and months Gunny found himself in the thick of it. Surviving battles at Mai Xai Chan, Lam Xuan (east), the Tet offensive and Dai Do, Gunny was eventually sent state-side for having been wounded three times. After spending a month in the states, he decided he couldn't stand being away from "his" Marines any longer so he signed a waiver to go back.

One day, shortly after he returned, while on patrol, a booby-trapped Claymore did what no NVA solider or enemy incoming had ever been able to do. It cut him down like a big oak tree. This time he was sent home for good. None of us who were familiar with the details of his last patrol ever expected to hear from him again. We were wrong. In all Gunny had been hit forty-three times… in both eyes, both arms, and both legs. Every rib, his left forearm, right leg, right wrist, right shoulder, and right knee was broken. He suffered stomach and right testicle injuries. His left thumb had been blown off as well as the tip of one finger and three knuckles had been broken as well.

The right side of his head had been torn in three places. Every tooth was loose. Holes had been punctured through his right ear and left lung. His spleen was removed and the lower intestines sewn over. Hundreds of pieces of metal were left in every part of his body.

With over twenty-five commendations, including four Purple Hearts, Vietnam Cross of Gallantry, Navy commendations with combat V and combat action ribbons, Gunny Brandon was retired from the Marine Corps.

For several years now we have been in contact by email and phone. As you can well imagine, he goes through some dark, dark days. I consider it my privilege and solemn duty as my part of remaining "always faithful" to maintain contact with my former Company Gunny Sergeant, Gunny Brandon, bringing him hope and what cheer I can during those troubled times. At this age 1 can say what my skewed macho mentality at that time, wouldn't allow me to. I love that man I am proud to call him my hero.

You don't have to have been in combat to know that Marines have a language of caring and concern all their own.

After reading many accounts of personal involvement and histories of battles and wars across the centuries, I am taken by a certain archetypal behavior. That is; when the conversation is limited to only two men—no more—it seems to be more acceptable and certainly easier, to express and experience that caring and concern. However, when you get a group of warriors together who love each other deeply, who respect each person's unique contribution to the fulfilling of the mission, who would literally take a bullet for one another, you can't get one of them to admit it.

Steve Klink

Appendix F
Additional Photos and Memorabilia

When I graduated from grade school in 1949, my mother gave me a little Brownie camera she'd found at a second hand store. It remained part of my equipment until it finally wore out, many years later.

I remember hearing (perhaps from my mother) the phrase "a picture is worth a thousand words" — so I'm going to share a few thousand words' worth of pictures taken as I went through life.

My Family — Then and Now

Us kids in the 1940s

Sister Tonie

Sister Jerry

Sister Joyce: died in a car accident in 1947

Brother Bill on leave from Vietnam

Family...

Us kids...a little older!

Mom & Dad

With Our Grandson

Family Portrait

March 2006: Me & Shirlie's 50th Anniversary

Fellow Marines — Where are they now?

Bert Thomas, McMinnville Oregon, 1995:
A long ways from Camp Pendleton!

Andy Kendall, Marine buddy and Retired
Light Heavyweight World Champ

1Sgt Taylor of Top Sergeant Gym in Arizona

WWII Marine Gordon Morgan

Still shows up when the Marines need him!

Fellow Marines…

Vietnam Buddies in Savannah, Georgia

Marine Buddy

DI Buddies, San Diego

Old DI Buddy Cruz, San Diego

Marine Buddies

My Drinking Days…

Veteran's Day, 1978: You can buy all you want at the PX!

No kidding! They let you wear a beard in the Army?

September 1984:

Left: "Hee Haw Gunny!"

Right: "I *AM* sucking my belly in!"

Bottom left: "Oh yeah? You and what fucking army?"

Bottom right: "Chief Bear-Tracks…311 pounds"

Drinking Days, continued…

February 1987: "Hey! This is only water!"

I swear this bird is after my food!

Don't look at me, Bud did it!

1982: Out front of the Veterans Club I built

So what if I need a haircut?
Tell someone who cares!

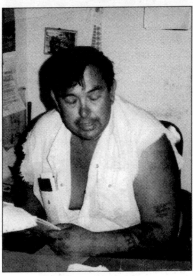

Okay, that's it, I'm quitting next Tuesday.
Not sure which month, though…

My Gym Days

Gunny's Gym in its heyday

My 1969 "Gunny-mobile"

*Best Body Contest, March 1984
(photo by Doreen Wynja)*

Weight Lifting Contest, 1985

*Halloween 1987: Gunny's Indian Dance
(photo by Doreen Wynja)*

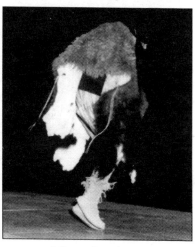

*…and Gunny danced some more
(photo by Doreen Wynja)*

Gym Days, continued…

Working my body back into shape…

Getting a kiss from Shirlie…
(photo by Doreen Wynja)

Tons of fun!

1999: Still got it!

Wanna piece of me?

300 pounds…one arm!

At the office…just enjoying life!

Friends, Acquaintances, and People I've Met

*Marine buddy and pro boxing referee Mills Lane
—he refereed the fight where Mike Tyson bit off
Evander Holyfield's ear!*

*Mills Lane in action:
"Let's Get It On!"*

*General Jones (Supreme Allied Commander
Europe) with Jim Deal (Army within Jones'
command), holding a copy of Gunny's book.*

*"Here I am in Vegas, just like I said, reading
your book and having a cold drink!"
—Lynn, a Marine Friend*

*December 17, 2006. From left to right, all guests
of Bill O'Reilly: Allen Walker, Jereme Coker, Jim
Sims, Bill O'Reilly, Gunny Brandon, and Tom
Wiggins. 12 purple hearts between the five.*

*December 2006:
Bill O'Reilly & Gunny enjoying a
quick stopover in Ireland on the way
home from a tour of the Middle East.*

Aloha! Photos from various trips to Hawaii…

My, my: a Mai Tai…

No limit to booze in Hawaii!

"In training" for my return trip

Me, Rita, Shirlie & the Brown Buddha

Oops! Must've been a 'wardrobe malfunction'

More Places I've Been...

Seattle: Oysters a-plenty at the Space Needle

Bottoms up!

2000 Rose Parade: rode ship from Longview, WA

Cruising up the Columbia River, 2000

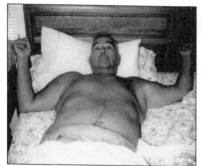

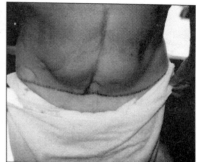

More surgery: St. Vincent's Hospital, September 2003

Things I've Done Since Vietnam…

1974: Chief Want-a-bee

1993: Moving the Spruce Goose from California to McMinnville

*McMinnville, 1984:
Attending Memorial Day Services with John*

McMinnville: Erecting the new flagpole in front of Rice Furniture

Grand Ronde, Oregon, 2000: Grand Ronde Indians Basketball Reunion, 1950-2000

Vehicles I've Restored

1930 Ford 1.5-ton: two years to restore   *The 1952 Jeep I restored…yes, it has gas!*

My Bid for County Commissioner

GUNNY BRANDON
YAMHILL COUNTY
COMMISSIONER
Position 2

We need his
strengths in our
local government

Almost won…but "close" only counts in horseshoes!

My Tattoos

Heck, no, it never hurt! (Okay, maybe a little) … Not shown: the tattoo on my pec:
"Semper Fi – Once a Marine, Always a Marine – 260 Pounds of Steel & Sex Appeal"

At the First Edition Book Signing, June 1995

Kaylee, age 8, sang "The Ballad of Gunny Brandon" for 300+ people

Flowers for My Love…

High School Graduation…50 Years Late

Willamina, 2004:

A Proud High School Graduate at last!

top: The ceremony

left & right: At home afterwards

Artwork & Other Memorabilia

Sketch by Ellen Keeland.

Ellen is the author of "The Lusty Life of Loon Lake Lloyd" about her husband Lloyd Keeland, a WWII Marine on Iwo Jima. During that battle, Lloyd's machine gun platoon took out nearly an entire company of Japanese soldiers.

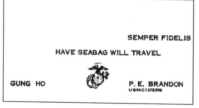

A calling card I used to hand out

A memorial for my dog Hooper...she could almost talk! Never liked Navy chow.

Lyrics to "The Marines' Hymn," which dates to the mid-1800s. The author is unknown.

Artwork…

Drawing by Art Inyo McKellips, a Marine of Osage ancestry who served in Korea. This drawing represents his thoughts of my brother being carried off the battlefield at Iwo Jima. McKellips' seven-foot-square wood carving of Babe Ruth and Hank Aaron ("Brotherhood of Excellence") is on permanent display at Atlanta Stadium.

The *USS Iwo Jima*...Long May She Sail

With Shirlie and a friend at the commissioning of the USS Iwo Jima *(Florida) in 2001*

My Memorial to Iwo Jima

Building the framework

Before landscaping

The finished memorial: Summer

"Gunny's Mountain"
by W. Dale Burkett — December 29, 2005

In McMinnville is Gunny's Monument,
Near the end of Booth Bend Road.
Where a bridge once crossed the river,
Carrying many a heavy load.

We came to Gunny's drive,
And there, plain as could be,
Was a monument raising Old Glory,
For all the world to see.

This was Gunny's Mountain,
With an old beat up truck nearby,
Rusted from standing and waiting,
While the years of that Hell passed by.

On top of the mountain a bunker,
And as I looked inside I see,
The smiling face of a soldier,
Staring up at me.

A sign at the base of the mountain,
Told of a fountain on top,
With a wish from Ole Gunny that says,
Have a drink whenever you stop…

The view in winter: hushed with snow…

Brothers In Arms

John Brandon, WWII

Howard Brandon, WWII
Killed on Iwo Jima, March 9, 1945

Remembering those who didn't return...

We Can Never Forget

About the Author

Percy Eugene "Gunny" Brandon joined the Marine Corps in January 1953 and served until May, 1969. At that time, he was temporarily retired. He was sent home to recover from fourth-time wounds and was retired April 1, 1973 with over twenty years' service.

The Brandon family came to Oregon from South Dakota. There were five brothers (all of whom served in the military) and four sisters. Brothers John and Gary served in the Navy, Bill in the Air Force, and Percy and Howard "Stubby" Brandon and in the Marines. Stubby was killed in Iwo Jima.

The Brandons are of mixed blood within the Rosebud Sioux and Cree Indian tribes. Percy was raised and schooled in Grand Ronde and Willamina, Oregon.

Gunny served during the Korean and Vietnamese conflicts as a company gunnery sergeant with the 2nd Battalion, 4th Marines: known as the "Magnificent Bastards." Their mission involved patrolling the demilitarized zone (Dm. Their enemy was the 320th Division of the North Vietnamese Army: hard-core, tough, combat-tested troops; given the name "Mr. Charles."

E. Michael Helms' book *THE PROUD BASTARDS* (published June 1990) tells of Vietnam and of the "2/4," their life and battles. Gunny Brandon was company gunny with F Company during that period.

Keith William Nolan, author of several books on Vietnam, published his last, *THE MAGNIFICENT BASTARDS*, in 1994, and tells about the battle of Dai Do that wounded nearly every officer and enlisted man in the company. Captains James E. Livingston and J.R. Vargas were both awarded the Medal of Honor, and Battalion Commander Colonel W. "Bill" Weise was awarded the Navy Cross. Sergeant Major "Big John" Malnar was awarded the Silver Star. He was a veteran of three wars—he was killed in the battle of Dai Do.